CLIMATE CHANGE: FROM SCIENCE TO SUSTAINABILITY

Stephen Peake and Joe Smith

THE ENVIRONMENTAL WEB

U316

Cover images from left to right: residents battling against 90 m.p.h. winds at Key West, Florida during hurricane George in September 1998 (Associated Press); a group of CO_2 emissions graphics typifying the 'contraction and convergence' approach to climate equity (courtesy of Ben Matthews); environmental protestors with slogans made into a giant ark, outside climate negotiations in Bonn, July 2001 (courtesy of Stephen Peake); second-hand car sales in the port of Cotonou, Benin, West Africa (© Panos Pictures/Sven Torfinn).

This publication forms part of an Open University course U316 *The Environmental Web*. The complete list of texts which make up this course can be found on the back cover. Details of this and other Open University courses can be obtained from the Course Information and Advice Centre, PO Box 724, The Open University, Milton Keynes MK7 6ZS, United Kingdom: tel. +44 (0)1908 653231, e-mail general enquiries@open.ac.uk

Alternatively, you may visit the Open University website at http://www.open.ac.uk where you can learn more about the wide range of courses and packs offered at all levels by The Open University.

To purchase a selection of Open University course materials visit the webshop at www.ouw.co.uk, or, contact Open University Worldwide, Michael Young Building, Walton Hall, Milton Keynes MK7 6AA, United Kingdom for a brochure: tel. +44 (0)1908 858785; fax +44 (0)1908 858787; e-mail ouwenq@open.ac.uk

The Open University
Walton Hall, Milton Keynes
MK7 6AA

First published 2003

Edited, designed and typeset by The Open University.

Printed and bound in the United Kingdom by The Bath Press, Glasgow.

ISBN 0 7492 5680X

1.1

u316 book 3i1.1

U316 *The Environmental Web* Course Team

Course Team Chair

Jonathan Silvertown, Department of Biological Sciences, Faculty of Science

Course Managers

Tracy Finnegan, Department of Biological Sciences, Faculty of Science
Marion Hall, Department of Biological Sciences, Faculty of Science

Course Team Assistant

Catherine Eden, Department of Biological Sciences, Faculty of Science

Open University Authors

Mark Brandon, Department of Earth Sciences, Faculty of Science
(Chair and author Block 1)
Nigel Clark, Department of Geography, Faculty of Social Science (Block 1)
Mike Dodd, Department of Biological Sciences, Faculty of Science (Block 2)
Marion Hall, Department of Biological Sciences, Faculty of Science (Block 1)
Stephen Peake, Department of Design and Innovation, Faculty of Technology
(Co-Chair and author Block 3)
Irene Ridge, Department of Biological Sciences, Faculty of Science (Block 2)
Jonathan Silvertown, Department of Biological Sciences, Faculty of Science
(Chair and author Block 2)
Sandrine Simon, Systems Department, Faculty of Technology
(Chair and author Block 4)
Joe Smith, Department of Geography, Faculty of Social Science (Co-Chair and author Block 3)

Web and Multimedia Producer

Gloria Medina, Faculty of Science

Software Development

Phil Butcher, Learning and Teaching Solutions (CD-ROM development)
Sophia Braybrooke, Learning and Teaching Solutions (CD-ROM development)
Andrea Goodinson, Learning and Teaching Solutions (Web development)
Jason Jarratt, Learning and Teaching Solutions (CD-ROM development)
Ross Mackenzie, Learning and Teaching Solutions (Web development)
Gloria Medina, Faculty of Science (Software Production Manager and academic liaison)
Trent Williams, Learning and Teaching Solutions (Web development)
Damion Young, Learning and Teaching Solutions (CD-ROM and Web development)

Editors

Sheila Dunleavy
Ian Nuttall
Bina Sharma
Dick Sharp

Graphic Design

Sue Dobson
Carl Gibbard
David Winter

BBC/OU Production Centre

Sarah Carr BBC OU Production Centre (Block 3 CD-ROM)
Sue Nuttall (Video for CD-ROM)

Other Contributors

Gary Alexander, Department of Telematics, Faculty of Technology (Block 4)
John Baxter, Faculty of Science (Community Interactions)
Roger Blackmore, Faculty of Technology (Day School, Project, activities for Block 1)
Gloria Medina (activities for Blocks 1 to 4)
Richard Treves, Faculty of Technology (Block 1)

Consultants

Claire Appleby, Open University Associate Lecturer (Block 4)
Hilary Denny, Open University Associate Lecturer (Associate Lecturer recruitment,
training and support, design of, and materials for, End-of-Course Assessment and Day School)
Sarah Hardy (ECA)
Alex Kirby, BBC News Online environment correspondent (activities for Block 3)
Bob MacQueen, Open University Associate Lecturer (Reader)
Jean Macqueen (Indexer)
Steve Millar, Open University Associate Lecturer (Reader)
Donal O'Donnell, Open University Associate Lecturer (Reader)
Julian Priddle, Science Teaching and Education Partnership (Block 1)

External Assessors

Professor Sandy Crosbie, Faculty of Science and Engineering,
University of Edinburgh (Course Assessor)
Dr Christopher Hope, Judge Institute of Management Studies, University of Cambridge (Block 3)
Dr John Shears, British Antarctic Survey, Cambridge (Block 1)
Mr David Streeter, School of Biological Sciences, University of Sussex (Block 2)
Dr Caroline Sullivan, Centre for Ecology and Hydrology at Wallingford, Oxfordshire (Block 4)

Contents

Chapter 1 The climate strikes back   9

1.1   Introduction   9

1.2   The central role of the Intergovernmental Panel on Climate Change   9

1.3   Climate change presents 'mind-blowing' political consequences   13

1.4   Climate change in the context of other eco 'gloom and doom' stories   18

1.5   What do we mean by 'climate change'?   21

1.6   So is it happening? Early warning signs of climate change   23

1.7   Why is climate change a problem? Who for, where and when?   25

1.8   Major reasons for concern about future climate change   28

1.9   How does driving a car make the sea-level rise?   30

1.10 Conclusion: a chain of causes and effects   42

1.11 Summary of Chapter 1   44

Learning Outcomes for Chapter 1   45

Questions for Chapter 1   45

References   47

Chapter 2 A citizen's guide to climate science   49

2.1   Introduction   49

2.2   The Earth's complex climate system   51

2.3   Fossil fuels and the carbon cycle   53

2.4   Uncertainties in our understanding of radiative forcing   60

2.5   Is climate change real and are humans the cause?   63

2.6   Future climate change   67

2.7   The science behind climate change is settling but remains unsettled   78

2.8   Summary of Chapter 2   81

Learning Outcomes for Chapter 2   82

Questions for Chapter 2   83

References   85

Chapter 3 Planetary engineering   87

3.1   Introduction   87

3.2   What took us so long to realize?   87

3.3   The United Nations Framework Convention on Climate Change
      and the Kyoto Protocol   91

3.4   One small step for the planet, one giant leap towards a global carbon economy   106

3.5   Summary of Chapter 3   116

Learning Outcomes for Chapter 3   117

Questions for Chapter 3   118

References   119

Chapter 4 Tuning in: integrated assessments of climate futures   121

4.1   Introduction   121

4.2   An integrated approach to thinking climate change through   121

4.3   From emissions to decisions: integrated assessment models   127

4.4   Models and policymakers   130

4.5   Future emissions: exploring the uncertainties   134

4.6   Emissions scenarios as a way of thinking about an uncertain future   138

4.7   Quantifying the challenge: baselines and target stabilization levels   144

4.8   Sharing the burden: equity and climate change   148

4.9   Summary of Chapter 4   154

Learning Outcomes for Chapter 4   156

Questions for Chapter 4   156

References   158

Chapter 5 Listening out: climate, politics, philosophy   159

5.1   Bringing strangers into the equation   159

5.2   Being fair to the future   166

5.3   People in place: connecting environmental change, philosophy and politics   175

5.4   Summary of Chapter 5   182

Learning Outcomes for Chapter 5   182

Questions for Chapter 5   182

References   183

Chapter 6 Climate change and sustainability — inseparable   185

6.1   Career of the concept of sustainable development   185

6.2   Intellectual foundations of sustainable development   194

6.3   Making sustainability count   197

6.4   Conclusion   201

6.5   Summary of Chapter 6   202

Learning Outcomes for Chapter 6   203

Questions for Chapter 6   204

References   205

Chapter 7 Changing the world   207

7.1   Introduction   207

7.2   Globalization and environmental change   208

7.3   Governance, citizenship and sustainability   214

7.4   Making it happen — sustainability in practice   227

7.5   Conclusion — the increasingly World Wide Web   237

7.6   Summary of Chapter 7   240

Learning Outcomes for Chapter 7   241

Questions for Chapter 7   241

References   242

Answers to Questions   243

Acknowledgements   257

Index   261

Chapter 1 The climate strikes back

Prepared for the course team by Stephen Peake

1.1 Introduction

Climate change is an urgent issue that demands clear and decisive action. It is one of the most complex, multilayered and interdisciplinary intellectual puzzles facing researchers. This book is going to help you to work with this difficult mix of urgency and complexity, and equip you to take an active part in debates that will shape all our futures.

The topic of global climate change occurs throughout the exploration of islands and Antarctica in Book 1, and biodiversity and ecosystems in Book 2. Climate change is an excellent topic to further explore the interconnections between the four key concepts of *The Environmental Web*: globalization, uncertainty, governance and sustainability. As we will see, this is because the map of causes, effects and consequences of climate change encapsulates the entirety of the living and non-living systems on Earth. Not surprisingly, then, climate change is a truly interdisciplinary subject. It mingles Earth sciences (e.g. geology, oceanography), biology, atmospheric chemistry, technology, design and innovation, economics, geography, politics, sociology, philosophy and ethics. It is a good topic to develop your interdisciplinary thinking skills on environmental issues.

Understanding how and why the issue of climate change has emerged so rapidly on to the international political agenda — it is just over a decade old — and what implications this may have for the potential for sustainable development for the rest of this century, requires thinking through the issue from start to finish. That means starting with Earth science observations and working through to an understanding of the dynamics of a possible global political agreement on what constitutes an equitable path towards sustainable economic, social and environmental development. To get there, you need to be not only scientifically literate but also deft at interpreting the science. You need to be aware of how the science is interpreted by the media. You also need to have access to some thinking tools to help you see the implications of various prescriptions of how humans could respond. This is an interdisciplinary book for an interdisciplinary audience: some of you will find some of the science very straightforward; others will have covered some of the philosophy or economics in greater depth in the past. The point about this book is that we expect to give all of you the challenge of weaving together these different strands in your mind. You will make the journey 'from science to sustainability'.

1.2 The central role of the Intergovernmental Panel on Climate Change

Climate change regularly makes the news. The reports are often about global environmental change on an unprecedented scale, of an emerging crisis alarmingly beyond human comprehension and control. When carefully and accurately communicated, the story typically takes on a shape something like the following:

> Concentrations of greenhouse gases in the atmosphere are rising. The Earth is rapidly warming and its climate is changing. In the years to come, there could be more frequent, more intense floods and droughts, more powerful storms,

polar ice-sheets may melt and retreat, seasons around the world may change, tropical diseases may spread, and the sea-level may rise significantly.

Just imagine it. You could be forgiven for thinking these observations and predictions sound a bit like an extract from the story line of a modern science fiction movie like *Armageddon* (1998) or *Deep Impact* (1999).

Suddenly, scientists, politicians and pundits are in the media regurgitating scary scientific conclusions about the effects of global warming. Given half a chance, weather presenters have trouble holding back on the topic. In the flux of daily news, the climate-change trump card is never far from being played by anti-consumption, anti-capitalist, anti-globalization voices that are steadily becoming louder.

Various pundits prescribe urgent measures to control the Earth's climate before it is too late and things get out of control. Many who become informed about the phenomenon of climate change seem to rapidly and deeply embrace the issue. It is used to legitimize many general concerns and fears about the damage being inflicted on the planet's living systems as a result of human aspirations and development patterns.

Environmental activists become very energized by the topic of climate change (Figure 1.1). On the one hand, it is a great attention grabber: the risks of irreversible large-scale environmental change and damage are real and significant. On the other hand, it attracts prescriptions about how humans should live properly and equitably together on the same planet — higher fuel prices, less air travel, smaller cars (or even no cars), and rafts of other energy-efficiency measures.

Figure 1.1 NGO campaigners demonstrate outside the climate negotiations in Bonn, July 2001.

Climate change is a pressing modern environmental issue, spawning connections to social and political processes that are breaking out all over the world. It is a lightning rod for those promoting sustainable development.

The information focus to which politicians, academics, civil servants, the media, and environmental activists turn to is an official scientific body known as the Intergovernmental Panel on Climate Change (IPCC; Box 1.1, p.12).

Every few years since 1990, the IPCC has produced an up-to-date assessment of climate change. The global scientific community's third assessment of the status of climate change was published in 2001. It is known as the IPCC **Third Assessment Report (TAR)**. It consists of four separate published volumes (Figure 1.2). Three working groups (referred to as Working Groups I, II and III, often abbreviated as WGI, etc.) each produced a report on a different aspect of climate change, and there is also a synthesis report. Such IPCC reports are usually weighty tomes.

Figure 1.2 Thud! Now decide on that! The IPCC TAR is in four volumes (IPCC 2001a, b, c, d). The four volumes are 3062 pages long, weigh 8.6 kilograms and are altogether 14 cm thick.

The TAR is without doubt the most influential and complete assessment of the scientific status of climate change available in the world today. How these scientific findings are translated, and what people decide to do about them, is going to affect each and every citizen in the world in some way or other.

Moreover, fed into the world of international development and technical cooperation, it is very likely that climate science will in one way or another affect patterns of economic and social development in developing countries for decades to come.

Although the IPCC has led to a growing scientific consensus on the causes and implications of climate change, the science is by no means universally accepted. A few scientists do continue to dispute some of the findings of the IPCC, in particular the extent to which observed climate change can be attributed to anthropogenic activity. Some scientific voices dispute the IPCC's interpretation of recent temperature measurements, whereas a handful of others continue to put forward various alternative theories other than the greenhouse effect to explain the Earth's rising mean surface temperature.

Scientific assessment underpins the global political response to climate change. It is a critical trigger in the policy process, and will continue to have an important checking effect on the social and political dynamics that are being unleashed and whipped up around this topic. Chapter 1 is designed to consolidate your existing knowledge of the science of climate change. It tunes into influential and high-level voices expressing concern, and joining the chorus of appeals for urgent action to combat climate change. The chapter takes a look at what evidence there is to date of the effects of climate change that have already taken place. Next we jump straight to the bottom line of the problem as we conceive it today, and look at the risks of rapid climate change.

By the end of the chapter, you should be able to explain why driving a car makes the sea-level rise. The chapter will consolidate and develop your knowledge of some of the most important features of basic climate science (and where and why it is uncertain).

Box 1.1 A new way of managing complex interdisciplinary scientific knowledge: the Intergovernmental Panel on Climate Change

The most authoritative and comprehensive source of information on climate change is the IPCC. 'Intergovernmental panels' are a relatively new type of international organization. They are promoted in Chapter 31 of Agenda 21*, which states, 'Intergovernmental panels on development and environmental issues should be organized, with emphasis on their scientific and technical aspects, and studies of responsiveness and adaptability included in subsequent programmes of action' (paragraph 31.6). There is also an Intergovernmental Panel on Forests, for example. Their role is partly scientific and partly political, providing mechanisms to enable the scientific and technological community to make a more effective contribution to decision-making processes concerning environment and development.

The IPCC is one of the largest and most sophisticated international interdisciplinary peer-review mechanisms ever established. Involving thousands of collaborating natural and social scientists, it comprises a significant proportion of global scientific, technical and socio-economic academic community involved in climate change-related research. In its own words:

> The role of the IPCC is to assess... The scientific, technical and socio-economic information relevant for the understanding of the risk of human-induced climate change... The IPCC does not carry out research nor does it monitor climate-related data or other relevant parameters. It bases its assessment mainly on peer reviewed and published scientific/technical literature...The Panel meets in plenary sessions about once a year.
> It accepts/approves/adopts IPCC reports, decides on the mandates and work plans of the Working Groups and the Task Force, the structure and outlines of its reports, the IPCC Principles and Procedures, and the budget.
> The Panel also elects the IPCC Chair...

(IPCC, 2002)

This large multicultural network of people discussing the complexities of climate change and its potentially serious implications is both scientific and political. In its work for the TAR, the IPCC divided up the enormous labour involved between three Working Groups (Figure 1.3):

- Working Group I assesses the scientific aspects of the climate system and climate change.

- Working Group II assesses the vulnerability of socio-economic and natural systems to climate change, the negative and positive consequences of climate change, and options for adapting to it.

- Working Group III assesses options for limiting greenhouse gas emissions and otherwise mitigating climate change.

* Agenda 21 is one of the so-called Earth Summit Agreements that emerged from the 1992 Rio Earth Summit. It is a comprehensive plan of action to be taken globally, nationally and locally by organizations of the United Nations system, governments, and major groups in every area in which humans impact on the environment.

Each Working Group published its findings for the TAR in 2001 (Figure 1.2). Each report contains a 'Summary for Policymakers' (SPM), a Technical Summary (a longer summary) and the main body of the text. The Summary for Policymakers is as an important part of each report. It is by far the most frequently quoted source used by journalists, and is painstakingly and carefully worded. So much so, that it must be agreed unanimously at the IPCC Plenary. This involves high-level government officials sitting behind national flags in UN fashion going through the summaries, line by line, word by word, and, frequently, comma by comma. This aspect of the IPCC process is highly political. Large fossil-fuel consuming or oil-producing nations do not ignore the chance to press their interests at this point. This is why the IPCC process as a whole goes to great pains to stress that it is 'policy relevant but not policy prescriptive'. In other words, it's up to others to interpret what the science suggests we do about climate change.

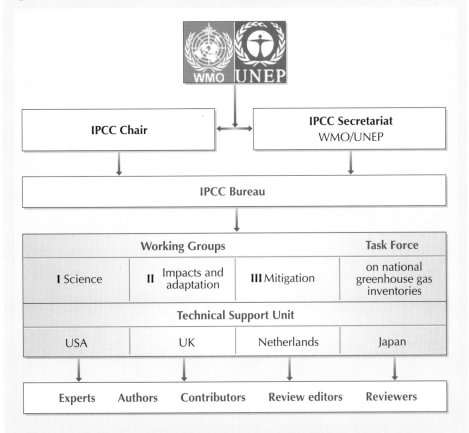

Figure 1.3 The structure of the IPCC in 2003. It was established by the World Meteorological Organization (WMO) and the United Nations Environment Program (UNEP).

1.3 Climate change presents 'mind-blowing' political consequences

Though the earliest scientific work to understand the Earth's climate dates back at least 100 years, international political discussion of the topic appeared only very recently. Following publication of the IPCC's First Assessment Report in 1990, the UN General Assembly passed a resolution to establish an INC (Intergovernmental Negotiating Committee) to draft a framework convention on climate change.

Since the early 1990s, many world leaders have spoken publicly about the consequences of climate change. Business chiefs and the leaders of various intergovernmental organizations (IGOs) and non-governmental organizations (NGOs) have added their voices too.

Climate change is now being billed as a major threat to humanity. Not surprisingly, then, it is not too difficult to find quote after quote on the subject from various public figures on the Web. Box 1.2 contains a selection of remarks on the subject of climate change collected by Guy Dauncey and Patrick Mazza (2003). You will return to these in Activity 1.1.

Box 1.2 Powerful voices on climate change on the Web

1   On the island where I live, it is possible to throw a stone from one side to the other. Our fears about sea-level rise are very real. Our Cabinet has been exploring the possibility of buying land in a nearby country in case we become refugees of climate change.

Teleke Lauti, Minister for the Environment, Tuvalu

2   The scientific consensus presented in this comprehensive report about human-induced climate change should sound alarm bells in every national capital and in every local community.

Klaus Töpfer, Executive Secretary of the United Nations Environment Program, commenting on the IPCC's Third Assessment Report, January 2001

3   This is not some slow, controlled change we're talking about. It's fast, it's unpredictable, and it's unprecedented during human civilization.

Adam Markham, World Wide Fund for Nature

4   There is broad agreement within the scientific community that amplification of the Earth's natural greenhouse effect by the build-up of various gases introduced by human activity has the potential to produce dramatic changes in climate. Only by taking action now can we ensure that future generations will not be put at risk.

Statement by 49 Nobel Prize winners and 700 members of the United States National Academy of Sciences, 1990

5   A child born in a wealthy country is likely to consume, waste, and pollute more in his lifetime than 50 children born in developing nations. Our energy-burning lifestyles are pushing our planet to the point of no return. It is dawning on us at last that the life of our world is as vulnerable as the children we raise.

George Carey, former Archbishop of Canterbury

6   As parliamentarians, we have to stand on platforms around the planet and explain to electors …why the forest is burning, the cattle are dying…why there is surf in the high street. To explain…that these are not Acts of God, but Acts of Man.

Tom Spencer, British Conservative Member of the European Parliament

7   Globally, emissions may have to be reduced, the scientists are telling us, by as much as 60% or 70%, with developed countries likely to have to make even bigger cuts if we're going to allow the developing world to have their share of growing industrial prosperity…The Kyoto Protocol is only the first rather modest step. Much, much deeper emission reductions will be needed in future. The political implications are mind-blowing.

Michael Meacher, UK Environment Minister, November 2000

8   Every generation faces a challenge. In the 1930s, it was the creation of Social Security. In the 1960s, it was putting a man on the moon. In the 1980s, it was ending the Cold War. Our generation's challenge will be addressing global climate change while sustaining a growing global economy.

Eileen Claussen, Pew Center on Global Climate Change

9   This is a huge problem. If we don't deal with this within just a few years, you will have island nations flooded; you will have the agricultural balance of most countries completely changed; you will have a dramatic increase in the number of severe, unmanageable weather events… And the good news is that we can now deal with this problem — and strengthen our economic growth, not weaken it.

former United States President Bill Clinton (Figure 1.4a),

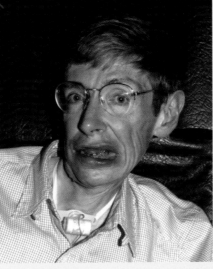

(a)   (b)

Figure 1.4   (a) Bill Clinton; (b) Stephen Hawking.

10   If it were only a few degrees, that would be serious, but we could adapt to it. But the danger is the warming process might be unstable and run away. We could end up like Venus, covered in clouds and with a surface temperature of 400 degrees. It could be too late if we wait until the bad effects of warming become obvious. We need action now to reduce emission of carbon dioxide.

Stephen Hawking (Figure 1.4b), physicist, on *Larry King Live*, 25 December 1999

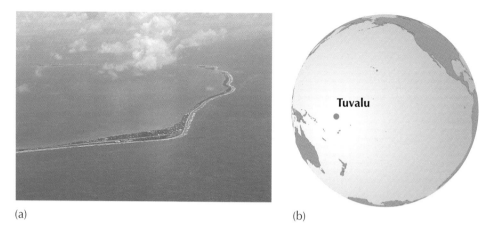

(a)   (b)

Figure 1.5 (a) 'Toodleloo Tuvalu' — the nation that is likely to be one of the first victims of climate change. (b) Tuvalu is located in the South Pacific. In 2002, its population was 11 146.

The vulnerability of small islands to climate change was introduced in Book 1. A number of island states (in the South Pacific and the Caribbean) are particularly low lying, several with maximum heights above sea-level of just a few metres. Tuvalu (Figure 1.5) is particularly vulnerable, with a coastline of just 24 km and a maximum height of just 5 m above sea-level. Such islands are particularly vulnerable to extreme storm events. An extreme weather event can devastate an island for decades. You also met the Alliance of Small Island States (AOSIS) in Block 1. AOSIS has been particularly vociferous in the climate-change negotiations. Teleke Lauti's remark (Box 1.2, quote 1) shows a startling degree of acceptance of climate change and a willingness to face up to its consequences.

Töpfer's notion of alarm bells (quote 2) very much instils a sense of panic about the problem, as does Markham (quote 3). The Nobel Laureates (quote 4) were commenting in 1990, around the time of the IPCC's First Assessment Report. A great deal more analysis has been presented by the IPCC since then. However, despite the relative lack of scientific consensus on the matter in 1990, there was enough concern for this influential group to call for urgent action.

Meacher's term 'mind-blowing' (quote 7) is a particularly strong expression. He has clearly thought about this problem deeply. Despite the uncertainties involved in climate prediction, some European leaders are actually engaging with the prospect of 60–70% cuts in emissions. This is evidence of acceptance of the 'precautionary principle' embodied in the climate convention and elsewhere in multilateral environmental agreements (MEAs).

Figure 1.6 The 'ark' theme has been widely used to communicate the implications of climate change. Here environmental NGOs have constructed an ark made from many boards carrying various messages about climate change at the climate negotiations in July 2001.

The ethical dimensions of climate change — and sustainable development in general — may play a particularly important role in any future global successes at managing the planet's atmosphere. The remark by Carey (quote 5) invokes ethical implications of both distant others (see Chapter 5) and future generations. Spencer (quote 6) explicitly connects the problem of climate change to the notion of Acts of Man rather than God. Many campaigning groups and commentators have made references, and associations, or invoked images of the story of Noah's Ark to communicate climate change. Figure 1.6 shows a climate 'ark' constructed by environmental activists during the resumed Sixth Conference of Parties to the United Nations Framework Convention on Climate Change in Bonn (Germany) in July 2001.

Claussen (quote 8) provides a helpful reminder that one way of understanding the possible political consequences of climate change is to view it in a historical context.

The notion that particular issues can rise to prominence and characterize a whole period will be helpful to us as we consider the degree of political support required to deal effectively with the problem. Clinton (quote 9) exercises an unusual combination of pessimism and optimism. It is not quite clear that climate impacts will happen in just a few years. Equally, many stakeholders are not so convinced that there can be a 'win–win' situation whereby effective action on climate change will inevitably lead to economic growth.

Hawking (quote 10) is a distinguished physicist/mathematician who is quite used to considering complexity, chaos and uncertainty. He has pondered the creation of the Universe, and debated the probability of the existence of a god or other supernatural creator. His maths and science skills applied to the risks of climate change have clearly convinced him we face a real and significant problem (Figure 1.7).

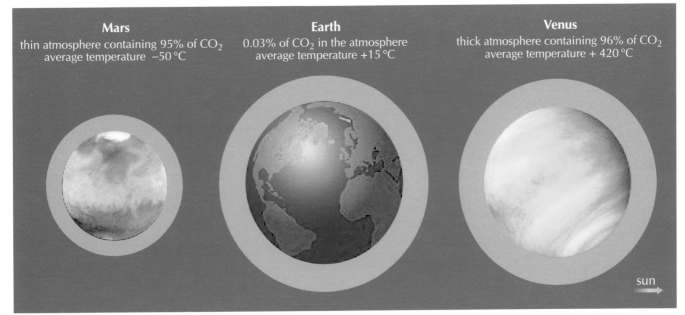

Mars
thin atmosphere containing 95% of CO_2
average temperature −50 °C

Earth
0.03% of CO_2 in the atmosphere
average temperature +15 °C

Venus
thick atmosphere containing 96% of CO_2
average temperature + 420 °C

sun

Figure 1.7   The surface temperatures of the inner planets are largely determined by the amount of carbon dioxide and other greenhouse gases in the planetary atmosphere. Although 95% of the Martian atmosphere is CO_2, its atmospheric pressure is less than 1% that of Earth! A great deal more CO_2 exists in the solid state of the poles as 'dry ice'. Stephen Hawking has suggested that if global warming on Earth becomes unstable, we could end up like Venus, covered in clouds and with a surface temperature of 400 °C. This is highly improbable (but scary anyway!). How the concentration of carbon dioxide (among other gases) affects the surface temperature of a planet will become apparent later in this chapter.

Activity 1.1: Communicating climate change

The quotations in Box 1.2 use a variety of devices to communicate the importance of climate change and the need for urgent action. Take a few minutes to find the best match between each quote and the following themes:

- economic and technological optimism;
- ethics/religion;
- brutal rationality;
- planetary consequences;
- panic;
- urgency;
- reasoned historical perspective.

Comment

One way of matching these would be:

- economic and technological optimism (Clinton);
- ethical/religious (Carey, Spencer, Meacher);
- brutal rationality (Lauti);
- planetary consequences (Hawking);
- panic (Töpfer, Markham);
- urgency (Nobel Prize winners);
- reasoned historical perspective (Claussen).

1.4 Climate change in the context of other eco 'gloom and doom' stories

Do you remember the last time you paused for a moment and found yourself thinking about the sheer number of people around you and the consequences of what they were up to — one of those slightly uncomfortable, slightly claustrophobic 'isn't it amazing how many people there are' moments? A host of different things might have triggered the feeling: the week before Christmas in a crowded shopping centre; the stadium or car park after a football match; a long queue at a crowded foreign airport; a jammed motorway; the checkout at your local supermarket; a session watching 24-hour international rolling news stories on the television; or perhaps the noisy crowd at one of your favourite beauty spots on a Sunday afternoon.

The chances are that on one of these occasions your mind may have jumped ahead a step further. Have you ever asked yourself how we manage to feed ourselves so well in rich developed countries? Or how is it that the petrol station always has fuel and the lights at home or in the office stay on? Will the food, petrol and electricity ever run out? It seems quite natural for us to worry from time to time about the finite limits to some of the resources we depend on. In reality we are worrying about the finite nature of the planet we live on — the small-world effect.

The human population continues to grow rapidly. In 2003 there were around 6.3 billion humans on the planet. Our present best estimate is that we expect the human population to peak around 9 billion or so (Figure 1.8). Although a peak in human population is envisaged, the present growth rate is still high and adds further pressure to some already intense environmental problems, such as food production, energy use, biodiversity (Block 2) and water shortage (Block 4).

To get an idea of the explosion in the human population relative to the time-scales involved in climate change (discussed in Chapter 2), we have to put the Industrial Revolution into a long-term perspective. For argument's sake, let us say that anatomically modern humans (*Homo sapiens*) have been around for 200 000 years. If we could fast forward through that time in, say, an hour from then to now, we would be travelling forward in time at the rate of 55.6 years per second. Imagine sitting quietly in a chair for an hour. The Industrial Revolution doesn't start until around 1750, by which time we have sat for approximately 59 minutes and 55 seconds. Just over a

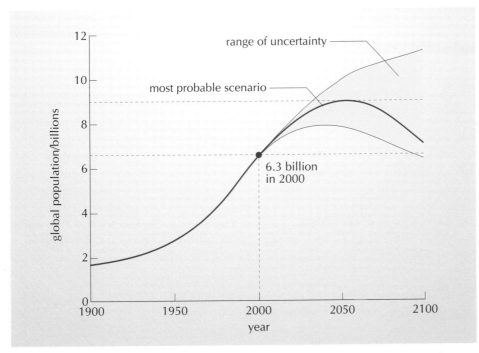

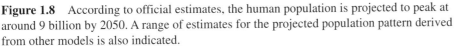

Figure 1.8 According to official estimates, the human population is projected to peak at around 9 billion by 2050. A range of estimates for the projected population pattern derived from other models is also indicated.

second later the human population reaches 1 billion (around 1825), and 3.2 seconds after that in 2003 its size is 6.3 billion. Within the next second after that, the world's population is projected to increase 50% again to 9 billion by 2050!

The impact that humans have had on the Earth's landscape has been dramatic. Some impacts are visible — for example, the scale and nature of land-use change. Flying over whole swathes of Europe on a clear day reveals the scale of change that human activity has had on the land (Figure 1.9). If you were to colour the places where

Figure 1.9 Not a corner untouched: an aerial photograph of a European landscape.

Figure 1.10 Just how did *The Limits to Growth*, a highly technical book on systems dynamics, succeed in selling over 1 million copies?

Figure 1.11 The 'Save It' campaign was a prominent part of the British Government's response to the oil crisis. We can make connections between early public awareness campaigns to save energy in the 1970s and implications for current climate policies.

human activity had been present for some time, there wouldn't be a white patch left. Satellite images can reveal land-use changes in the last few decades, including, for example, deforestation and afforestation. However, we cannot easily *see* the impacts that humans are having on the climate on the street or from an aeroplane — not yet anyway!

Fears about the consequences of the scale of human population increase seem to ebb and flow in popular culture. The last significant period of mass anxiety about population levels and growth was in the late 1960s/early 1970s. This anxiety was powerfully summarized in an influential report entitled *The Limits to Growth* (Meadows *et al.*, 1972 — Figure 1.10), which sold over 1 million copies world wide. The book used simple modelling techniques to make a dramatic prediction about the consequences of rising human population, economic growth and expectations about consumption. The report concluded that in a closed system such as the Earth, simultaneous exponential growth in several factors, such as population, food production, the consumption of natural resources and environmental pollution, would sooner or later lead to a dramatic system collapse around the second half of the 21st century.

The doom-mongers were centre stage for a while in the early 1970s. Fears about the growing global dependence on fossil fuels and their finite supply were particularly acute. The world's first major oil shock unfolded in October 1973 at the time of the outbreak of the Yom Kippur War between Egypt and Israel. Oil prices rose dramatically, and, for a moment, systems thinking about populations, their energy consumption and its relationship to economic growth, became as basic and fundamental to governments as defence and national security have always been. Fears about energy security gripped the developed world. Perhaps for the first time outside the macroeconomics profession, a new generation of professionals began deftly using systems-modelling approaches to point towards economic impacts and policy implications for governments and markets. Although entirely coincidental, the 1973 oil crisis came just in time for proponents of *The Limits to Growth*; it seemed to be a tangible illustration of what the future may hold. Nevertheless, there remained a good deal of scepticism about the argument.

The impact of 1970s events on climate policies today is clearly traceable. It is around this issue that many economists and social scientists working in the IPCC cut their teeth. Deeply held views about what is and is not technically, economically or politically feasible were formed around this time (Figure 1.11).

Interestingly, in the 1960s and 1970s some scientists began exploring the possibility that we were heading rapidly towards another ice age (Box 1.3, p. 22). Later on, when you come to examine the evidence yourself, you may see why this seemed plausible.

Whether we know enough about the science, the politics or the systems dynamics of climate change, we should not ignore the fact that current fears are leading to extraordinary statements on the problem. Just consider the quotes in Box 1.3. We need to remind ourselves that climate change is only the latest global crisis to affect the human outlook. Whatever the science, it must have come as a tremendously welcome boost to the ever-present community of gloom and doomsayers. This is not to reject the science, but only to remind us that scientific processes are cultural, and have their own evolutionary (sometimes revolutionary) dynamics, and are capable of rapid transformations and turns.

In this context, climate change is the new limits-to-growth story. It arrived just in time for those who had pinned their arguments on fossil fuels running out. As you will see in Chapter 2, we are still far from running out of fossil fuels: we have only burned a small fraction of what's still in the ground. The threat has been neatly transformed from one of the geopolitical risks of finding and securing adequate supplies of fossil fuels to the geopolitical risks of combusting them.

1.5 What do we mean by 'climate change'?

In the remainder of this chapter and in Chapter 2, we shall consider the scientific evidence for climate change. Before we do, it will help us to be clear about exactly what we mean by '**climate change**'. It is not an intuitively obvious thing to understand. To understand climate change, we must first understand what we mean by '*climate*'. In Block 1, you calculated average temperatures for Antarctica. Crudely, you can think of climate as average weather. Alternatively, climate is what you expect; weather is what you get. We can begin to think more scientifically about climate by first thinking about the weather. What is the weather like outside right now? You can probably give a fairly detailed description in terms of temperature, rain, wind-strength, sunshine, cloud cover, perhaps even humidity. The different components that make up the weather are readily observable and easily understandable. Weather is pretty easy to understand: it hits you in the face, soaks you, blows you about, burns you, makes you freeze, makes you sad or happy. That's weather!

Now think about the climate of your country. Looking out of the window doesn't help much in describing the climate because, unlike the weather, it is not possible to observe the climate directly. Instead, you probably think about your own climate in terms of it being generally warm, wet, windy, dry or sunny. In this sense, 'climate' describes *average* weather conditions in a given place. Quantitatively, this might involve the arithmetic mean (over a defined period) of the various elements of the weather (e.g. 30 mm rainfall per month, 3.2 hours of sunshine per June day, an average April wind speed of $1.3 \, \mathrm{m \, s^{-1}}$, etc.). Climate can also be quantified as the *variability* of mean weather, including extremes — for example, average lows of $4.5 \, °C$ in the winter months, average highs of $18 \, °C$ in summer months, and so on.

But what if you were asked to describe the climate in your *region* of the world? Thinking about the climate over a region is still more complicated. Even across relatively small regions such as the 2500 km or so between Edinburgh in Scotland and Montpellier in the South of France, the climate varies dramatically and is dependent on factors such as latitude, height above sea-level, proximity to the coast, and local topography. As we define still larger geographical regions, the idea of an 'average' climate becomes even harder to conceive, as in the case of Europe as a whole. There are such climatic differences between say the Nordic countries and those in the Mediterranean that we can't really speak of a 'European' climate as such. This is even more the case at a *global* scale (Figure 1.12). Again, we must fall back on statistical data, this time involving global averages for the parameters mentioned above, and the variability in these characteristics around such averages.

So what on earth does climate change mean? We'll see in Chapter 2 that the basis of evidence of global climate change is changes in a group of variables averaged over the globe as best we can. These include: **global mean surface temperature** (GMST; discussed in more detail in Section 1.9.1), carbon dioxide and other greenhouse gas concentrations, changes in sea-level, precipitation patterns, and the frequency and intensity of extreme weather events.

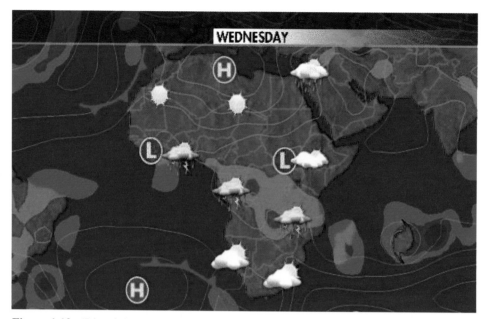

Figure 1.12 'It's raining in Africa'. Forecasting climate change at a global level is even less meaningful.

Bear these thoughts in mind as we begin our brief tour of some of the key aspects of the scientific assessment of climate change.

Box 1.3 The 1970s ice age scare

You may be surprised to learn that the theory that we were heading into another 'ice age' was really quite topical and scientifically respectable in the 1970s. In fact, the theory was partly fuelled by long-term temperature measurements that showed a consistent cooling effect happening in the post-war years. You can see this clearly if you look at Figure 1.13, and, in particular, the years between 1940 and 1970.

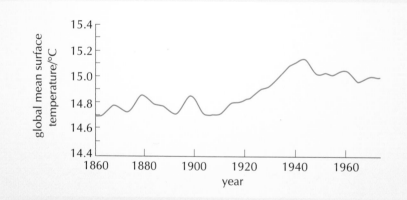

Figure 1.13 Evidence for a possible approaching ice age (Source IPCC 2001a).

What do these data tell you? Some people didn't need too much convincing. This was enough evidence to support the theory of the coming of a new ice age, set against the general backdrop of concern, gloom and doom. Some environmental scientists were particularly interested in the suggestion that an increase in natural and anthropogenic **aerosols** (liquid or solid particles suspended in a gas which lead to air pollution) would have a significant cooling effect on the climate. In fact, the scientific logic was correct (see Chapter 2), but the effect was not enough to outweigh the warming caused by increasing concentrations of greenhouse gases. Here are just a few quotes, which together give you a sense of how the issue was presented and how it evolved:

> Certain signs, some of them visible to the layman as well as the scientist, indicate that we have been watching an ice age approach for some time without realizing what we are seeing... Scientists predict that it will cause great snows which the world has not seen since the last ice age thousands of years ago.
>
> Betty Friedan, 'The Coming Ice Age', *Harper's Magazine*, September 1958

> An increase by only a factor of 4 in the global aerosol background concentration may be sufficient to reduce the surface temperature by as much as 3.5 K [degrees kelvin, K, in this context is the same as degrees Celsius]. If sustained over a period of several years, such a temperature decrease over the whole globe is believed to be sufficient to trigger an ice age.
>
> S. I. Rasool and S. H. Schneider, *Science*, **173**, p. 138, July 1971

> The threat of a new ice age must now stand alongside nuclear war as a likely source of wholesale death and misery for mankind.
>
> Nigel Calder, *International Wildlife*, July 1975

> This [cooling] trend will reduce agricultural productivity for the rest of the century.
>
> Peter Gwynne, *Newsweek*, 1976

> This cooling has already killed hundreds of thousands of people. If it continues and no strong action is taken, it will cause world famine, world chaos and world war, and this could all come about before the year 2000.
>
> Lowell Ponte, *The Cooling*, 1976

1.6 So is it happening? Early warning signs of climate change

The first page of the IPCC TAR Working Group II report deals with the interrelated themes of impacts, adaptation and vulnerability, followed by a summary of what is termed 'emergent findings'. The report concludes that there is high confidence (67–95%; see Box 1.4 overleaf) that recent regional changes in mean temperatures have had an impact on many physical and biological systems.

Box 1.4 What risk means to the IPCC (IPCC 2001b, p. 24)

You were introduced to the IPCC's *qualitative* approach to the assessment of uncertainty in Book 1 (Box 1.1). In the TAR, the IPCC also uses a more *quantitative* approach to the assessment of uncertainty:

Five levels of confidence are distinguished, namely:

very high	95% or greater
high	67–95%
medium	33–67%
low	5–33%
very low	less than 5%

According to the IPCC (2001b, p. 3), a literature survey of papers documenting the biological and physical changes associated with regional climate change reveals with high confidence that the following observations are related to climate change:

- shrinkage of glaciers;

- thawing of permafrost;

- later freezing and earlier break-up of ice on rivers and lakes;

- lengthening of growing seasons in mid- to high latitudes;

- poleward and altitudinal shifts of plant and animal ranges;

- decline of some plant and animal populations;

- earlier flowering of plants, budding of trees, emergence of insects and egg-laying in birds and amphibians. The effects of climate change on ecosystems were introduced in Book 2, Chapter 3.

○ List the four methods of investigating how climate change affects ecosystems mentioned in Book 2, Chapter 3.

○ (i) Phenology and physiology of organisms; (ii) shifts in the range and distribution of species; (iii) community shifts; (iv) changes in the structure and complex dynamics of ecosystems (Book 2, p. 59).

Figure 1.14 shows locations where temperature-related climate impacts on physical and biological systems have been clearly established by the IPCC. Systems affected include:

- hydrology and glaciers;

- sea-ice;

- animals;

- plants.

Observed changes in birds, glaciers, plants, invertebrates, amphibians and mammals are all in the direction we would expect from a warming world. The IPCC TAR is confident that there is negligible probability that the observed changes happened by chance, given what is known about various mechanisms of change in biological and physical systems. In other words, a large proportion (over 80–90%) of observed changes in biodiversity and physical processes are in the direction consistent with well-established temperature relationships. However, the TAR notes that around 20% of bird observations do not fit these relationships.

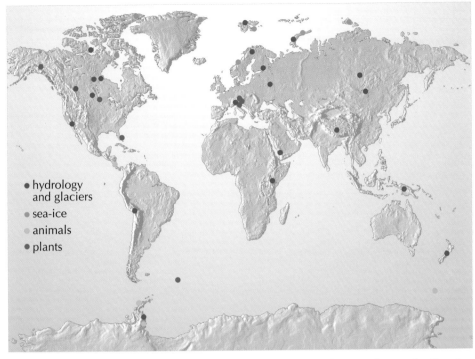

Figure 1.14 Clear physical and biological evidence of climate impacts that can be directly attributed to temperature change is hard to gather, but is nevertheless quickly accumulating.

1.7 Why is climate change a problem? Who for, where and when?

Is climate change a problem? The answer is complex and depends on the amount of climate change envisaged. It is not automatically obvious that climate change presents a 'net' problem — that is, after balancing the costs with the benefits. After all, won't there be some benefits from a slightly warmer world? Policymakers and scientists recognize that a 1–2 °C average warming does not sound particularly alarming to large, rich populations in many northern developed countries. This is particularly so at higher latitudes and in the context of winter. In Northern Europe, North America, Central and Eastern Europe and Northern Asia, a slight warming must sound positively attractive to many. Asking Northern Europeans to take action to prevent this happening doesn't seem to be a particularly easy marketing task.

However, populations in sub-tropical, tropical and equatorial climates may perceive a 1–2 °C increase in mean temperature very differently.

When we think about the 'problem' of climate change, we ought to be thinking about a whole variety of different possible problems. Evidence of the effects of climate change that are already apparent is given in Box 1.5 (overleaf). An increase in GMST will have various effects on regional climates. Models of the various systems that are affected by climate change show a variety of climate impacts occurring as GMST increases (Chapter 2).

Climate change will deliver a vast number of possible impacts. In terms of human welfare, some impacts will be positive and others negative (Figure 1.15 overleaf).

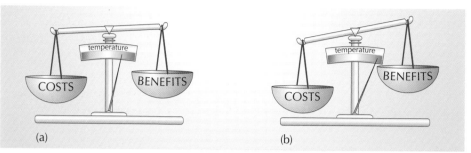

(a)   (b)

Figure 1.15   Climate change is not all doom and gloom. Initially there will be winners as well as losers. Average temperature increases of 1–2 °C (a) will benefit some regions and systems, and damage others. But as the global temperature increases further beyond 3–4 °C (b), the costs begin to rapidly outweigh benefits.

Box 1.5 Climate change is already a reality (UCS, 2003)

Here is just a handful of the sorts of stories that are now emerging out of scientific research demonstrating real evidence of rapid climate change:

1   Since 1945, the Antarctic Peninsula has experienced a warming of about 2.5 °C, which is five times the global average. The annual melt season has increased by 2 to 3 weeks in just the past 20 years.

2   Mount Kilimanjaro, Tanzania (Figure 1.16). 82% of Kilimanjaro's ice has disappeared since 1912, with about one-third melting since 1990. At this rate, all the ice will be gone by about 2015. Scientists hypothesize that less snow on the mountain during the rainy season decreases the surface reflectiveness, leading to higher rates of absorption of heat and increased ice melt (an example of positive feedback).

Figure 1.16   Melting snows of Kilimanjaro: The Landsat 5 and Landsat 7 satellites captured this pair of images over Mount Kilimanjaro on February 17, 1993 (left), and February 21, 2000 (right). The snow and ice on the summit of Mount Kilimanjaro is melting so fast that some scientists believe its ice cap could be gone by the year 2015.

3   Galapagos Islands, Ecuador. In March/April 2002, sea-surface temperatures rose above 27.5 °C several times, causing repeated coral bleaching events. This eventually kills corals and causes a decline in associated marine species.

4   New York City, July 1999. New York City had its warmest and driest July on record, with temperatures climbing above 35 °C for 11 days — the largest number ever in a single month.

5   Chokaria Sundarbans, Bangladesh. Rising ocean levels have flooded about 7500 hectares of mangrove forest during the past three decades. Global sea-level rise is aggravated by substantial deltaic subsidence in the Ganges delta, with rates as high as 5.5 mm yr^{-1}.

6   United Kingdom. The average first flowering date of 385 British plant species has advanced by 4.5 days during the 1990s compared with the previous four decades: 16% of species flowered significantly earlier in the 1990s than previously, with an average advancement of 15 days in a decade. These data reveal the strongest biological signal yet of climatic change. Flowering is especially sensitive to the temperature in the previous month, and spring-flowering species are most responsive.

7   Samoa has experienced shore recession of about 46 cm per year for at least the past 90 years.

The IPCC summarizes the projected negative impacts for small increases in GMST as:

- *Crop yields*: reductions in crop yields in most tropical and sub-tropical regions, even at small projected increases in temperature; larger temperature increases would lead to reductions in crop yields in regions in mid-latitudes.

- *Water resources*: increasing scarcity for many regions already suffering from shortage of water, particularly in the sub-tropics (in Book 4 you will learn more about linkages between climate change and water issues).

- *Disease*: increasing population exposed to vector-borne diseases (e.g. malaria) and water-borne diseases (e.g. cholera), as well as increase in deaths caused by heat stress.

- *Flooding*: increased risks for tens of millions of people in many countries from heavier rainfall, storms and sea-level rise.

- *Energy consumption*: could increase as a result of people relying more on air conditioning in summer (where electricity and air conditioners are available).

For small increases in GMST, the IPCC summarizes the projected beneficial impacts as:

- *Crop yields*: could increase for some regions at mid-latitudes for small increases in temperature.

- *Timber supply*: could increase from sustainably managed forests (see Chapter 7).

- *Water resources*: more precipitation could improve the situation in some water-scarce regions, such as parts of South-East Asia.

- *Winter deaths*: fewer in mid to high latitudes.

- *Energy consumption*: could decrease because of reduced need for space heating due to higher winter temperatures.

There is a strand of climate modelling and research that quantifies the benefits and the costs of climate change. *Integrated assessment models* (IAMs; see Chapter 4) are evolving rapidly. They are becoming more and more capable of translating climate impacts into impacts on human welfare.

On balance, integrated assessment models suggest that climate change is a net negative cost to human welfare; that is, it's a problem. But this is *on balance*, and only if you add up all the changes and look at winners and losers for a small degree of warming. We shall look at potential impacts in more detail in Chapter 2.

The distribution of positive impacts (e.g. higher crop yields from the enhanced fertilization effect of higher atmospheric carbon dioxide concentrations) and negative impacts (e.g. increased probability of storm damage) depends on location, and on the size and rate of increase in global and regional mean temperatures. Generally, there can be simultaneous positive and negative impacts on crops, water scarcity problems, or human health, for example.

1.8 Major reasons for concern about future climate change

The IPCC TAR correlated the magnitude of climate change with five categories of 'reasons for concern'. The five categories are listed in Table 1.1, together with illustrative examples.

The IPCC has summarized the relationship between these various categories of risk and temperature increase (Figure 1.17).

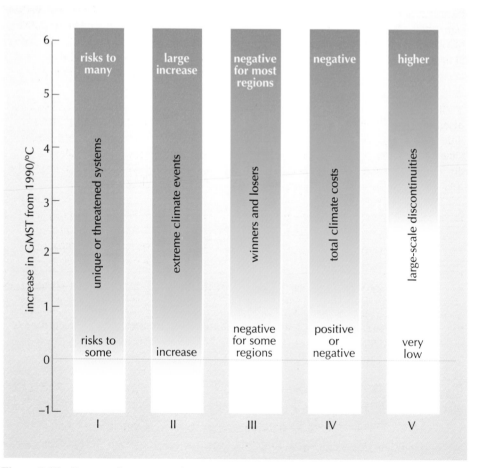

Figure 1.17 Reasons for concern about projected climate change (numbers refer to the risk categories given in Table 1.1).

Table 1.1 The IPCC's five categories of 'reasons for concern' about climate change (Source IPCC 2001b)

Risk category	Examples
I Risks to unique and threatened systems	Tropical glaciers, coral reefs, mangroves, biodiversity hotspots and transition areas between different environments, habitats or ecosystems.
II Risks from extreme climate events	Floods, droughts, storms, unusually high or low temperatures, and fires.
III Risks due to the distribution of impacts (This is not easy to understand, but can be crudely thought of as relating partly to some notion of political risk — that is, which countries are most vulnerable.)	Climate impacts will not be the same in all countries: there will be winners and losers for various sectors in various countries. In general, richer countries may be able to cope better than poorer countries, particularly if the latter are more vulnerable. The risks stem from the inequalities and unevenness of the impacts that climate change will bring, especially in its early phases (i.e. when the temperature increase is low).
IV Risks due to aggregate impacts (This category of risk is reasonably controversial, as it involves putting an economic value on costs and benefits of climate change, and then looking at the net result.)	'Aggregate impacts' is a measure of the total cost of climate change on the economy. The size of the human welfare loss is usually measured in terms of % of GDP, taking into account costs and benefits of climate change for a particular increase in global mean surface temperature.
V Risks due to future **large-scale discontinuities** ('Large-scale discontinuities' means significant and sudden change in a system, way outside the normal variability inherent in it. Risks from large-scale discontinuities are poorly understood; they are changes in the climate system that would have widespread and sustained impacts.)	The possibility of dramatic and sudden cooling in the UK as a result of the weakening or loss of the Gulf Stream is an example. Others include: possible large retreat of the Greenland and West Antarctic Ice Sheets, accelerated warming due to carbon cycle feedbacks in the terrestrial biosphere and releases of terrestrial carbon from permafrost regions and methane clathrates[a] in coastal sediments.

[a] A clathrate compound involves a gas molecule enclosed within a matrix of another compound. In the case of the methane clathrates, the methane is trapped in a water matrix, which is why they are sometimes referred to as 'methane hydrates'. If this methane is released by a rise in seawater temperature, it could have a profound effect on GMST. However, according to best current estimates, it could take tens of thousands of years for the ocean floor temperature to rise sufficiently for that to happen.

Figure 1.17 uses a colour code to indicate three increasing levels of risk. The IPCC's official explanation of the colour key is:

white indicates neutral or small negative or positive impacts or risks;

orange indicates negative impacts for some systems or low risks;

red means negative impacts or risks that are more widespread and/or greater in magnitude.

However, the IPCC does not quantify 'low' and 'high' risk in this context. For our purposes, we can interpret the key in clearer terms:

white means little reason for concern — low risk;

orange means considerable reason for some concern — intermediate risk;

red means many reasons for great concern — high risk.

○ Using Figure 1.17, summarize in your own words the relationship between reasons for concern and projected increase in GMST.

● The main points to note are that:

- for small projected mean temperature increases (up to 2 °C), there are no or low risks (various costs and benefits depending on location, reason for concern, etc.);
- for larger projected mean temperature increases (>3 °C), the risks from climate change rise; above 3–4 °C there are high risks in all categories of reasons for concern.

1.9 How does driving a car make the sea-level rise?

You are no doubt reasonably familiar with the terms **global warming**, **greenhouse effect** and **greenhouse gases** (GHGs). But how much of the basic scientific mechanisms and processes at play in the process of global warming can you describe simply and easily?

○ Can you readily describe the scientific steps that explain why burning fossil fuels leads to climate impacts such as sea-level rise? Sketch out the chain of causality between greenhouse gas emissions and sea-level rise, as you understand it.

● Keep your notes — we'll return to them at the end of Section 1.10.

Don't you find it just slightly bizarre, perhaps even confusing in some way, that climate change — arguably the most important and urgent environmental issue humanity faces today — is somehow inextricably connected to the notion of a greenhouse? The word 'greenhouse' is a very important one at the beginning of the 21st century. It is printed in (English language) newspapers and magazines, and said on radio and television thousands of times a week in the context of climate change. Let's review the basic science behind terms such as 'global warming', the 'greenhouse effect' and 'greenhouse gases'.

1.9.1 Global warming

Let's start with the notion of global warming. What exactly do we mean by global warming? We mean that the Earth is warming up. Well yes, of course, but which bit? Do we mean all of it, or just some of it? Think about it for a moment. It's a simple question, but the answer isn't at all straightforward. This is because temperatures around the Earth vary dramatically in both space and time. 'Global warming' is the term used to describe the recent observed increase in GMST. Book 1 looked in some detail at the question of mean surface temperatures in summer and winter in Antarctica as well as the seasonal cycle of atmospheric temperatures. Now imagine thinking about such questions on a global basis — across all latitudes and longitudes. The temperature at the South Pole ranges from −30 to −60 °C, and at the North Pole is in the range

0 to −30 °C; the maximum temperature in hot climates is 40 to 50 °C. So the difference between minimum and maximum temperatures in the biosphere is in the range 70 °C to 110 °C. In any one place, temperature changes over the course of a day, throughout the week, over the month, and by the season. Temperatures vary from one place to another depending on latitude and local climate factors. Temperatures vary from land to air to sea. They also vary according to altitude: it gets cooler as you walk up a mountain or jet up into the sky (see Figure 1.21). So how do we know the Earth is warming and what exactly do we mean? The answer isn't trivial and is keeping many scientists busy (Box 1.6). In brief, we take into account the variety of different temperatures on the Earth and average these over different places and different seasons. The result is an artificial globally averaged temperature called global mean surface temperature (GMST).

Box 1.6 Measuring the temperature of the Earth's atmosphere is not a simple task. Where on earth do you stick the thermometer?

What do we mean precisely by the 'global mean surface temperature'? GMST is actually measured using a network of observation stations on both land and sea.

There are several different networks of temperature observation stations for:

- land surface (various altitudes);

- ocean temperatures.

The global mean surface temperature is an index made by combining and weighting thousands of measurements from the global climate observing system (GCOS). The GCOS comprises a network of thousands of land and marine monitoring stations, buoys and ships (Figure 1.18).

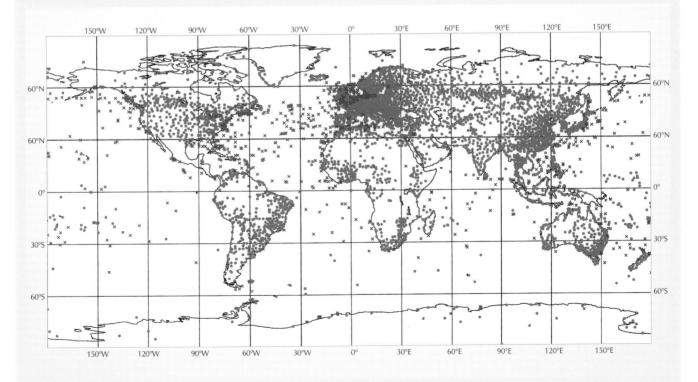

Figure 1.18 The distribution of surface temperature measurements reported on a particular day. (The total number of observations was 12 683.)

The notion of a global mean surface temperature is extremely artificial. In fact, although it is one of the most important tangible pieces of evidence of climate change, some climate scientists are becoming frustrated with the notion. There are two good reasons for this:

(a)   Current measurements of GMST are not based on a truly globally averaged temperature (the measurement points are not evenly spaced). Although it is true that GMST has increased, the data show that this is mainly because of temperature increases at night, in the winter, in cold places.

(b)   Even if we measured GMST more accurately, the mean temperature may be unhelpful. There is now plenty of evidence that climate change and its impacts are likely to be a lot more dependent on regional temperature changes.

1.9.2 The greenhouse effect

So what is the mechanism behind global warming? This is the famous 'greenhouse effect'. The term is used to communicate the idea that the Earth's atmosphere behaves a bit like a greenhouse (though in a rather simplistic way, as you will see). The air inside a greenhouse is warmer than the surrounding air. The Earth is around 33 °C warmer than it would otherwise be without its atmosphere, so in that sense the Earth's atmosphere is behaving like a greenhouse. This has been the case for millions of years and, thankfully for humans and other life forms, has kept the Earth warmer than it would otherwise be given its position in space as 'the third rock from the Sun', 150 million kilometres away (Figure 1.7). This is the 'natural' greenhouse effect.

So how exactly does the atmosphere act like a greenhouse? The rather surprising answer, in fact, is that the atmosphere behaves very unlike a greenhouse! The label 'greenhouse effect' is scientifically quite misleading, and in some ways is quite unfortunate. However, it is now the key term used to describe the mechanism underlying global warming (the increase in GMST), and it seems as though we are stuck with it. The air inside a greenhouse is warmer than the outside mainly because the glass traps warm air that would otherwise escape through the process of convection. The Sun shines on the greenhouse and warms the air inside. Air expands, becoming less dense than surrounding air, and flows (convects) upwards inside the greenhouse. A small amount of the warming that takes place inside a greenhouse is due to a process very different from convection and heat trapping, and it is here that we can make a connection between the atmosphere and a greenhouse. The warming we experience in sunlight is chiefly due to radiation in the infrared region of the electromagnetic spectrum (Figure 1.19).

Not only does the glass act to trap the infrared radiation that would otherwise escape, but it also reflects some of it back into the greenhouse. The selective absorption of infrared radiation in daylight, and its subsequent re-emission back into the greenhouse is the essence of the science that explains why the Earth's atmosphere is warmer than would otherwise be the case. (But it is not the main reason why greenhouses are warm.)

1.9.3 The science behind the greenhouse effect

So the Earth is not a warm place because heat is somehow trapped at the top of the atmosphere due to some physical barrier as it is in a greenhouse. This is why the analogy with a greenhouse is really not a good way to understand how the atmosphere traps heat from the Sun and keeps the Earth 33 °C warmer than it would otherwise be.

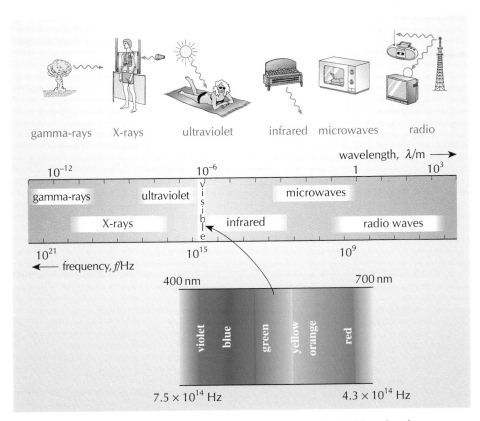

Figure 1.19 Electromagnetic radiation subdivided by wavelength. Note that the wavelength increases from left to right, so that (for example) infrared radiation has longer wavelength than visible radiation.

The beginning of an understanding of this mystery came in 1860, when John Tyndall described the infrared 'excitability' of water vapour (Box 1.7 overleaf).

There is a lot of water in the atmosphere (around 15 000 km³; see 4). Each day around 10% of it falls as precipitation, and is replaced by an equivalent amount through evaporation and transpiration. Moreover, water vapour is the most important greenhouse gas in the Earth's atmosphere, and without it the Earth would be a much cooler place. Humans affect the hydrological cycle in many ways (this is the topic of Book 4). However, the volume of water evaporating into the atmosphere every day is so large compared with the disturbance that human activity causes in the hydrological cycle, that we can assume that humans have negligible, if not zero, impact on global average atmospheric water vapour concentrations. The human perturbation on the carbon cycle is much greater than on the hydrological cycle. Human activity *directly* affects the atmospheric carbon dioxide concentration, but does not directly affect water vapour concentrations on a global scale, whereas it can do so locally as, for example, when forests are cut down. However, human activity does influence the global water vapour concentration *indirectly* through the **enhanced greenhouse effect** (see also Chapter 2).

Although water vapour is a powerful greenhouse gas, and there is lots of it in the atmosphere, its concentration varies significantly (0.5–4%) with latitude, longitude, altitude, and at any single place over time. For this reason Table 1.2 relates to the *dry* atmosphere.

Box 1.7 Water vapour: 'More necessary to the vegetable life of England than clothing is to man'

One of the main climate research institutes in the UK is in Norwich. It is called the Tyndall Centre after John Tyndall (Figure 1.20), the physicist who was one of the first scientists to recognize the 'natural greenhouse effect' taking place in the Earth's atmosphere. Tyndall was an early climate change researcher. In 1860, he suggested that slight changes in the atmospheric composition could bring about climatic variations. He was exploring radiation passing through the atmosphere and noted that:

> The waves of heat speed from our earth through our atmosphere towards space. These waves dash in their passage against the atoms of oxygen and nitrogen, and against molecules of aqueous vapour. Thinly scattered as these latter are, we might naturally think of them merely as barriers to the waves of heat.

Figure 1.20 John Tyndall (1820–1893) was a late starter in his academic life, only beginning his formal studies at the age of 28, when he enrolled for a course in Marburg, Germany, presided over by Robert Bunsen (famous for his burner). After he graduated, he joined the Royal Institution, where he earned considerable renown for presenting science to the public. Apart from being a pioneer in climate research, he contributed to the advancement of science in various areas such as glacier motion, the germ theory of disease, and the diffusion of light in the atmosphere, where he was honoured for his explanation of why the sky is blue — the Tyndall effect.

Tyndall's main interest was with water vapour and its impact on radiation. Most importantly he identified that there was a greenhouse effect, whether natural or anthropogenic. For water vapour he noted that:

> The aqueous vapour constitutes a local dam, by which the temperature at the earth's surface is deepened; the dam, however, finally overflows and we give space all that we receive from the sun…This aqueous vapour is a blanket more necessary to the vegetable life of England than clothing is to man. Remove for a single summer night the aqueous vapour from the air that overspreads this country, and you would assuredly destroy every plant capable of being destroyed by a freezing temperature. The warmth of our fields and gardens would pour itself unrequited into space, and the sun would rise upon an island held fast in the iron grip of frost…Its presence would check the earth's loss; its absence without sensibly altering the transparency of the air, would open wide a door for the escape of the earth's heat into infinitude.

90% of the total mass of the atmosphere (excluding water vapour) lies in the troposphere (Figure 1.21). Of this, 98.5% is nitrogen and oxygen, and just under 1% is argon (Table 1.2). The last 0.57% comprises trace amounts of a large variety of gases, some of which are greenhouse gases.

Table 1.2 The gaseous composition of dry air in the troposphere

Component	Composition/volume %
nitrogen (N_2)	77.6
oxygen (O_2)	20.9
argon (Ar)	0.93
neon, krypton, helium, xenon	traces
Gases regulated under the Kyoto Protocol [a] (data as of 2000)	
carbon dioxide (CO_2)	0.037
methane (CH_4)	0.000 174 5
nitrous oxide (N_2O)	0.000 031 4
hydrofluorocarbons (HFCs; e.g. HFC-23)	0.000 000 001 4
perfluorocarbons (PFCs; e.g. CF_4)	0.000 000 008 0
sulfur hexafluoride (SF_6)	0.000 000 000 45

a The Kyoto Protocol is discussed in Chapter 3.

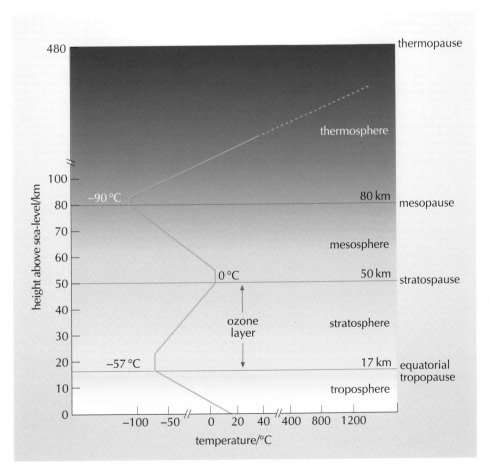

Figure 1.21 The structure of the Earth's atmosphere is like a series of concentric shells defined by gaseous composition and temperature bands (troposphere, stratosphere, mesosphere, thermosphere). The diagram shows a plot of atmospheric height against temperature; note that the curve changes direction at particular heights (tropopause, stratopause, mesopause).

The spectrum of radiation emitted by a planetary (or other) body is a function of its temperature. The Sun is very hot — about 6000 °C — and most of the radiation it emits is in the visible region. The Earth, however, is much cooler, and its radiation spectrum is wholly in the rather lower energy infrared region (Figure 1.19). That infrared radiation would escape the Earth's atmosphere altogether were it not for the presence of water vapour and some of the trace gases in Table 1.2, notably carbon dioxide, which absorb it, and in so doing make the atmosphere and the surface of the planet warmer. These are the 'greenhouse gases', and the phenomenon by which it happens is the 'greenhouse effect'. The scientific principles underlying it are outlined in Box 1.8.

Box 1.8 How carbon dioxide gets excited

The main mechanism by which a gas absorbs infrared radiation is vibration. It turns out that the criterion for a gaseous molecule to interact with infrared radiation is that there must be a *change in the* **dipole moment** during the vibration. But what is a 'dipole moment'?

Although molecules as a whole are electrically neutral, those that are composed of atoms of more than one element have an unequal distribution of charge (electron density), because the atoms of different elements have different capacities for attracting electrons. The disparity in this electron-attracting power is quantified as the dipole moment, which has both magnitude and direction; it is governed by the difference in the electron-attracting power *and the separation of the atoms* (this is significant). Hence, oxygen molecules (O_2) and nitrogen molecules (N_2), being composed of two atoms of the same element, have zero dipole moment.

But what about carbon dioxide (CO_2)? This is a linear molecule, comprising a central carbon atom, with two flanking oxygen atoms (Figure 1.22). An oxygen atom is able to attract electrons to itself more than carbon, so does carbon dioxide have a dipole moment? The answer is 'no', because the molecule is symmetrical: the partial dipole moment of one carbon–oxygen bond is cancelled out by the partial dipole moment of the other carbon–oxygen bond, which is in the opposite direction.

So why is carbon dioxide a greenhouse gas? To answer this, we need to think again about the criterion mentioned above for absorption of infrared radiation.

- What is the critical feature of this condition for absorption of infrared radiation?

- A *change* in the dipole moment during a vibration.

Molecules vibrate in different ways. In particular, bonds can stretch or the molecule can bend. For carbon dioxide, the most obvious way we can imagine a stretching vibration is when both the carbon–oxygen bonds expand together and contract together; this is called a 'symmetric stretch' (Figure 1.22a); at all times during such a vibration there is no change in the dipole moment. Hence this form of vibration for carbon dioxide is not infrared active.

However, if one bond expands while the other contracts (asymmetric stretch), and vice versa (Figure 1.22b), the size of the dipole moment will change during the vibration. So this type of vibration is infrared active. Similarly, the bending form of vibration involves a change in dipole moment, so it too is infrared active (Figure 1.22c).

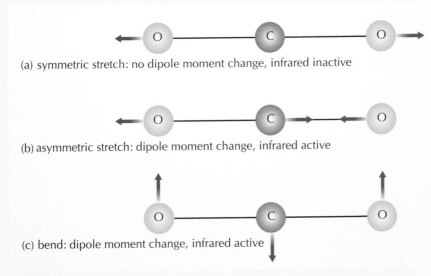

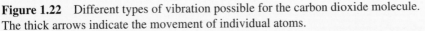

(a) symmetric stretch: no dipole moment change, infrared inactive

(b) asymmetric stretch: dipole moment change, infrared active

(c) bend: dipole moment change, infrared active

Figure 1.22   Different types of vibration possible for the carbon dioxide molecule. The thick arrows indicate the movement of individual atoms.

Every type of molecule that is infrared active has characteristic frequencies (the inverse of wavelength) of vibration, so will absorb infrared radiation of these frequencies; equally it emits radiation of the same frequency when it loses energy. The process is analogous to the resonation of a wine glass when a musical note of the right frequency (pitch) is played.

All the gases that are designated as 'greenhouse gases', such as water, methane and nitrous oxide are composed of atoms of more than one element, and so fulfil the criterion for being infrared active in the same way as carbon dioxide. Together, they account for the fact that the Earth is 33 °C warmer than it would otherwise be; it is the warming caused by the *additional* amount of these gases that have been generated by human activities since the Industrial Revolution that constitutes the **enhanced greenhouse effect**.

1.9.4 The Earth's energy balance and deviations from it

Let's now put some numbers on to the concepts that we have discussed so far. Figure 1.23 (overleaf) shows a schematic diagram of the balance of energy flows towards and away from the Earth.

The Earth emits an amount of energy equivalent to the solar energy it absorbs; if it did not, it would constantly heat up or cool down.

○ Using Figure 1.23, describe how the balance of different rates of energy gains and losses leads to thermal equilibrium.

● The net energy gain due to incoming solar radiation shown in Figure 1.23 (yellow arrows) is 69 units (100 incoming − 31 outgoing = 69 units). The net loss of infrared energy escaping to space (red arrows) is also 69 units (57 + 12 = 69 units). The incoming and outgoing radiation is therefore balanced, and the Earth is in thermal equilibrium.

Look carefully at the red arrows indicating infrared radiation in Figure 1.23. There are actually relatively high rates of energy being exchanged between the Earth's surface and the atmosphere. In fact, Figure 1.23 shows a mini-cycle of energy exchange, beginning with 114 units of infrared radiation emitted by the Earth's surface, 102 units of which are absorbed by the atmosphere. This combined with 20 units of incoming solar radiation directly absorbed by the atmosphere leads to 95 units of infrared atmospheric radiation absorbed by the surface, and so on. Relatively high rates of energy are being exchanged between the surface and the atmosphere.

Incoming solar radiation that is absorbed by the gases in the atmosphere is re-emitted at longer wavelength as infrared radiation. 49 units of solar radiation get through to the ground. The surface and the atmosphere both emit infrared radiation. Eventually, 69 units of infrared radiation escapes to space, but not before there has been some more absorption and re-emission in the meantime. The net effect of the absorption of outgoing radiation and re-emission at higher altitudes and lower temperatures is a warming of the lower atmosphere and surface.

Altering the concentrations of gases in the atmosphere that absorb infrared radiation (Box 1.8) therefore interferes with the 'natural' internal recycling of heat between the atmosphere and land.

⬤ Using Table 1.2 (p. 35), what percentage of the dry atmosphere do the six Kyoto categories of greenhouse gas make up? Your answer should be to five decimal places (that is, four significant figures).

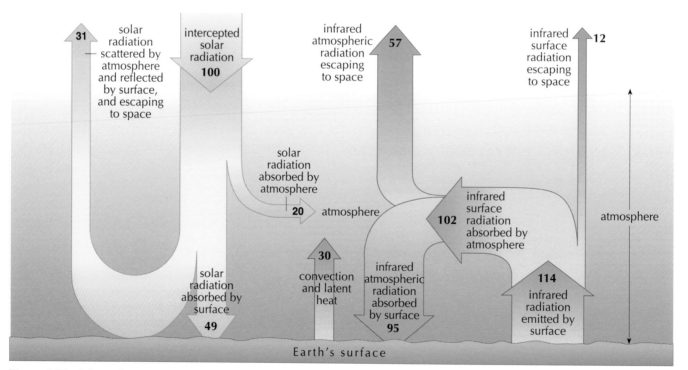

Figure 1.23 Schematic representation of rates of energy gain and loss by the Earth's surface and atmosphere. Note that although the arrows starting and stopping in the atmosphere do so in a small region in the centre, the atmospheric gains and losses that they represent take place throughout the atmosphere. 100 units represent the rate at which solar radiation is intercepted by the Earth. The width of each arrow is proportional to the rate of energy transfer.

● Concentrations of HFCs, PFCs and SF_6 are extremely low, and can be regarded as zero to the level of accuracy demanded in the question. Adding up the percentages of CO_2, CH_4 and N_2O, the total is

0.037 205 9 ≈ 0.037 21 to five decimal places

This means just a tiny proportion of the gases in the atmosphere is responsible for the increase in GMST that can be attributed to the enhanced greenhouse effect. However, although the concentrations of greenhouse gases in the atmosphere are relatively small, they exert a powerful effect on the planet's climate. Small changes in the concentrations of these greenhouse gases can have a measurable effect on GMST.

● What would be the effect on GMST of increasing the concentration of a greenhouse gas like carbon dioxide in the atmosphere?

● Higher concentrations of carbon dioxide would result in more atmospheric absorption and subsequent emission of infrared radiation into the atmosphere, and hence an enhanced greenhouse effect.

The temporary change in net outgoing radiation is referred to as **net radiative forcing**. Increased concentrations of greenhouse gases are increasing the rate of internal thermal recycling, which, in turn, is resulting in some extra radiation being directed towards the Earth's surface instead of escaping. This is the reason that higher greenhouse gas concentrations are causing global warming.

1.9.5 The concepts of 'radiative forcing' and 'direct global warming potential'

So far, we have only considered the two main greenhouse gases in the atmosphere: water vapour and carbon dioxide. There are, in fact, many other greenhouse gases, which all have their individual infrared absorption and re-emission frequencies; in addition, they remain in the atmosphere for different periods. Because the greenhouse gases that we are interested in are present in relatively small quantities, the scientific community has adopted the 'parts per million', 'parts per billion' or 'parts per trillion' method of describing their concentrations (Box 1.9 overleaf).

The composition of the atmosphere at any moment is in fact a snapshot of a very dynamic system. Each of the gases present in the atmosphere is engaged in some cycle or other. They are in the process of being mixed within one component of the climate system or exchanged between one part and another (we shall look at the climate system in Chapter 2).

● Name some of the important cycles you already know about and which are associated with the gases listed in Table 1.2.

● The carbon cycle is clearly associated with carbon dioxide concentrations and also methane concentrations. Nitrous oxide is part of the nitrogen cycle. The gases are involved in different chemical, physical and biological processes. Their life expectancies in the atmosphere depend on the speed of the cycles they are involved in (Chapter 2).

An indicator has been developed to measure the *relative* power of a given amount of different greenhouse gases. This is known as the **Direct Global Warming Potential** (DGWP) of the gas. The index measures the 'power' of the compound as a greenhouse gas *relative to carbon dioxide*. The DGWP of a gas is a measure of how powerful it is as a greenhouse gas. It is a complex combination of its 'effectiveness' and its lifetime in the atmosphere. Recall that the warming effect caused by a greenhouse gas is called 'radiative forcing'.

Radiative forcing is the amount of additional energy that a higher concentration of a particular greenhouse gas reflects back into the atmosphere. We measure radiative forcing in units of W m^{-2} (watts per square metre). Other things besides gases can have radiative forcings. Aerosols and clouds, for example, reflect solar energy back out to space, so they have negative radiative forcings. In detailed and sophisticated debates about the science behind climate change — in particular, when climate models are being discussed — you will frequently come across statements such as 'the current predictions are based on models with new assumptions about forcings'. Scientists are still busily working out radiative forcings for greenhouse gases, clouds and aerosols.

The more powerful a particular greenhouse gas (the higher its DGWP), the greater the radiative forcing effect it will have on the climate for a particular increase in concentration. The radiative forcing effect of the release of a unit (say, a tonne) of CO_2 measured over 100 years later (i.e. its cumulative effect integrated over the time period) is indexed to 1. The power of the equivalent mass of any other gas over 100 years is then expressed relative to this. Table 1.3 lists the DGWPs for the greenhouse gases covered by the Kyoto Protocol (the Kyoto Protocol is discussed in Chapter 3).

Table 1.3 shows us that carbon dioxide is a relatively weak greenhouse gas. The reason it is given such prominence is that humans are responsible for generating so much more of this gas than any other.

- How many tonnes of CO_2 would have to be absorbed by forests to have the same effect on the climate as fixing a leaking gas main, thereby avoiding the emission of 1 tonne of methane?

- A single tonne of methane released into the atmosphere has a warming effect on the planet (on a hundred-year time-scale) 23 times that of a single tonne of carbon dioxide. The forest would therefore have to **sequester** (absorb) 23 t of CO_2 to have the same effect as preventing the release of 1 t of methane from a gas leak.

Box 1.9 '500 p.p.m.' will be an everyday phrase for tomorrow's politicians

You are familiar with the notion of 'per cent'. But we could equally say 'parts per hundred'. Instead of describing the proportion of carbon dioxide in the atmosphere as '0.037%' it could be described as '0.037 parts per 100'. Or we could express this as parts per million (p.p.m.). Expressed in parts per million, the proportion of carbon dioxide in the atmosphere is 370/1 000 000 or '370 p.p.m.' Hence, we can say that the atmospheric carbon dioxide concentration is 370 p.p.m. Concentrations of rare greenhouse gases in the atmosphere are sometimes expressed in units of 'parts per billion' (p.p.b.), or 'parts per trillion' (p.p.t.). This system is more succinct than using percentages with many zeros as we did in Table 1.2.

In reports of political negotiations on climate change, you will come across politicians and other stakeholders sometimes discussing climate change using data such as '500 p.p.m.' (Figure 1.24). This is particularly the case when safe or target levels for stabilization of greenhouse gas concentrations in the atmosphere are being discussed.

Figure 1.24 What would you call your climate-related business? According to the 500 PPM company, 'Our name is our mission: 500 PPM means 500 parts per million — a crucial value for climate protection, because it describes the point at which the concen–tration of greenhouse gases in the atmosphere should be stabilized.'

Table 1.3 Direct global warming potentials (100 years) for greenhouse gases regulated under the Kyoto Protocol (Source IPCC 2001a)

Gas	DGWP for 100-year time horizon[a]
carbon dioxide (CO_2)	1
methane (CH_4)	23
nitrous oxide (N_2O)	296
hydrofluorocarbons (HFCs)	12–12 000 depending on the gas
perfluorocarbons (PFCs)	5700–11 900 depending on the gas
sulfur hexafluoride (SF_6)	22 200

a The choice of the 100-year time-scale is arbitrary, but is generally chosen to avoid problems using shorter or longer time-scales for comparison.

Direct global warming potentials are a convenient tool for getting an overview of, for example, the impact of various climate policies resulting in the reduction of various greenhouse gases (e.g. CO_2 and CH_4). Instead of having to say, for example, 'our climate program resulted in the reduction of 1 Mt of carbon dioxide and 25 000 tonnes of methane', using DGWPs we can say that the program resulted in the reduction of 1.575 Mt of **carbon dioxide equivalent** (1 Mt from CO_2 and 25 000 × 23 t (575 000) from methane = 1 575 000 t). 'Carbon dioxide equivalent' is abbreviated as 'CO_2e'.

Activity 1.2: Mixing up greenhouse gases

Anthropogenic emissions of the six greenhouse gases covered under the Kyoto Protocol for the European Union as a whole in the year 2000 are shown in the accompanying table derived from UNFCCC data:

Greenhouse gas	Quantity/Mt
carbon dioxide (including changes due to land-use change and forestry)	3144
methane	16
nitrous oxide	1
hydrofluorocarbons (HFCs), perfluorocarbons (PFCs) and sulfur hexafluoride (SF_6)	63 CO_2e

(a)   Express the grand total of European emissions of the six greenhouse gases in 2000 regulated under the Kyoto Protocol as a single number in terms of megatonnes of CO_2 equivalent.

Answer

3871 Mt CO_2e. Emissions of carbon dioxide, HFCs, PFCs and SF_6 are given in units of megatonnes of CO_2 and CO_2e. These can simply be added together. However, the values for methane and nitrous oxide must first be converted into units of CO_2e using their respective 100-year DGWPs of 23 and 296 (from Table 1.3). To convert 16 Mt of methane to its equivalent in CO_2e, we multiply by 23 — that is, 16 × 23 = 368 Mt CO_2e. To convert 1 Mt of nitrous oxide to its equivalent in CO_2e, we multiply by 296 — that is, 1 × 296 = 296 Mt CO_2e. The total contribution of the six gases expressed in Mt CO_2e can now be added up. This comes to 3871 Mt CO_2e.

(b)   How important were emissions of each of the categories of greenhouse gases listed above expressed as a percentage in relation to the grand total for all six gases?

> **Answer**
>
> The relative contribution of carbon dioxide is therefore: $3144/3871 \times 100 = 81.2\%$.
>
> The figures for methane and nitrous oxide are 9.5% and 7.6%, respectively. The relative contribution of HFCs, PFCs and SF_6 was 1.6%.
>
> In other words, statistics for the European Union in 2000 show that emissions of carbon dioxide were responsible for over 80% of the region's total contribution to global warming. Emission of methane and nitrous oxide were each responsible for around 8–9% of Europe's contribution to global warming in 2000. The combined contribution of the other three greenhouse gases was only 1.6%. The emissions profile of Europe is typical of other industrialized countries. Carbon dioxide is the main contributor to the enhanced greenhouse effect not because it is a particularly powerful greenhouse gas, but simply because we produce so very much more of it than any of the other gases.

In summary, to find out what the sum total effect that the emissions of various anthropogenic greenhouse gases is having on the internal rate of heat exchange between the surface and the atmosphere, we need to take into account:

- the relative contribution of each different gas to infrared absorption — how 'powerful' the greenhouse gas is (the DGWP value);
- the relative amounts of each gas released into the atmosphere.

1.10   Conclusion: a chain of causes and effects

Now let's try to consolidate our understanding of different aspects of the mechanisms at play in the greenhouse effect that contribute to climate change. To help us, let's briefly consider for a moment the mechanisms at work in other environmental issues. Think about a classic environmental pollution problem — pollution in a river, particulate matter in the air, or radiation leakage from a nuclear power station. In what ways are these environmental problems? What are the mechanisms at play that cause the problem? We can be very specific:

- Pollution dissolves in water; fish exposed; chemical absorbed; dose taken; effects produced; fish dies.
- Air inhaled into deep lung with small particulates carrying partially or unburnt volatile organic compounds (e.g. benzene), in contact with lung tissue (alveoli); dose received; effects produced (e.g. lung cancer).
- Radiation released; human exposed; dose received; effects produced (e.g. genetic mutation occurs causing cancer in a mother and deformity in her newly born child).

Activity 1.3: So how *does* driving a car make the sea-level rise

Now take a few minutes to write down the various steps in the chain of cause-and-effect relationships that link driving a car with sea-level rise.

Comment

Driving a car is linked to sea-level rise by the following chain of causes and effects in the climate system (Figure 1.25):

- Human activity causes the release of greenhouse gases.
- Emissions of greenhouse gases into the atmosphere alter the chemical composition of the atmosphere; in particular, greenhouse gas concentrations rise.
- Higher greenhouse gas concentrations increase the rate of recycling of infrared energy between the surface and the atmosphere. The effect is a temporary decrease in the amount of infrared radiation escaping to space.
- This has a positive radiative forcing effect on the atmosphere, causing an increase in the GMST.
- Various possible physical and biological changes can occur as a result of higher temperatures, including, for example, sea-level.
- You will see in Chapter 2 that the recently observed rise in sea-level is primarily due to the thermal expansion of seawater rather than the melting of polar ice caps.

Now compare the above with your notes on the answer you made at the start of Section 1.9. Did you include all the steps? You should now feel you would have no trouble answering the question 'how does driving a car make the sea-level rise?', at least in outline.

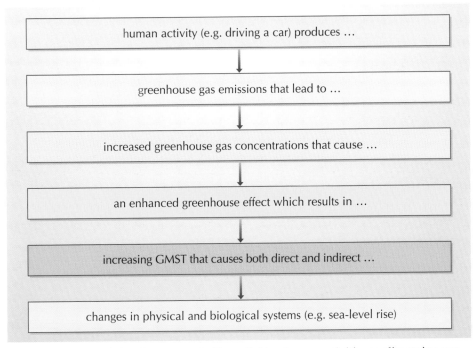

Figure 1.25   The chain of causes, and effects, linking human activities to climate impacts.

You should now go to the Web and do the activities associated with Chapter 1.

1.11 Summary of Chapter 1

1.1 The IPCC's Third Assessment Report is the most comprehensive and authoritative source of scientific information on the current status and future implications of climate change. However, the dynamics of the formal IPCC peer review process combined with the complexity of the underlying science provide plenty of opportunities for sceptics to point towards many remaining uncertainties in this assessment of climate change.

1.2 Climate change is now a key component of global political and cultural consciousness and is being linked to the broader notion of sustainable development (see also Chapter 6).

1.3 Clear evidence of temperature-related changes in various physical and biological systems is mounting, which together constitute early warning signs of global climate change. If the IPCC's projections of the scale of future climate change over the rest of the century are reasonably accurate, the warning signs are likely to become much clearer and louder within the next two decades or so.

1.4 Climate change will have negative and positive effects on different parts of the climate system and in different regions of the world. There will be some clear losers and some winners. Overall, the latest integrated assessment models suggest that climate will be a net problem for humanity; that is, its costs will outweigh any benefits. As GMST rises, the overall cost increases significantly.

1.5 Climate change presents a variety of different types of risk associated with increases in global mean surface temperature. Those risks increase dramatically as projections of temperature change increase.

1.6 The greenhouse effect is not about imaginary glass sheets at the top of the atmosphere. It is more accurately described as the absorption and re-emittance of solar radiation that has been re-emitted by the surface and the atmosphere as infrared radiation by some trace gases such as carbon dioxide.

1.7 A small change in the concentrations of greenhouse gases acts to temporarily increase the internal rate of thermal recycling between the atmosphere and the surface. The contribution of different greenhouse gases to global warming can be compared using the Direct Global Warming Potentials. DGWPs allow the warming effect of different quantities of different greenhouse gases to be expressed in mass units of CO_2e. Climate change is the result of a causal chain of effects, processes and consequences as shown in Figure 1.25.

Learning Outcomes for Chapter 1

When you have completed this chapter, you should be able to:

1.1 Define and use, or recognize definitions and applications of, each of the terms given in **bold** in the text.

1.2 Describe the function and significance of the IPCC. (Question 1.1)

1.3 Give examples of the early warning signs of climate change that are being detected, and list various reasons for concern about the potential scale and pace of climate change during the course of this century. (Questions 1.2–1.4)

1.4 Explain the enhanced greenhouse effect, and use the concept of Direct Global Warming Potential (DGWP) to perform simple calculations of the relative contribution of a variety of greenhouse gases included in the Kyoto Protocol to global warming. (Questions 1.5–1.8)

1.5 Describe in detail the causal steps that link human activity to physical and biological impacts in the climate system. (Question 1.9)

Questions for Chapter 1

Question 1.1

Which of the following statements about the IPCC are accurate?

(a) The IPCC conducts research into climate change, its causes and consequences.

(b) Every line of an IPCC report is negotiated word by word by government representatives during IPCC plenary sessions.

(c) The IPCC aims to be policy relevant, but not policy prescriptive.

Question 1.2

(a) Name four physical and biological systems where studies have revealed temperature-related climate change impacts.

(b) Give five examples of physical and biological changes associated with regional climate change observed in these systems.

Question 1.3

Which of the following could be affected both positively *and* negatively by climate change in different regions at different times?

(a) crop yields;

(b) water resources;

(c) disease;

(d) flooding;

(e) energy consumption.

Question 1.4

Rearrange the table below so that the risk categories match the examples given.

Risk category	Examples
risks due to future large-scale discontinuities	net human welfare loss due to a 2 °C warming equivalent to 5% of GDP
risks due to aggregate impacts	increases in frequency and intensity of tropical cyclones
risks due to distribution of impacts	severe famine and drought in East Africa
risks from extreme climate events	impacts on mangrove ecosystems
risks to unique and threatened systems	possible large retreat of the Greenland and West Antarctic Ice Sheets

Question 1.5

Explain why the term 'greenhouse effect' is not the most appropriate term to use from a scientific perspective for describing the mechanism that links increasing concentrations of carbon dioxide to increases in global mean surface temperature.

Question 1.6

Which of the following are not greenhouse gases?

(a)   carbon dioxide;

(b)   nitrogen;

(c)   methane;

(d)   nitrous oxide;

(e)   water vapour;

(f)   oxygen.

Question 1.7

Over a 100-year time-frame, which of the following releases of emissions would cause the greatest warming:

(a)   850 t of CO_2;

(b)   3 t of N_2O;

(c)   30 t of CH_4;

(d)   50 g of SF_6.

Question 1.8

Explain why, although carbon dioxide is a relatively weak greenhouse gas, globally, it is by far the main contributor to the enhanced greenhouse effect. Illustrate your answer using the example of European emissions of CO_2, CH_4 and N_2O in 2000 (Activity 1.2).

Question 1.9

Describe the main steps in the chain of causes and effects that links human activity to climate impacts (e.g. sea-level rise).

References

Dauncey, G., and Mazza, P. (2003) [online] Stormy weather: 101 solutions to global climate change. Available from: http://www.earthfuture.com/stormyweather/quotes/ [Accessed 17 March 2003]

IPCC (2001a) *Climate Change 2001: The Scientific Basis. Contribution of Working Group I to the Third Assessment Report of the Intergovernmental Panel on Climate Change.* Cambridge: Cambridge University Press.

IPCC (2001b) *Climate Change 2001: Impacts, Adaptation and Vulnerability. Contribution of Working Group II to the Third Assessment Report of the Intergovernmental Panel on Climate Change.* Cambridge: Cambridge University Press.

IPCC (2001c) *Climate Change 2001: Mitigation. Contribution of Working Group III to the Third Assessment Report of the Intergovernmental Panel on Climate Change.* Cambridge: Cambridge University Press.

IPCC (2001d) *Climate Change 2001: Synthesis Report. Contribution of Working Groups I, II and III to the Third Assessment Report of the Intergovernmental Panel on Climate Change.* Cambridge: Cambridge University Press.

IPCC (2002) [online] About the IPCC. Available from: http://www.ipcc.ch/about/about.htm [Accessed 30 December 2002]

Meadows, D. H., Meadows, D. L., Randers, J., and Behrens, W. W. (1972) *The Limits to Growth: a Report for the Club of Rome's Project on the Predicament of Mankind.* London: Earth Island.

Tyndall Centre [online] Available from: http://www.tyndall.ac.uk/ [Accessed 5 December 2002]

UCS (2003) http://www.climatehotmap.org [online] [Accessed 1 May 2003]

500ppm [online] Available from: http://500ppm.com/ [Accessed 24 April 2003]

Chapter 2 A citizen's guide to climate science

Prepared for the course team by Stephen Peake

2.1 Introduction

The Earth's climate system is mind-bogglingly complex. We don't satisfactorily understand how it works. To have even a basic idea of how the climate system's various geophysical, chemical and biological sub-systems interact, we would need to blend information and skills from across a number of disciplines and topics including:

- Earth sciences (oceanography, meteorology, geology, atmospheric physics and chemistry);
- biogeochemistry (the carbon cycle and biology);
- energy-economics (dynamic systems and general equilibrium modelling, policy and political sciences).

Tens of thousands of natural and social scientists are currently working on the thousands of separate pieces that make up the jigsaw puzzle of the climate system. Many people are spending large parts of their working lives refining knowledge of what amounts to one small element of a much bigger picture (Figure 2.1). Their contribution could be: singling out the signature of solar variation on the global temperature record; how a particular chlorofluorocarbon greenhouse gas (a 'CFC' gas) mixes in the upper atmosphere; refining one equation within one sea-ice model for Antarctica; tracking how one particular bird species is responding to climate change; or predicting the future cost of a specific type of new energy technology such as the fuel cell.

Fortunately, IPCC scientists have been hard at work doing a good job of summarizing this vast body of knowledge for us. This chapter reviews the emerging scientific consensus and some key remaining uncertainties. It is essential background to making sense of the global political response to climate change covered in the rest of the block.

(a)　　　　　　　　　　　　　　　　(b)

Figure 2.1　Unlocking secrets of climates past: (a) coral paleoclimatologists extracting a core from a *Porites lobata* colony on the Clipperton Atoll in the Pacific Ocean. (b) Ice taken from Lake Vostok is stored inside the US National Ice Core Laboratory (the clear ice is coated with brown kerosene used as a drilling fluid). Paleoclimatology underpins the international political response to climate change.

Activity 2.1: Imagine you *really* had to understand the science behind climate change

Imagine yourself in *one* of the following roles:

- A climate policy decision-maker. You have to get your facts right, and may need to defend your ideas against sceptics or cynics, particularly if your ideas are unpalatable to various economic and political interests.

- A climate sceptic. You have heard gloom and doom scenarios before (such as the coming of a new ice age mentioned in Chapter 1): climate change may turn out to be a false alarm. You could be the government relations representative for a large multinational oil company.

- A concerned citizen — wanting to do your bit for the planet. What is the exact nature of the evidence of climate change? Is it enough to make you change your patterns of consumption? What would it take to significantly reduce your use of cars or aircraft? Or influence where you live or whether you pay for flood insurance?

Whether you are trying to save the world from climate disaster, increase your company's oil revenues, or become an informed citizen, you are going to need to understand the key certainties and weaknesses in the evolving science of climate change.

Write down some of the key questions you think you would need answers to in your chosen role.

Comment

It's likely that many of your questions relate to the level of certainty about various aspects of climate change such as:

- Is climate change really happening?

- How do we know?

- We can't predict weather very far into the future, so how can we predict climate change?

- How much will sea-level rise?

- Could the world supply itself with enough energy from renewable sources to maintain current living standards?

- What are the costs of acting versus a 'wait and see' (do little or nothing) policy?

In this chapter we pose and answer the following questions:

- How well do we understand how the climate actually works?

- How sure are we that the Earth's climate is changing, and that humans are the cause?

- How sure are we about the nature of future climate change?

- What could happen to ecological and socio-economic systems as a result of future climate change?

We begin the chapter with a review of the main components of the Earth's climate system, and examples of some of the interactions that make it so complex.

2.2 The Earth's complex climate system

So how much do we know about how our climate really works? Extending from the edge of the Earth's atmosphere to the bottom of the deepest oceans, the Earth's climate system is incredibly complex. It is important that we realize just how complex it is. The **climate system** consists of five main components (Figure 2.2):

- atmosphere (the envelope of gases surrounding the Earth);
- hydrosphere (oceans, seas, rivers, freshwater, underground water);
- cryosphere (snow, sea-ice, ice-sheets, glaciers and permafrost);
- land surface;
- biosphere (all ecosystems and living organisms).

There are many reasons why the Earth's climate changes over the long term. Climate scientists distinguish between two different kinds of influence on the climate:

- 'Internal' changes in the interactions between the different components of the climate system (the composition of the atmosphere, the oceans, etc.). The IPCC has concluded that humans are now having an unprecedented impact on various aspects of the planet's climate system as a result of burning fossil fuels and the release of terrestrial carbon (in plants and soils) into the atmosphere from agriculture and land-use change.

- 'External' changes, such as fluctuations in solar radiation and volcanic activity, over which humans have no influence.

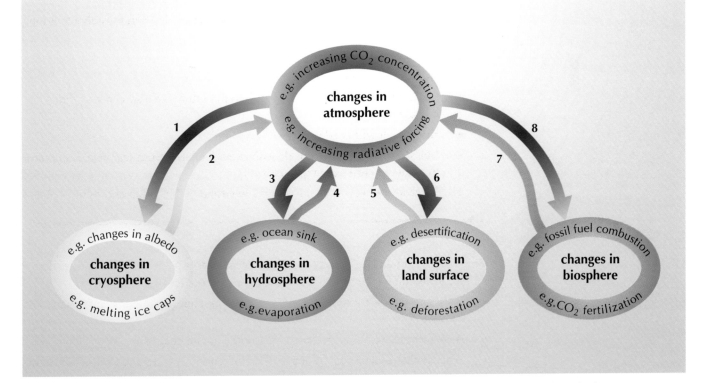

Figure 2.2 The Earth's climate system comprises five main subsystems. In this representation the atmosphere is shown as the keystone to the whole system, dynamically interacting with the other four subsystems. (The numbered interactions are discussed on p. 52).

In Chapter 1, we reviewed how the enhanced greenhouse effect influences global mean surface temperature (GMST). However, the enhanced greenhouse effect is just one small factor influencing a very complex climate system.

We know that changes in the chemical composition of the atmosphere are causing the Earth to trap more heat in its atmosphere and therefore to warm up. Atmospheric concentrations of various greenhouse gases are increasing because of many interacting physical, chemical and biological processes within the climate system.

Examples of interactions between different elements of the climate system shown in Figure 2.2 include:

1   Increasing GMST leading to melting snow and ice.

2   A reduction in the extent of snow- and ice-covered areas leading to a reduction in surface **albedo**, which, in turn, leads to warming.

3   Oceans absorbing large quantities of carbon dioxide (systems that absorb greenhouse gases are sometimes called **sinks**).

4   Water evaporating from the oceans, carrying thermal energy and water vapour into the atmosphere.

5   Deforestation releasing carbon dioxide into the atmosphere, thereby increasing the atmosphere's carbon dioxide concentration.

6   Desertification (not covered further in this chapter but referred to in Block 4) as a result of changes in regional temperature and precipitation patterns.

7   Fossil-fuel combustion and land-use change release carbon dioxide into the atmosphere, thereby increasing the atmosphere's carbon dioxide concentration. Methane enters the atmosphere from anaerobic decomposition in bogs or sediments, or from cattle belching, thereby increasing methane concentrations.

8   Plants absorbing carbon dioxide from the atmosphere, temporarily storing the carbon as plant biomass (another example of a sink; see later in this chapter).

Such interactions are examples of **couplings** between the different components of the climate system:

- Atmospheric and oceanic circulations are strongly coupled through exchange of water vapour, carbon dioxide and heat (interactions 3 and 4 in Figure 2.2).

- The biosphere is coupled to the atmosphere through photosynthesis and respiration, human activity in the form of fossil-fuel combustion and land-use change (interactions 7 and 8 in Figure 2.2; the human perturbation of the carbon cycle is described in Book 2, Chapter 1).

When a series of such interactions or couplings act in sequence to form a closed loop process, they set up a **feedback** within the climate system. There are many examples of **positive** and **negative feedbacks** at play in the climate system. Three such examples are:

- Changes in sea-ice extent and snow cover: a warming Earth leads to melting ice caps and less snow cover, which, in turn, reduce the Earth's albedo and make the planet less reflective of solar radiation, leading to greater warming (positive feedback, interactions 1 and 2 in Figure 2.2).

- The water vapour positive feedback (type 3 and 4 interactions in Figure 2.2): a warming Earth leads to increased water vapour concentrations in the atmosphere; in turn, such increases lead to greater warming (recall that water vapour is a powerful greenhouse gas), greater evaporation and higher water vapour concentrations, and so on.

- Carbon dioxide fertilization is an example of a negative feedback. Higher CO_2 concentrations speed up plant growth and carbon uptake, partially reducing CO_2 concentrations (type 7 and 8 processes in Figure 2.2). Another important negative feedback is radiative damping; a warming Earth results in an increase in infrared radiation emitted back to space, which, in turn, cools the Earth.

These different processes happen at different scales and speeds. It is clear from Figure 2.2 that the atmosphere is very much at the centre of many of these processes. As a result, it is the most unstable and rapidly changing part of the overall climate system.

A very important property of any system is how fast it responds when something in it changes. Systems that take a long time to respond to a change are said to be **inertial**. All systems exhibit inertia. Different processes within the climate system have different speeds, and this means that climate changes occur across different **time-scales**. There is a wide range of time-scales (Figure 2.3 overleaf) associated with the different components of the climate system, from two years (mixing of greenhouse gases in the atmosphere) to over ten thousand years (sea-level response to temperature change). The main inertias in the climate system' are the slow mixing of heat and carbon dioxide into deep oceans, and to a lesser extent the slow response of the terrestrial biosphere (especially soils).

- Use Figure 2.3 to make an argument as to why we ought to be extremely concerned about climate change.

- If climate change is a big problem — and there is a high chance it could be (see Chapter 1 and later sections of this chapter for the reasons for concern) — we may be already facing significant risks. We are conducting an experiment the consequences of which may last for centuries. Heat circulation in the oceans can take hundreds of years to settle down (Figure 2.3a). The result is that even if we dramatically reduce global CO_2 emissions in the course of this century, sea-levels would continue to rise for centuries to come (initially due to thermal expansion of water, and then as a result of melting ice caps; see Figure 2.3b). The quantity of greenhouse gases emitted since the beginning of the Industrial Revolution is going to affect us for centuries, no matter what we do or don't do from now on. Could it be then that the early warning signs and record temperatures we have already detected are just the tip of the iceberg (so to say)? It is possible — just possible — that we may be facing a human-induced global disaster on a previously unimaginable scale. Then again, the risks we face may not be quite so dramatic.

2.3 Fossil fuels and the carbon cycle

The Earth as a system is unintentionally being used as a living laboratory demonstrating what happens when the atmosphere receives a sudden, significant and sustained injection of greenhouse gases caused by human activity. Book 2, Chapter 1 described how carbon flows in a cycle between the land, the atmosphere and the oceans. The additional carbon dioxide (CO_2) that humans have added to the atmosphere has been relatively large compared with the ability of the carbon cycle to respond. If the carbon cycle were somehow naturally able to respond to emissions caused by human activity by absorbing an equivalent amount in oceans and the terrestrial sinks (plants), then a great deal of the problem of climate change would be avoided (ignoring other greenhouse gases).

Unfortunately, the climate system doesn't seem to be quick at counteracting the effect that humans have had on atmospheric greenhouse gas concentrations. The rate that oceans absorb CO_2 is limited by the finite speed of vertical mixing of water layers, whereas long-term storage of carbon in wood represents only a relatively small fraction of total plant carbon (in the absence of land-use change).

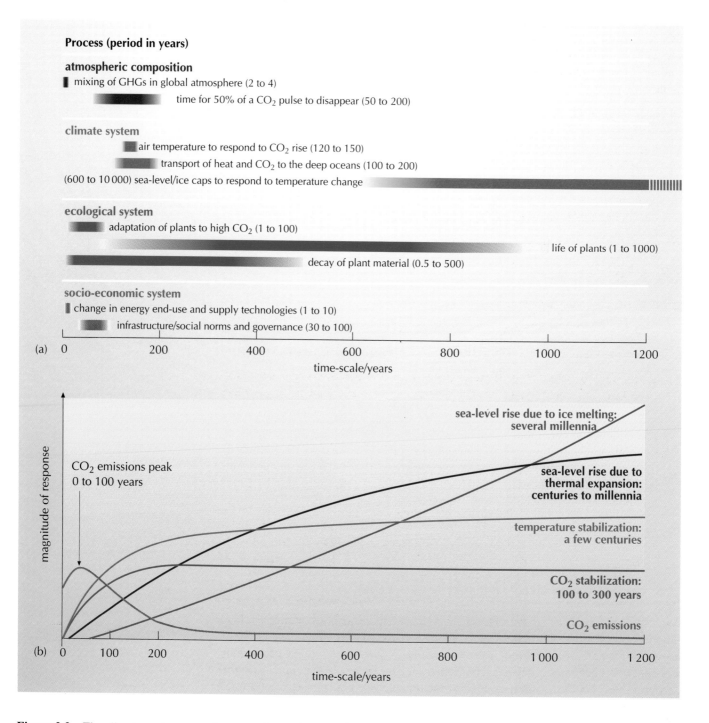

Figure 2.3 The climate system comprises some fast and some incredibly slow processes: (a) comparative time-scales of various physical and socio-economic systems (the size of the coloured bar gives an indication of the range of a particular process); (b) various climate processes plotted against their relative predicted responses over time (adapted from IPCC 2001d).

Humans are increasing CO_2 concentrations by approximately 0.4% per year, which is equivalent to a *net* flux of carbon into the atmosphere of 3.2 ± 0.1 PgC yr^{-1} (Book 2, Section 1.4.2.). Box 2.1 (p. 56) explains the different systems used for carbon counting.

Activity 2.2: Manipulating 'carbonistics' to get your message across

Make sure you have read Box 2.1 before you attempt this activity. You will constantly come across information and analysis about climate change, which use masses of either CO_2 or C as units. Sometimes it can be helpful to deliberately choose a unit that suits a specific purpose, for example to shock people or to sell some sort of new technology. Under what circumstances do you think it would help to count carbon in terms of tonnes of CO_2?

Comment

Say you wanted to shock people: 'hey, did you know that you emit 25 kg of carbon dioxide driving to work each week.' This sounds more dramatic than 6.82 kg of carbon. A given mass of CO_2 sounds smaller if you strip out the oxygen and just count the carbon. On the other hand, suppose we were trying to sell the public a new technology that could reduce CO_2 for a cost of $20 per tonne of CO_2.

What is $20/t$CO_2$ in terms of $ per tonne of carbon?

Answer

$74.1tC (which sounds a lot more expensive!)

This is $20/t$CO_2$ = $20 per 0.27tC = $20/0.27tC = $74.1tC

You will obtain a slightly different value if you used 12/44 in your calculator.

If you want to make climate technologies or measures appear cheaper, use tonnes of CO_2. If you want to make investing in the carbon market look more attractive, use tonnes of carbon; for example, 'If you plant trees, you could earn $50 per tonne carbon sequestered in your field'.

What is $50 per tonne of carbon expressed as $ per tonne of CO_2?

Answer

One tonne of carbon is equivalent to 3.67 t of carbon dioxide. You would need to sequester 3.67 t of carbon dioxide to earn $50. Sequestering 1 t of carbon dioxide would earn you $50/3.67 or $13.62. $50/tC is therefore the same as $13.62/t$CO_2$. What would you rather earn: $50/tC or $13.62/t$CO_2$? The first sounds more attractive, but in fact they are both the same thing.

So how much carbon dioxide remains in the atmosphere and how much has been absorbed by the oceans or terrestrial ecosystems? According to Table 2.1, the IPCC estimates that emissions of CO_2 from fossil-fuel burning (and cement production) from 1850 to 1998 were approximately 270 ± 30 GtC. On top of that, approximately 136 ± 55 GtC has been emitted as a result of land-use change (agriculture and urbanization), mainly from forest ecosystems.

The amount of CO_2 in the atmosphere has increased by 176 ± 10 GtC. But this leaves 230 ± 95 GtC unaccounted for. This is thought to have been taken up by the oceans and by terrestrial ecosystems.

Box 2.1 The needless complexities of carbon counting

It's impossible to read about climate change without having to wade through some strange and unfamiliar ways of measuring emissions and other factors. If politicians are seriously convinced about climate change and want the public to understand its implications, scientists are going to have to help make life simpler.

Imagine an estate agent in London advertising a £1.2m apartment for 1.2 *megapounds* (or, worse still, 0.12 *gigapence*), or the Chancellor of the Exchequer launching a new £25 billion programme to boost the National Health Service announcing he is spending 25 *gigapounds* (or 2.5 *terapence*). Unfortunately, in the TAR, the IPCC says it has 'deliberately not harmonized' various units in common usage (IPCC 2001a, p. 870). Thanks a million! Or should that be thanks a mega (Figure 2.4)!? — read on…

Quantities of carbon can be expressed in various ways depending on:

- the choice of either units of carbon, carbon dioxide or carbon dioxide equivalent;
- the choice of mass units between tonnes and grams;
- the choice of prefixes.

Figure 2.4   The Count (who likes to count) from *Sesame Street* would have a field day teaching climate numeracy. Many climate policy analysts and observers are themselves sometimes confused by the different ways of counting carbon.

We have already met three different ways of measuring carbon: tonnes carbon (tC), tonnes of carbon dioxide (tCO_2) and tonnes of carbon dioxide equivalent (CO_2e). To convert from tonnes of carbon dioxide to tonnes of carbon we must multiply by the factor 12.0/44.0 (= 0.27), the ratio of the relative atomic mass of carbon to the relative molecular mass of carbon dioxide. To convert from tonnes of carbon to tonnes of carbon dioxide we must multiply by the factor 44.0/12.0 (= 3.67).

- How much carbon is there in 10 t of carbon dioxide?

- 2.7 t. We multiply 10 by the factor 0.27: $10t \times 0.27 = 2.7t$.

IPCC scientists also use a range of different mass measures including grams and tonnes (one tonne is a million grams). It seems slightly odd that scientists and policymakers are using mass units as small as grams to measure a planetary scale phenomenon such as climate change. Scientists also use a series of different prefixes associated with the SI system of units to say exactly the same thing. A million tonnes is the same as a megatonne, and a billion tonnes is the same as a gigatonne.

The key SI prefixes you need to know in order to navigate climate science are:

mega, meaning a multiple of 1 000 000 (10^6, abbreviated 'M');

giga, meaning a multiple of 1 000 000 000 (10^9, abbreviated 'G');

tera, meaning a multiple of 1 000 000 000 000 (10^{12}, abbreviated 'T');

peta, meaning a multiple of 1 000 000 000 000 000 (10^{15}, abbreviated 'P')'.

● One tonne (1 t) is the same as 10^6 grams. How many tonnes are equivalent to (a) 1 petagram; (b) 1 teragram?

● (a) 1 billion tonnes, 10^9 t or 1 gigatonne (Gt); (b) 1 million tonnes, 10^6 t or 1 megatonne (Mt).

We can easily become frustrated at the plethora of different units being used to communicate climate change. Don't let the various units and prefixes get in the way of your understanding and ability to communicate the issues of climate change.

Table 2.1   Where has all the carbon gone? (Source: IPCC, 2000 p. 4)

Global carbon stock	Carbon mass/GtC (10^9 tonnes of carbon)
1 Total emissions of CO_2 to atmosphere from fossil-fuel burning and cement production[a] 1850–1998	270 ± 30
2 Emissions as a result of land-use change	136 ± 55
3 Increase in carbon dioxide in atmosphere	176 ± 10
4 Remainder (1 + 2 − 3) is what is estimated to have been taken up by oceans and forests	230 ± 95

[a] A large amount of CO_2 is generated during the manufacture of cement, principally by the elimination of CO_2 from limestone ($CaCO_3$); hence this is not a combustion process.

● Look at the uncertainty expressed against the different stocks in Table 2.1. Can you explain why they are relatively large for the ocean and land components, and relatively small for the atmosphere? Name two ways in which human activities are resulting in positive fluxes of carbon into the atmosphere.

● The atmospheric increase can be estimated from direct measurements of the atmospheric carbon dioxide concentration. We know what the concentrations are and how big the atmosphere is, so it is a relatively simple calculation to do. We cannot directly measure exchanges of CO_2 between atmosphere and ocean, and atmosphere and land; these have to be estimated. This is the reason for the difference. Humans are contributing positive fluxes to the atmosphere as a result of burning fossil fuels and land-use changes.

A key point is that although we have some idea of how much carbon has been released into the atmosphere by humans, and have some clues as to where it has gone, there is lots of uncertainty in these values. There is also a great deal of uncertainty about how the Earth's climate system will behave in the future. The climate system has many feedbacks in it, particularly between the carbon cycle and the atmosphere. Even if we knew our future global emissions trajectory into the next century with complete accuracy, there would still be a great deal of uncertainty around future atmospheric greenhouse gas concentrations.

To help put the carbon cycle into better perspective, we can relate carbon flows to stocks with historical and possible future fossil-fuel emissions (Table 2.2).

From Table 2.1 we see that between 1850 and 1998 humans have pumped around 270 ± 30 GtC into the atmosphere through burning fossil fuels. The key point is that according to Table 2.2 we have only burned about a fifth (295 GtC) of the reserves of carbon we *know* are in the ground (1549 GtC), and possibly as little as around a twentieth of what *might* be there (4959 GtC). When you hear stories about the world running out of fossil fuels, you have to appreciate that the figures are constructed in a particular way. In fact, those seeking to be pessimistic about future fossil fuel supply focus in particular on our rates of consumption of different fuels relative to known reserves.

Table 2.2 Estimates[a] of how much fossil carbon is still left in the ground (expressed in GtC)

Fuel	Consumption 1860–1998	Consumption in 1998	Reserves	Resources [b]	Resource base [c]
oil					
conventional	97.1	2.7	118	153	271
unconventional [d]	5.7	0.2	132	308	440
sub-total	102.8	2.9	250	461	711
natural gas					
conventional	35.9	1.2	82	179	261
unconventional	0.5	0.1	123	165	288
sub-total	36.4	1.3	205	344	549
coal	156	2.4	1094	2605	3699
total	295.2	6.6	1549	3410	4959

[a] Source: IPCC 2001c, Table 3.28b.

[b] Resources = resources yet to be developed as reserves and reserves yet to be discovered.

[c] Resources base = sum of reserves + resources.

[d] Unconventional occurrences include: oil shale, tar sands, coalbed methane clathrates. According to the IPCC, unconventional deposits require different and more complex production methods, and, in the case of oil, need additional upgrading to usable fuels. In summary, if unconventional deposits were processed today, they would cost more, and sometimes a lot more.

● Use the information in Table 2.2 to calculate how many years of reserves of *conventional* sources of oil, gas and coal we have left at 1998 rates of consumption. (Ignore completely the data on unconventional sources and rates of consumption.)

● We have 118 GtC in known reserves of oil. At the 1998 rate of consumption of conventional oil of 2.7 GtC yr^{-1}, this is equivalent to almost 44 years (118/2.7) remaining. We have around 68 years (82/1.2) of conventional natural gas left and 456 years (1094/2.4) of conventional coal left.

These figures would be a lot greater if we compared current consumption to the total resource base and not just known reserves. Also, if we included unconventional sources, the figures would be even greater still. Of course, if we allow for growing consumption, then in all cases the figures will be lower.

We only barely begun to tap into the fossil fuels that are present in the Earth. According to Table 2.1, we are just 406 GtC ($\pm$ 85) into disrupting the carbon cycle (taking into account emissions from land-use change). But, already the Earth's climate is registering a strong warning signal and signs of climate change. Imagine how much more climate change there would be if all the fossil fuel reserves lying dormant in the ground (and under our oceans) were exploited!

Simple carbon cycle mathematics tells us that if we are going to stabilize greenhouse gas concentrations, at some stage we are going to have to drastically reduce our emissions back down to levels that the climate system can cope with. We are going to have to put a limit on the emissions that humans began injecting into the atmosphere around 200 years ago (that is, the sum total of what we have already released into the atmosphere since the year 1750 from burning fossil fuels and other sources of GHGs, plus future emissions). In effect, to achieve stabilization, we are going to have to limit the sum total anthropogenic emissions within some overall cap — the lower the cap, the lower the level of stabilization, and vice versa.

Activity 2.3: Brush up your back-of-the-envelope climate modelling skills

(a)   First back-of-the-envelope insight into the Earth's climate system

Current climate models are telling us that if we want to stabilize the atmospheric CO_2 concentration at, say, 450 p.p.m., then the total of past and future cumulative emissions needs to be less than around 670 GtC (IPCC, 2001c, p. 237).

If we wanted to stabilize CO_2 concentrations at 450 p.p.m., what is the maximum total amount of emissions we can put into the atmosphere in the future?

Answer

264 GtC. From Table 2.1 we know that the total cumulative historical emission from burning fossil fuels and land-use changes is 406 $\pm$ 85 GtC. We are told that to stabilize at 450 p.p.m., the cumulative total should be below 670 GtC. There are therefore approximately 264 GtC (670 − 406) of emissions that can be emitted if we are to stabilize at 450 p.p.m. This is approximately what we have already emitted due to the burning of fossil fuels since the onset of the Industrial Revolution.

(b)   Second back-of-the-envelope insight into the Earth's climate system

Total cumulative anthropogenic emissions of carbon dioxide during the last 200 years come to 406 GtC. This comprises 136 GtC from land-use change and 270 GtC due to the burning of fossil fuels. The pre-industrial atmospheric concentration of CO_2 was 280 p.p.m. and is now 370 p.p.m., which represents an increase of around 90 p.p.m. It turns out that a 90 p.p.m. increase in the atmospheric CO_2 concentration is equivalent to an additional 190 GtC in the atmosphere. But cumulative emissions up to 1998 were 406 GtC. 190 GtC is approximately 47% of the 406 GtC that have been emitted since the start of the Industrial Revolution. The conclusion is that over a 200-year period, the atmosphere has accumulated around 47% of carbon dioxide emissions. (The rest was absorbed by the land and the oceans in roughly equal measure.)

Based on these new insights into the Earth's climate system, use a crude 'back-of-the-envelope' method for estimating the total cumulative emissions (historical plus future) of CO_2 in GtC corresponding to a stabilization of the CO_2 concentration at 650 p.p.m.

Answer

650 p.p.m. is 280 p.p.m. higher than today's concentration. We were told above that 90 p.p.m. is equivalent to an additional 190 GtC. An increase of 280 p.p.m. is just over three times (3.11) what is already observed. If the climate system is linear (a big assumption!), a 280 p.p.m. would correspond to:

$$3.11 \times 190 \, GtC = 591 \, GtC$$

However, 591 GtC is just 47% of what would have been the total emissions. The total cumulative emissions associated with 650 p.p.m. would therefore be $(100/47) \times 591 = 1257 \, GtC$.

Assuming that the Earth's climate system will behave in the future as it did in the last 200 years (a very big assumption), stabilization at 650 p.p.m. corresponds to cumulative total carbon emissions of

$$406 \, GtC^* + 1257 \, GtC^\dagger = 1663 \, GtC$$

or four times what we have generated so far from fossil fuels and land-use changes.

All these calculations assume that the relationship between CO_2 emissions and atmospheric concentration is linear. It is not! This is why scientists construct complex climate models to predict such values. But our 'envelope' is not that big, and crude calculations are still informative.

* from 280 p.p.m. in 1750 to 370 p.p.m. today.
† from 370 p.p.m. today to 650 p.p.m. in the future.

2.4 Uncertainties in our understanding of radiative forcing

How sure are we about the relationship between the atmospheric CO_2 concentration and temperature increases? Our best estimate of the increase in GMST for a doubling of the atmospheric CO_2 concentration from 280 p.p.m. to 560 p.p.m. is 1.5 °C–4.5 °C. The term used for our best estimate of how much the world might warm for a doubling of carbon dioxide concentrations is **climate sensitivity**. The IPCC TAR estimates that stabilization of carbon dioxide at 450 p.p.m. and 1000 p.p.m., respectively, would result in an equilibrium temperature rise from 1990 to 2100 of 0.9 °C–2.5 °C and 2.9 °C–7.5 °C, respectively. Increases in the concentrations of other greenhouse gases would increase these estimates.

In Chapter 1 we reviewed how increasing greenhouse gas concentrations produce a net positive radiative forcing effect and therefore lead to global warming. Now we need to go a bit further and understand that GMST is influenced by several factors that each have various effects on radiative forcing. GMST is really just an abstract statistic. It is true that what actually contributes to the climate (wind, clouds, rain storms, etc.) is differences in temperature between one region and another. However, for our purposes, GMST is a useful device for understanding how various factors influence the climate. It is an accessible way of understanding uncertainties in simple climate prediction models.

There are many aspects of the functioning of the Earth's climate that are still not properly understood. We are, however, increasingly gaining a better understanding of how various factors affect the Earth's GMST and therefore, in turn, a variety of aspects of the climate.

GMST is particularly important in determining other climatic variables. Many climate variables (precipitation, extreme events, cloud cover, sea-level) are closely related to GMST. This is why so much effort and care goes into refining models of natural and enhanced radiative forcing. All modelling and policy-making rests firmly in the first instance on radiative forcing. It is going to be very important later on to understand what affects GMST when we come to ask reasonable questions about what we know and don't know about climate change. Overall, the GMST of the Earth is determined by a number of diverse factors (explained in more detail later) including:

- atmospheric properties that affect solar radiation: aerosols (content, type, altitude) and clouds (cover, type, altitude and thickness);

- atmospheric properties that affect infrared radiation: clouds and aerosols again as well as greenhouse gas concentrations;

- surface properties that affect solar radiation: albedo of surfaces free of ice and snow; fraction of surface covered by ice and snow;

- 'external' or 'natural' factors: solar variability and volcanic eruptions.

Our knowledge about the forcing effects of the various factors that affect GMST is summarized in Figure 2.5. The most important thing to glean from Figure 2.5 is that direct forcing from the four main sources of anthropogenic greenhouse gases is by far the most significant effect (2.4 W m^{-2}) and the one we know with the highest certainty. There are a lot of smaller forcings that we are much less sure about. In other words, we are still not very sure about the science behind, for example:

- aerosols;

- the contribution of aircraft to climate change;

- the impact of land-use changes on albedo;

- solar variation;

- tropospheric ozone.

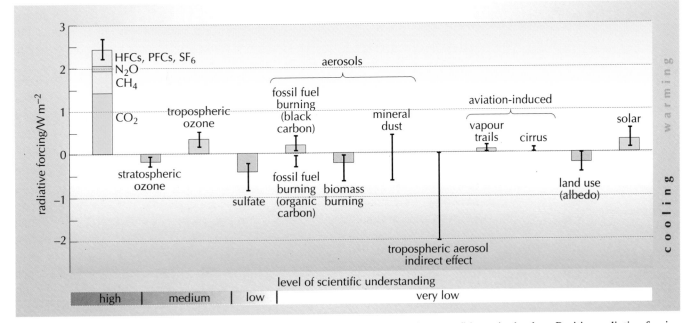

Figure 2.5 The radiative forcing effects of various factors, arranged in order of our confidence in the data. Positive radiative forcing effects are outlined in orange, and negative effects in blue. The black vertical lines indicate the range of estimates for these forcings. (Source: IPCC 2001a)

Aerosols

Aerosols include, for example, dust from volcanic eruptions, soot and sulfates from the burning of fossil fuels and biomass. The effect of aerosols on the climate is complex and not well understood. Aerosols do various things including:

- scattering part of the incoming solar radiation back into space, and therefore having a cooling effect (or negative radiative forcing effect) on GMST;

- absorbing and re-emitting infrared radiation (a warming effect);

- affecting the formation and properties of clouds, which in turn affects the climate in various ways.

The physics and chemistry of atmospheric aerosols are complex. There are several different 'species' of atmospheric aerosols including sulfates, black carbon, organic carbon, biomass burning and mineral dust. Our current estimation is that sulfates (largely derived from fossil fuel and biomass combustion), wood burning and the release of organic carbon (a by-product of fossil fuel and biomass combustion) have a negative radiative effect (i.e. cooling effect), whereas black carbon from fossil-fuel combustion produces a positive effect (Figure 2.5). We are not sure whether mineral dust has a cooling or warming effect. The dust thrown into the atmosphere from volcanic eruptions has a cooling effect, which typically lasts a few years.

Effect of clouds

Clouds reflect sunlight back into space. Think about what happens to you on a spring day as the Sun dips behind a cloud. You can instantly feel chilly. Where did that lovely heat go? Some of it was reflected back into space off the cloud. Clouds can also trap heat: starry nights are generally colder than cloudy ones. As clouds are made of water vapour, they also contribute to the thermal warming of the atmosphere through infrared absorption and re-emittance. High clouds have a net warming effect, whereas low clouds have a net cooling effect. The net effect of a cloud on the balance of radiative forcing depends on the type of cloud and its altitude.

But the effect of clouds on radiative forcing is a major uncertainty in climate prediction, 'probably the greatest uncertainty' according to the TAR (IPCC, 200lb, technical summary p. 49).

Change in surface albedo

Changes in various surface properties of the Earth can affect albedo (the amount of reflected solar radiation). Snow-covered forested areas reflect less light back to the atmosphere than open deforested snow-covered areas. Cutting down trees in snow-covered areas can have a cooling effect because more radiation is reflected back to space. Sea-ice reflects more incoming radiation than seawater. It also insulates the sea from heat loss during the winter. Overall, a reduction in the area of sea-ice has a positive effect on radiative forcing, and so has a warming effect.

External or natural factors

Two major natural factors that have a significant influence on radiative forcing are:

- changes in the level of the Sun's solar activity;

- major volcanic eruptions.

We think that changes in the Sun's solar radiation may have increased radiative forcing by +0.3 W m^{-2} since 1750. The major volcanic eruptions that occurred between 1880 and 1991 had a net negative radiative forcing effect. Overall, the combined effect of changes in solar variation and volcanic aerosols in the last few decades has been a cooling.

2.5 Is climate change real and are humans the cause?

One of the most frequent citations from the IPCC TAR is the conclusion from the summary for policymakers of the report of Working Group I that 'There is new and stronger evidence that most of the observed warming of the past 50 years is attributable to human activities' (IPCC 2001a, p. 10).

The IPCC TAR is a hugely rich source of virtually all the known parameters that influence climate change. Even the summaries for policymakers and technical summaries are very densely packed and carefully worded. To answer the question 'Is climate change real and are humans the cause?', we are going to extract and focus on three specific pieces of scientific evidence of climate change from the IPCC TAR:

- measurements of greenhouse gas concentrations in the atmosphere;
- temperature records;
- measurements of changes in some climate variables that we consider are important.

Changes in atmospheric concentrations or GMST and other climate variables can be measured or estimated using two types of method and sources of evidence (Box 2.2).

Box 2.2 Various direct and indirect ways we can measure climate change

There are two basic ways of measuring climate change:

1 Measurements taken directly using dedicated instruments. This 'instrumental record' consists of:

- direct measurements of surface temperature since the middle of the 19th century;
- precipitation and wind measurements since around 1900;
- sea-level measurements from about 1900 (however, most of the tide gauge record is over a shorter time-scale);
- surface ocean observations made from ships since the 1850s (a network of dedicated buoys was established in the 1970s);
- sub-surface ocean temperature measurements since the 1940s;
- upper air observations since the 1940s (since 1958 using weather balloons);
- Earth observation satellite measurements since 1979.

2 Measurements taken indirectly using climate change indicators from the paleoclimatic record. This pre-instrumental proxy record includes:

- trees (tree ring data can be well calibrated and verified);
- corals (Figure 2.1a; they often live for several centuries, and variations in their skeletal density and geochemical parameters can provide accurate annual age estimates, and therefore climate information);
- borehole measurements (provide direct estimate of ground surface temperature from assumptions about the geothermal properties of the Earth near the borehole);
- ice cores (Figure 2.1b) provide much information about past climate via the concentrations of stable (i.e. not radioactive) isotopes, the rate of accumulation of sediments, concentrations of various salts and acids and trapped trace gases.

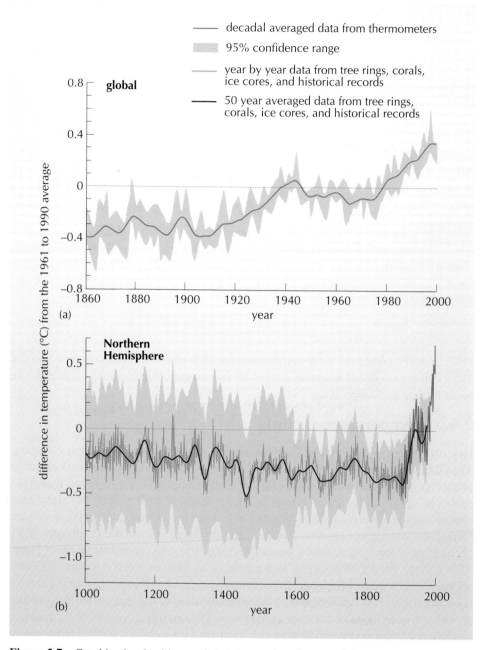

Figure 2.7 Graphic visual evidence of global warming. As you might expect, there is a lot more uncertainty about the historical data derived from proxy temperature measurements (b), than there is from recent direct measurements (a). Hence the confidence interval gets narrower as time passes, and our confidence in the data grows. (Source: IPCC 2001a)

Figure 2.7a shows clearly that global average surface temperature has increased by 0.6 ± 0.2 °C since the late 19th century. The IPCC concludes that 'indications from the pre-instrumental proxy record suggest it is likely that the rate and duration of the warming of the 20th century is faster and longer, respectively, than at any other time during the last 1000 years'.

What other stories could you write about temperature records from the data in Figure 2.7a?

In fact you will notice that we have had record-breaking years in the period 1930–1940, and consistently from around 1980 onwards. Newspapers only began running 'warmest year on record' stories recently. Alternatively, you might have chosen to describe the significant cooling that occurred between 1940 and the mid-1970s. It was this interlude that helped fuel the short-lived mini ice age scare referred to in Box 1.3. The IPCC TAR concludes that the main factors causing this were aerosols and solar variability.

2.5.3 Observed changes in other climate variables

Other climate variables provide supporting evidence of climate change. Box 2.3 mentions some of the non-temperature related changes that have been observed.

The evidence presented in Box 2.3 indicates that the relatively rapid warming now taking place in the Earth's climate system is highly unusual from a long-term perspective, and that, for the first time, humans, rather than other internal or external factors, are responsible. Moreover, because of fundamental inertias within the climate system, there is every likelihood that more climate change is already 'in the pipeline', no matter what is done to try to forestall these changes.

Recall that in Section 1.5 we posed the question 'what do we mean by *climate change*?'. We can now revisit that question, and translate it into the terminology and concepts of climate science. In practice, 'climate change' is used scientifically to mean the following things interchangeably:

- global warming — the year-on-year increase in GMST;
- changes in key climate variables such as sea-level rise, precipitation, and patterns of extreme events.

Because we are more certain about how greenhouse gases affect GMST than we are of how GMST affects climate variables, we can say that we are currently more confident about 'global warming' than we can be about 'climate change' (sea-level rise, changes in precipitation, frequency of extreme events, ice extents).

2.6 Future climate change

What will our future climate be like? Wouldn't we all like to know that! Thousands of scientists are working on complex climate models to try to help us answer this question. We can logically unpack some of the uncertainties inherent in this question. Let's try to think about the answer by working backwards. By 'future climate', we mean future sea-level, levels of precipitation, frequencies of severe storms, etc. In other words, our future climate can be described in terms of future climate variables. However, these depend largely on regional climate as well as on the overall increase in GMST. In turn, as we have seen, GMST depends partly on increases in atmospheric greenhouse gas concentrations, and also partly on a range of other factors. Future greenhouse gas concentrations are in large measure dependent on how humans are going to behave in the future — that is, on the quantity of CO_2 emissions pumped into the atmosphere as a result of fossil-fuel burning, cement production and changing land-use patterns.

By now, you probably have a sense that detecting and attributing cause and effect to *historical* climate change is a complex task. Predicting *future* climate change is even more complex and uncertain. It involves simulating the behaviour of the different components of the climate system (atmosphere, ocean, land surface, cryosphere and

Box 2.3 Other indicators of recently observed climate change

A variety of observations of different climate variables indicate a rapidly warming planet. The IPCC's TAR identifies the following indicators:

- Global mean sea-level has risen in the range 1.0 mm to 2.0 mm per year over the 20th century.

- It is likely that total atmospheric water vapour has increased by several per cent per decade over many regions of the Northern Hemisphere.

- The pattern of changes in precipitation is mixed. In recent years (since about 1995), annual land precipitation has continued to increase in the middle and high latitudes of the Northern Hemisphere at a rate of around 0.5%–1.0% per decade, except over Eastern Asia. Over the northern sub-tropics (10°N–30°N), land surface rainfall has decreased on average at a rate of 0.3% per decade. There has been an increase of 2%–4% in the frequency of heavy precipitation events in the latter part of the 20th century in the Northern Hemisphere.

- Cloud cover for the mid- and high-latitude continental regions of the Northern Hemisphere has increased by around 2% since 1900.

- There has been a 10% decrease in the extent of snow cover since the 1960s. Northern Hemisphere sea-ice extents are decreasing, but there are no significant trends in the Antarctic sea-ice extent. There is likely to have been an approximate 40% decline in Arctic sea-ice thickness in late summer to early autumn between the period of 1958–1976, and again during the 1990s, with a substantially smaller decline in winter.

- Changes in atmospheric and oceanic circulation patterns are still being assessed. Compared with the previous 100 years, the El Niño Southern Oscillation (Book 1, Box 3.2) has been more frequent, persistent and intense, relative to its cool phase, since the mid-1970s.

- Analyses of extreme weather and climate events reveal (a) pronounced increases in heavy and extreme precipitation events in the mid- to high latitudes of the Northern Hemisphere; (b) no compelling evidence of changes in tropical storms; and (c) no long-term changes in severe local weather events (tornadoes, thunderstorms and hail) in selected regions (Figure 2.8).

Figure 2.8 An Act of God? As we learn to live with global warming and climate change, we also learn to expect it. The media now connect any weather event to global warming theory, but so far there is no compelling evidence that the frequency or intensity of extreme storms has changed.

biosphere) under different possible future levels of greenhouse gas emissions and atmospheric concentrations. The only way to do this is by using sophisticated and complex modelling techniques. The most complex climate models are known as comprehensive *atmosphere–ocean general circulation models* (AOGCMs). These models incorporate sub-models of the five main components of the climate system outlined in Figure 2.2 (see Box 2.4).

Emissions over the course of this century, however, are highly uncertain, and dependent on a diverse set of factors such as projections of population, the size and distribution of world incomes, and the rate of take-up of energy technologies. The IPCC has considered various possible combinations (or scenarios) of these factors, together with different future global emissions trajectories. (We shall look more closely at emissions projections in Chapter 4.) According to these scenarios, the emissions of carbon dioxide may

Box 2.4 An introduction to climate models

Climate modellers are very busy slicing, dicing (and cubing and layering!) sectors and quadrants of our oceans, atmosphere and land surfaces. Three-dimensional atmospheric general circulation models (AGCMs), for example, slice the atmosphere up into small pieces. We are familiar with 1×1 km grid squares on a map. Now imagine layers of those grids on top of one another, 1 km thick. We can slice the atmosphere up into 1 km^3 chunks or smaller if we like. We can then imagine that each block has assigned to it a specific average value for its temperature, density, atmospheric composition, etc. The models then perform calculations involving every block. This is climate modelling.

Ocean general circulation models (OGCMs) slice oceans up into layers and grids in much the same way, typically on a grid of 1–2° latitude and longitude. Meanwhile, sophisticated satellite imagery at sub-kilometre scales is being used to map land use to feed into models of the terrestrial carbon cycle.

A large number of models has been built involving the five main components of the climate system (Figure 2.2). These include ocean models, models of radiative forcing mechanisms, ice-sheet and carbon cycle models. As we saw in Figure 2.2, there are couplings between different parts of the climate system, and many feedbacks within it. The most complex climate models combine all these sub-models, and are called coupled *atmosphere–ocean general circulation models* (AOGCMs). They model climate at relatively high spatial and temporal resolutions and take many weeks to run. For this reason, scientists have developed a series of intermediate complexity and simpler climate models to explore alternative climate scenarios more readily. Their results can be calibrated against the more complex AOGCMs.

We have only limited capabilities to model the behaviour of the climate. Different climate models behave broadly similarly under certain conditions, but most of the time they give significantly different results.

Nearly all models give credible simulations of annual mean climate at continental scales. However, clouds and humidity remain serious headaches for climate modellers. Not all of our current climate models can reproduce the 20th-century warming trends. They tend to diverge in their prediction of extreme events and the simulation of past climates. There also remains a lot of uncertainty about tropical cyclones and the behaviour of aerosols in the atmosphere. Clearly, climate modellers are going to be busy for many years to come.

increase dramatically; however, they may even decrease. The shape of our future global emissions trajectory is highly uncertain and dependent on a number of factors, each of which has associated uncertainties.

Figure 2.9 summarizes the IPCC's key modelling results predicting climate change for the 21st century. Global CO_2 emissions (and SO_2 emissions) drive the results for temperature change, which, in turn, drive the results for sea-level. The figure shows different predictions of CO_2 and SO_2 emissions, CO_2 concentrations, temperature change and sea-level rise for various emissions scenarios (these are the different coloured lines). These particular scenarios assume that we make no attempt to control emissions in the future: they are alternative predictions of what might happen without strong intervention to control climate change. The scenarios have awkward coded names such as 'A1B', but don't let that distract you. We shall return to these scenarios in Chapter 3.

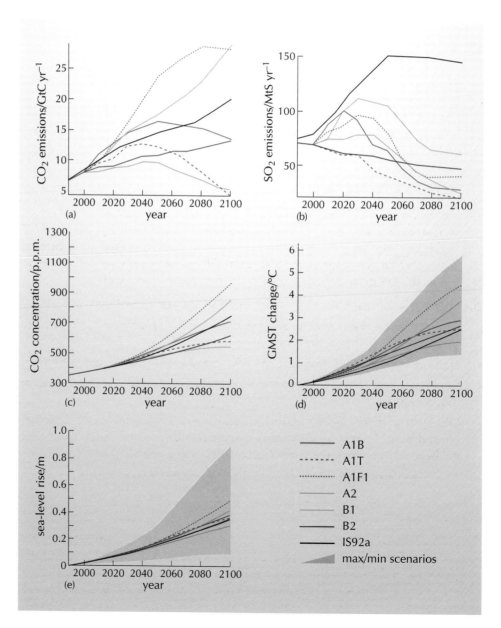

Figure 2.9 Climate change in the 21st century according to various scenarios. (Source: IPCC 2001d)

Activity 2.4: The global climate of the 21st century

Study Figure 2.9 carefully, and then answer the following questions.

(a) Look at the whole set of graphs together. Which graphs are most jagged and why do you think this might be?

Answer

CO$_2$ and SO$_2$ emissions are most jagged. This is because the models that produce them contain switches that kick in at a particular point as population, economic activity or technology factors suddenly change. For example, in the cycle of renewal of technology described by economists as 'capital stock turnover', power stations last between 20 and 50 years, cars about 12 years, and houses around 100 years.

(b) Why would we expect the graphs of CO$_2$ concentrations, temperature change and sea-level rise to be smooth?

Answer

Because of the time-scales and inertias of the various processes in the climate system.

(c) What is the range of predictions (using these scenarios) for CO$_2$ concentrations, temperature change and sea-level rise in 2100?

Answer

Predictions of CO$_2$ concentrations in 2100 range from just over 500 p.p.m. to just over 900 p.p.m. GMST is projected to increase by 1.5 °C–6 °C (accurately 1.4 °C–5.8 °C) over the 21st century (a rate of temperature increase unprecedented during the last 10 000 years). Global mean sea-level is projected to rise by 0.1–0.9 m (accurately 0.09–0.88 m) during the 21st century.

Climate models are also predicting changes in other climate variables:

- Global average water vapour concentration and precipitation are projected to increase.
- Northern Hemisphere snow cover and sea-ice extent are projected to decrease further.
- Glaciers and ice-caps are projected to continue their widespread retreat during the 21st century.
- The Antarctic ice-sheet is likely to grow (gain mass) because of greater precipitation, whereas the Greenland ice-sheet is likely to lose mass (in this case the increase in melting will exceed gains from precipitation).

There is even less confidence about how climate change might affect El Niño, monsoons and ocean currents (e.g. the Gulf Stream).

Figure 2.10 (overleaf) places the rate and scale of the rise in greenhouse gas concentrations into a much longer geological time perspective. It would seem prudent to be fairly alarmed by this graph. In fact, if Figure 2.10 doesn't scare you, then frankly nothing in the IPCC TAR will! How will Earth systems react to this sudden and unprecedented (in over 400 000 years) injection of CO$_2$ into the atmosphere? If data

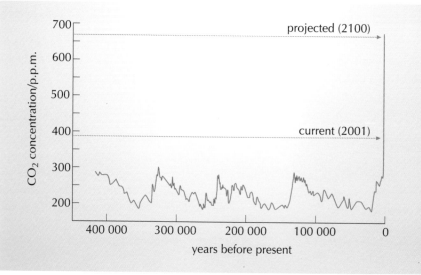

Figure 2.10 Never in half a million years: recent and projected increase in atmospheric CO_2 concentration is unprecedented and dramatic. (Source: IPCC data)

like those in Figure 2.10 were introduced in a timely manner into delicate international negotiations, it could result in moments of unity normally unattainable in the present international political system.

Figure 2.11 explains why there would be a significant change in the frequency of extreme events — record hot weather, for example — for a change in the mean value and variance of temperature. Projected changes in the pattern of extreme events are summarized in Table 2.4.

Table 2.4 Projected changes in the patterns of extreme events and their likelihood

Changes in extreme event	Confidence of projection (over 21st century)
higher maximum temperatures and more hot days over nearly all land areas (Figure 2.11)	very likely (90–99% chance[a])
higher minimum temperatures; fewer cold days and frost days over nearly all land areas (Figure 2.11)	very likely
reduced diurnal temperature range over most land areas	very likely
increase in *heat index*[b] over land areas	very likely, over most areas
more intense precipitation events	very likely, over many areas
increased summer continental drying and associated risk of drought	likely (66–99% chance) over most mid-latitude continental interiors (lack of consistent projections in other areas)
increase in tropical cyclone peak wind intensities	likely, over some areas
increase in tropical cyclone mean and peak precipitation intensities	likely, over some areas

[a] Note that here we have yet another scheme from the IPCC TAR, assigning qualitative assessments of confidence levels. 'Very likely' in this context means a 90–99% probability, whereas 'very high' (Box 1.4) means 95% probability or greater.

[b] A measure of how humidity acts along with high temperature to reduce the body's ability to cool itself.

Figure 2.11 schematically shows the distribution of temperature, randomly scattered around a mean according to a bell curve. At the tail ends of the distribution are record cold (left) and hot weather (right). In (a), an increase in mean temperature shifts the whole bell curve to the right, resulting in more hot weather. In (b), an increase in the variance ('squashing the curve') also results in more hot weather. In (c), the two effects are combined to produce even more record hot weather.

● Suggest some possible potential impacts (positive or negative) of an increase in maximum temperatures, and more hot days.

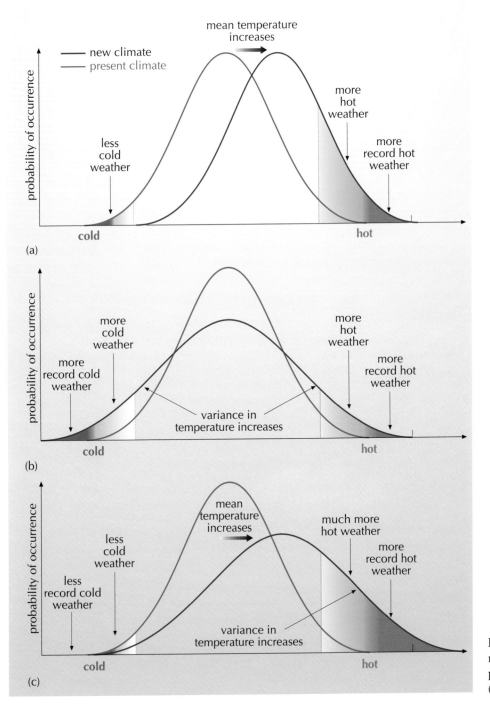

Figure 2.11 How a change in the mean and variance in temperature produces more record hot weather. (Source: IPCC 2001d, Fig. 4-1)

- Increased death and serious illness in older age groups and urban poor;
- increased heat stress in livestock and wildlife;
- shift in tourist destinations;
- increased risk of damage to a number of crops;
- increased electric cooling demand.

What potential impacts (positive or negative) are associated with an increase in minimum temperatures, and fewer cold days?

- Decreased cold-related human illness and death;
- decreased damage to a number of crops, and increased risk to others;
- extended range and activity of some pest and disease vectors;
- reduced heating energy demand.

How will climate change affect ecological and socio-economic systems? What actual difference might it make to the lives and livelihoods of this and future generations?

Weather and climate are inextricably linked to many aspects of our economies and societies. Climate change could bring about significant impacts on the economy, both positive and negative. For example, increased carbon dioxide concentrations help plants photosynthesise, and therefore speed up their growth rates. In many existing agricultural areas, yields will rise (if sufficient water is available). On the other hand, higher temperatures and reduced rainfall in drought areas will exacerbate already difficult agricultural conditions. Climate-change impacts are therefore varied and uncertain, and are likely to include both positive and negative environmental, ecological and socio-economic changes (Figure 1.17). However, it is generally assumed that the *net* outcome of climate change will be largely negative for human and non-human life on the planet, particularly for a large increase in GMST.

Some countries are more vulnerable to the potential impacts of climate change than others. Often the most vulnerable are among the poorest in warm climates, since poor countries have less ability to *adapt* to climate change than rich ones (see Chapter 4).

The following human systems are all particularly sensitive to climate change:

- water resources;
- agriculture, forestry, fisheries;
- human settlements;
- industry, energy, financial services.

In some cases, such sensitivities can lead to vulnerabilities with respect to food and water security, incomes and livelihoods, human health and infrastructure.

Box 2.5 illustrates the potential impacts of climate change across a range of *sectors* (IPCC, 2001b, Technical Summary, Section 4). We should, of course, remember that not all these impacts will manifest themselves in the same way in different regions.

Box 2.5 Sectoral impacts of climate change

Hydrology and water resources   Possible impacts include: relative increases/decreases in water flow in rivers depending on the region; a shift in peak stream flow from spring to winter in many areas where snowfall is a driver of the water balance; disappearance of many small glaciers; increased concentration of microbes in rivers (but this could be offset in some cases by higher flows); increases in flood magnitude and frequencies in most regions; increased needs for irrigation.

Coastal zones   Possible impacts include: increasing flood-frequency probabilities and accelerated coastal erosion; inundation via rising water tables; salt-water intrusion and associated biological effects. Each of these, in turn, will have impacts on water resources, agriculture, human health, fisheries, tourism and human settlements.

Agriculture   Potential impacts include: changes in the location of optimal growing areas for particular crops, resulting in a shift in crop zones; changes in size and type of crop yields; changes in the location and intensity of pests and diseases. Such impacts may, in turn, result in changes in farming practices, land-use patterns, food security and import/export dependency. As well as microeconomic changes in production, farm income and rural employment, there may be associated macroeconomic changes in the structure of GDP.

Range land/livestock   Possible impacts include: changes in trace element concentrations in soil water; in plant or forage quantity and quality; in plant adaptability or shifts in species; in livestock adaptability. Such impacts may, in turn, result in changes in food production and security, incomes, biodiversity and habitat impacts.

Human health   Possible impacts of climate change could include: increased heat-related death and illness; increase in photochemical and other forms of air pollution, with resulting increase in respiratory illness; increased mortality and morbidity as a result of increased frequency of floods, storms and other natural disasters; loss of habitable land, contamination of freshwater supplies, damage to public health infrastructure. Indirect health effects of climate change could include changes in the distribution and seasonal transmission of vector-borne diseases (e.g. malaria).

Energy   Possible impacts of climate change include energy consumption as well as production. Climate change will have impacts on the demand for air conditioning, space heating, water pumping, refrigeration and water heating. Hydroelectric energy production and, to a lesser extent, the thermal efficiencies of fossil fuel electricity generation, may be directly affected. Energy production facilities located on rivers or coastal zones may be at increased risk of flooding.

Forestry   Possible impacts include: shifts in the geographical area that can support forests; changes in the species composition of mixed-species forests; changes in the production of timber per unit area; changes in the type, location, or intensity of pest and disease, and fires; changes in biodiversity via afforestation or deforestation as a result of land competition with agriculture.

Biodiversity   Possible impacts include species adapting to climate change in different ways (Book 2, Chapter 3). Those dependent on ecosystems that are now more fragmented will be more at risk of being unable to adapt at an appropriate rate; there could be strong negative impacts on migratory species as a result of shifts in the timing of annual seasonal events; in some cases there will be an acceleration of existing problems such as invasive 'alien' plant species; there will also be negative impacts on arctic and alpine species as the extent of their native cold areas decline.

Fisheries   Possible impacts involve each of the three principal categories of fisheries — marine, coastal and estuarial — which may be affected by climate change in different ways. These include: potential loss of coastal wetlands and estuary habitats due to altered currents and sea-levels; changes in the quality and/or availability of suitable habitats for different species; alteration of food webs; shifts in the extent and locations of fishing grounds, together with associated socio-economic effects.

information the IPCC has presented about the various inertias within the climate system. Even if we engage in further actions to reduce GHG emissions, the models tell us that anthropogenic climate change will continue for centuries (Figure 2.3b). Politically, however, the authors may have thought it wise to imply that urgent action now might result in benefits that would avoid harmful climate change, even if the horse has, in some respects, bolted.

2.7 The science behind climate change is settling but remains unsettled

It is clear that our knowledge of the science of climate change is evolving extremely rapidly. The scientific and international policy communities are taking climate change very seriously, even in the face of considerable economic consequences and attendant political pressures. By now we hope you will have realized that there remain considerable uncertainties and gaps in scientific skill and understanding of the impacts of climate change. There is no point pretending this is not the case. It is tempting for many observers to rest their arguments firmly on IPCC summaries, negotiated in detail. But between the lines of the main reports there are all kinds of admissions of uncertainties and gaps. Climate science is far from settled:

- There is a great deal of uncertainty about basic climate system dynamics.
- Major improvements have been and continue to be made.
- The IPCC TAR contains a great deal of information.
- Part of the TAR is negotiated (the summary for policymakers); part is the responsibility of the teams of lead and contributing authors for each particular chapter.

Each time an IPCC assessment is released, one or two key phrases receive much more media attention than others. In the IPCC's 1995 Second Assessment Report, it was the statement that 'humans are having a discernible influence on the Earth's climate'. In its 2001 Third Assessment Report, it was 'most of the observed warming of the past 50 years is attributable to human activities'.

Behind the public, government-negotiated face of the IPCC consensus, is a lot of uncertain and messy science. Given the growing political importance of climate change, it is quite natural for some scientists to want to scrutinize these scientific assessments. Beyond their roles as concerned scientists and citizens, major careers are being built on the voluntary work that scientists give to the IPCC process. There is enormous constructive competition among scientists: their funding and status depends on their IPCC credentials and whether their work is used and cited. Their abilities to work together, choose who to work with, and how to work are very human. All the complex climate models on which a great deal of the work on climate change is based are linked by the same subsets of data and premises, so the same equations and techniques recur throughout them all; errors in one will therefore occur in others. There are relatively few models and modellers; the climate prediction business is a small tight-knit community, in which data and techniques are often jealously guarded. Climate models are important pieces of intellectual property.

However, the communication of the range of thinking on climate change has not been well served by the media, who love to play with opposing angles or viewpoints on a story; it's one of the basic principles taught in journalism schools. Climate change stories are no different from the general rule. The reports of climate change in the 1990s contain many examples of such stories. Individual academics who are not part of the IPCC process, as well as experts from the fossil-fuel businesses (e.g. the notorious and now largely defunct Global Climate Coalition, a business NGO comprising several large multinational fossil fuel companies), have weighed in with their own perspectives, which have also been extensively reported in recent years. Even the internal political machinations of the IPCC process are fertile areas for journalists seeking a different slant on climate change. The election of the new head of the IPCC in April 2002, Rajandra Pachauri, received global coverage with headline news around the world.

Our climate system is complex. The official 'handbook' to its functioning only began to be written around 1990. It is going to take many more years before the citizen's guide to climate science is widely comprehensible, and anywhere close to being adequate for the political decisions we may need to take.

To make matters more confusing for the concerned citizen, there are scientists who contest basic climate science. Figure 2.13 is a picture of the Lempriére–Ross mark. Under a news story headline 'Is this the picture that takes the heat out of global warming?', the BBC report says (BBC, 1999):

> It shows an Ordnance Survey Bench Mark engraved into a rock face on a little island near Port Arthur, Tasmania. It was put there in 1841 by the famous Antarctic explorer Captain Sir James Clark Ross and amateur meteorologist Thomas Lempriére to mark mean sea-level. What is so fascinating is that the mark appears to some to be 30 centimetres above the current mean sea-level.

It would be very unusual if everyone agreed on something, so it is heartening that some scientists are still asking fundamental questions about climate science outside the IPCC process. In the meantime, the IPCC is the voice of the scientific establishment, and is now regarded as an authority by the international political system; it is therefore now a driving force behind it. Let's consolidate the material in this chapter by summarizing what we know and don't know about the science behind climate change.

We have no idea how humanity is going to react to the scientific knowledge on climate change. Will governments, the business world and other stakeholders cooperate to find ways of implementing a precautionary approach to climate change in a peaceful and sustainable world? Or will the world's poorest nations insist on their rights to power their industrialization on cheap fossil fuels, just as the West has done up to now? Will rich countries be able to give up their carbon-intensive lifestyles?

Figure 2.13 The idea of a 'global mean sea-level' is just as helpful, though no less problematic, as 'global mean surface temperature'. The world's oceans are, in fact, 'bumpy'. The Lempriére–Ross mark suggests that sea-level has dropped 30 cm in Tasmania since 1841. Explaining this is not simple.

Chapter 3 Planetary engineering

Prepared for the course team by Stephen Peake

3.1 Introduction

The Earth's climate system is changing rapidly in response to human activities. In turn, various species are responding, including humans. We are at the beginning of an unprecedented and epic tale of how humans are attempting to knowingly restore thermal equilibrium to the biosphere. The task is possibly the ultimate engineering challenge — climate air conditioning on a global scale.

In the battle to control climate change and manage its consequences, our most powerful weapon is our own behaviour. Our society's response could be a critical negative feedback in the overall climate system. The kernel of that response is an emerging regime of international climate change negotiation and governance. This chapter describes the steps taken so far to control climate change at the international level, and some of the issues this generates around the themes of governance, uncertainty, globalization and sustainability.

3.2 What took us so long to realize?

We have graphic evidence of rising atmospheric CO_2 concentration and global mean surface temperature (Figure 3.1), as well as a growing database of emerging biogeochemical consequences and impacts (Box 2.3). We now realize what is happening. As you saw in Chapter 2, the release of around 270 GtC into the atmosphere from fossil fuel combustion and a further 136 GtC from land-use change is a major perturbation in the carbon cycle, with consequences throughout the overall climate system.

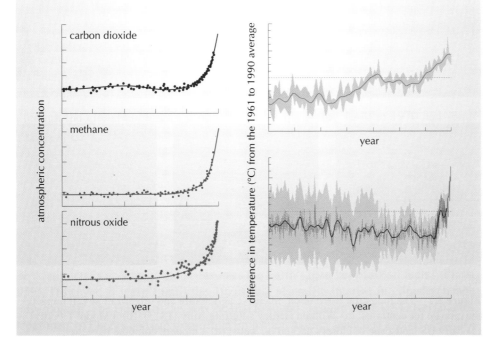

Figure 3.1 It all seems so obvious in retrospect: the outline shapes of the key scientific evidence of climate change (Figures 2.6 and 2.7).

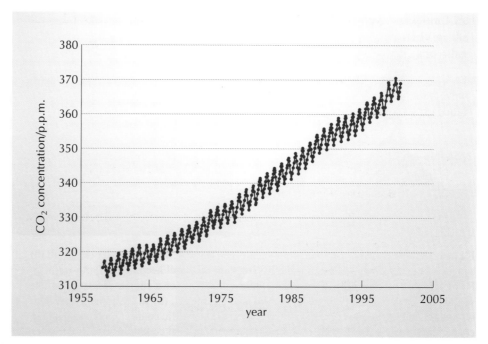

Figure 3.4 Data for atmospheric CO_2 concentration from Mauna Loa, a mountain in Hawaii, from 1958 to 2000; the wavy line shows that there is a seasonal variation as well as the long-term trend.

the international political agenda. The US remains massively involved in the international business of climate prediction and assessment to this day. Some of the key events that transformed climate change from scientific curiosity to global political issue are summarized in Box 3.1, p. 92.

Activity 3.1: Time-scales in climate science and politics

Let's step back and reflect on the different time-scales of the science and the politics. Just as the climate system contains different processes and cycles occurring at different speeds (Figure 2.3), so too does the human world.

Here is a list of the different time-scales you have so far encountered in this block and that are associated with different aspects of climate change:

400 000 years

10 000 years

1000 years

250 years

100 years

10 years

2–4 years

Which of the following best matches one of the above time-scales?

(a) time-scale of our global mean surface temperature records;

(b) time-scale of the life of the UNFCCC;

(c) time-scale for sea-levels or ice caps to fully respond to temperature change;

(d) time-scale of the evolution of scientific understanding of climate change;

(e) time-scale over which we have some knowledge of historical carbon dioxide concentrations;

(f) time-scale of atmospheric mixing of greenhouse gases;

(g) the Industrial Revolution.

Answers

(a)   1000 years (Figure 2.7b);

(b)   10 years (the UNFCCC was opened for signature in 1992);

(c)   10 000 years (Figure 2.3a);

(d)   100 years (from Tyndall's research in the 1860s to the Villach Conference);

(e)   400 000 years (Figure 2.10);

(f)   2–4 years (for carbon dioxide, methane and nitrous oxide; see Figure 2.3a);

(g)   250 years (taking 1750 as the start of the Industrial Revolution).

We have been puzzling over the climate jigsaw for well over a century. But it wasn't until the late 20th century that the science triggered a global political response and the UNFCCC was established. Understanding climate change requires that we make connections between different processes that span a vast range of time-scales:

- geological and climate system processes ranging from half a million years to a few weeks;

- socio-economic transformations over the course of 250 years;

- the evolution of scientific understanding of the order of a century to decades;

- political processes of the order of decades.

Before we discuss the international response to climate change in some detail, have another look at Figure 2.3 (p. 54). How many other international political issues require thinking at time-scales of a millenium?

3.3 The United Nations Framework Convention on Climate Change and the Kyoto Protocol

The international political response to climate change has been to set up an international convention. This is not at all surprising. There are over 200 international conventions dealing with regional and global environmental issues, all of them established since the early 1950s.

Which two international conventions dealing with aspects of the global environment have you already encountered in earlier parts of the course?

The Antarctic Treaty (Book 1, Chapter 6) and the Convention on Biological Diversity (Book 2, Chapter 1).

Box 3.1 Global science precipitates a global political response

Figure 3.5 Organized international science triggers a global political response: a cover from the IPCC's 1990 First Assessment Report.

1979 First World Climate Conference adopted climate change as a major issue and called on governments 'to foresee and prevent potential man-made changes in climate.' The conference was one of the first major international meetings on climate change.

1985 The famous (in climate circles) Villach (Austria) conference was the first major international conference to consider the greenhouse effect. The conference concluded that greenhouse gases will 'in the first half of the next century, cause a rise of global mean temperature which is greater than any in man's history', that sea-levels may rise by up to a metre by 1990, and that gases other than CO_2, such as methane, ozone, CFCs and nitrous oxide, also contribute to warming.

1988 The UN called for the establishment of the IPCC to analyse and report on scientific findings. Global warming begins to attract worldwide headlines. A meeting of climate scientists in Toronto calls for 20% cuts in global CO_2 emissions by the year 2005.

1990 The first report of the IPCC (Figure 3.5) found that the planet had warmed by 0.5 °C in the 20th century, and warned that only strong measures to halt rising greenhouse gas emissions would prevent serious global warming. The report provides the scientific basis for UN negotiations for a climate convention. The UN General Assembly convenes an Intergovernmental Negotiating Committee to begin drafting a UN Convention on Climate Change.

1992 The Intergovernmental Negotiating Committee concluded negotiations on a climate change convention. The Convention was adopted on 9 May 1992, and opened for signature a month later at the UN Conference on Environment and Development in Rio de Janeiro, Brazil (Figure 3.6).

1994 The United Nations Framework Convention on Climate Change (**UNFCCC**) came into force on 21 March 1994 and became the centrepiece of the global human response to climate change. A new era in international global environmental governance began (*New Scientist*, 2003 and UNFCCC, 2003).

Figure 3.6 George Bush senior attending the Rio Earth Summit in 1992. The US was a key player in paving the way for the UNFCCC.

The UNFCCC was one of the three new Conventions established at the 1992 Earth Summit in Rio de Janeiro. The others (Figure 3.7) are the Convention on Biological Diversity (CBD) and the Convention to Combat Desertification (CCD). There was also an attempt in Rio to establish a convention on forests, though an agreement to establish a formal convention was not reached. Given the long-term and global characteristics of climate change, it was highly likely that a global convention on this issue would happen. Nevertheless, the scale, complexity and potential risks associated with climate change make the UNFCCC one of the most important and unique international legal regimes to be created to date. The UNFCCC is ostensibly the legal basis for what must be the single most ambitious goal in the history of humanity's recent attempts to manage its relationship with the natural world — to restore thermal equilibrium to the Earth (the political reality is different, as we shall see later). It has near universal membership, and is the basis of a 'living' regime of international climate governance.

CBD

CCD

3.3.1 The F word

The F in UNFCCC stands for **Framework**. The UNFCCC sets out the broad framework of objectives and guiding principles in relation to the roles and responsibilities of participating countries — that is, those states that have ratified the Treaty, and therefore have formally become a 'Party' to it. It is one of the key international arenas in which we can glimpse how countries debate a host of thorny economic and political issues that are bundled under the broad umbrella term 'sustainable development' (Chapter 6).

UNFCCC

Figure 3.7 Symbols of sustainable development political turf inside the UN: each of the three 'Rio Conventions' has its own secretariat, idiosyncratic political dynamics and 'personality.'

The core of the 'F' in UNFCCC is a mixture of the following:

- a central **Objective** in Article 2;
- some guiding **Principles** in Article 3;
- a series of general **Commitments** in Article 4.

Every word and punctuation mark of an international agreement is carefully constructed, scrutinized and negotiated. Where nations cannot agree, a word or phrase is often chosen that satisfies all sides of an argument. In this way, international environmental law often produces the 'lowest common denominator' of political agreement. Clues to the strategic economic, social and political interests of nations are therefore scattered throughout the Treaty. In the next few pages we shall explore the UNFCCC with this in mind.

3.3.2 The objective of the UNFCCC

Having studied the ambiguous language contained in Article IV of the Antarctic Treaty (Box 6.1, Block 1), it will be less surprising to you to discover ambiguity at the heart of the UNFCCC. The overriding objective of the climate convention is stated in its Article 2. It is *not* a clear goal:

> The ultimate objective of this Convention and any related legal instruments that the Conference of the Parties may adopt is to achieve, in accordance with the relevant provisions of the Convention, stabilization of greenhouse gas concentrations in the atmosphere at a level that would prevent dangerous anthropogenic interference with the climate system. Such a level should be achieved within a time-frame sufficient to allow ecosystems to adapt naturally to climate change, to ensure that food production is not threatened and to enable economic development to proceed in a sustainable manner.

Activity 3.2: Planetary management

Clear goals are those about which we can readily answer the following basic questions:

- Who?
- What?
- When?
- How?

Study Article 2 of the UNFCCC carefully, and write a couple of sentences in your own words in answer to the following questions:

(a) Who is involved?

(b) What needs to be achieved?

(c) When must the goal be reached?

(d) How must the goal be achieved?

Comment

Here are the course team's answers and a little further explanation:

(a)   'The **Conference of the Parties**' is the answer to 'who?' A **Party** is any government that has legally ratified the Convention. There are over 180 Parties to the UNFCCC, including all developed and almost every developing nation, so the Convention has near-universal membership, and therefore applies to more or less everyone on the planet. When nations meet to deliberate progress on the UNFCCC (usually once per year), the conference is called a 'Conference of the Parties' or 'COP' for short.

(b)   The answer to 'what needs to be achieved?' is the 'stabilization of greenhouse gas concentrations in the atmosphere at a level that would prevent dangerous anthropogenic [human related] interference with the climate system'. There is no doubt that stabilization is the goal, but the level is unclear. What does 'dangerous' mean? It is a complex matter for scientific and political judgement as to what constitutes 'dangerous' interference with the climate system.

(c)   In answer to the question of 'when', the objective does not mention specific dates. It mentions a time-frame defined as 'sufficient to allow ecosystems to adapt naturally to climate change, to ensure that food production is not threatened and to enable economic development to proceed in a sustainable manner'. What sort of time-frame is this — 20, 50, 100 or 1000 years? Natural ecosystem time-frames can be of the order of 1000 years (e.g. the lifespan of a North American Redwood tree; Figure 2.3). There is a lot of political uncertainty here.

(d)   The answer to the question of 'how the goal must be achieved' is 'in accordance with the relevant provisions of the Convention'. This condition is extremely important in understanding the Convention. There are a lot of other relevant provisions in other articles of the Convention and to make sense of Article 2, we have to make sense of those too. We'll come to some of the most important ideas in Article 4 shortly. Article 2 also refers to 'sustainable' economic development — another term giving rise to a great deal of ambiguity and uncertainty, which we shall consider in more detail in Chapter 6.

Despite not being quite as clear a goal as at first sight, Article 2 makes the UNFCCC an international legal instrument with an aim of nothing less than environmental management on a planetary scale, and over project management time-scales not encountered since the Roman Empire. It's hard not to smile when you consider the objective of the UNFCCC and the time-scales involved! The characteristic features of the climate issue that make it an exercise in planetary-scale management are that climate change is: (i) a truly global problem involving a wide range of human activity, many biogeochemical and socio-economic systems and many different greenhouse gas pollutants; and (ii) a truly long-term problem with consequences that stretch many centuries and even millennia into the future. How will this aspect of the history of early 21st century post-industrial cyber society look to students in say 2200?...

> 'And 200 years ago, the UNFCCC marked the first human steps to restore thermal equilibrium to planet Earth — an experiment in air conditioning at the planetary scale.'

3.3.3 Principles of the UNFCCC

Article 3 of the UNFCCC sets out five general Principles to guide nations in their pursuit of climate stabilization (i.e. Article 2). The Principles are reproduced in Box 3.2 (overleaf). As you are reading through them, take note of any terminology that is not immediately clear to you.

Activity 3.3: Identifying the political landmines in the Principles of the UNFCCC

Study the five Principles in Box 3.2 carefully, and identify *one* term or expression from each Principle that you think could be a source of political uncertainty and disagreement between nations.

Comment

> Here are the course team's answers. All the terms chosen are potential sources of political uncertainty and disagreement:
>
> Principle 1: 'equity', 'common but differentiated responsibilities', 'take the lead';
>
> Principle 2: 'specific needs and special circumstances', 'vulnerable';
>
> Principle 3: 'precautionary measures', 'serious or irreversible damage', 'cost-effective';
>
> Principle 4: 'sustainable development', 'specific conditions of each Party', 'economic development is essential for adopting measures to...';
>
> Principle 5: 'supportive and open international economic system', 'sustainable economic growth', 'address the problems of climate change'.
>
> In the remainder of the block we are going to illustrate some of the political dynamics at play when nations attempt to act within the framework of these Principles. In one way or another, most of the politics of climate change can be explained in terms of differences of opinion between different groups of nations about how to interpret these issues.

Box 3.2 Article 3 Principles of the UNFCCC

In their actions to achieve the objective of the Convention and to implement its provisions, the Parties are guided, *inter alia*, by the following:

1. The Parties should protect the climate system for the benefit of present and future generations of humankind, on the basis of equity and in accordance with their common but differentiated responsibilities and respective capabilities. Accordingly, the developed country Parties should take the lead in combating climate change and the adverse effects thereof.

2. The specific needs and special circumstances of developing country Parties, especially those that are particularly vulnerable to the adverse effects of climate change, and of those Parties, especially developing country Parties, that would have to bear a disproportionate or abnormal burden under the Convention, should be given full consideration.

3. The Parties should take precautionary measures to anticipate, prevent or minimize the causes of climate change and mitigate its adverse effects. Where there are threats of serious or irreversible damage, lack of full scientific certainty should not be used as a reason for postponing such measures, taking into account that policies and measures to deal with climate change should be cost-effective so as to ensure global benefits at the lowest possible cost. To achieve this, such policies and measures should take into account different socio-economic contexts, be comprehensive, cover all relevant sources, sinks and reservoirs of greenhouse gases and adaptation, and comprise all economic sectors. Efforts to address climate change may be carried out cooperatively by interested Parties.

4. The Parties have a right to, and should, promote sustainable development. Policies and measures to protect the climate system against human-induced change should be appropriate for the specific conditions of each Party and should be integrated with national development programmes, taking into account that economic development is essential for adopting measures to address climate change.

5. The Parties should cooperate to promote a supportive and open international economic system that would lead to sustainable economic growth and development in all Parties, particularly developing country Parties, thus enabling them better to address the problems of climate change. Measures taken to combat climate change, including unilateral ones, should not constitute a means of arbitrary or unjustifiable discrimination or a disguised restriction on international trade.

3.3.4 Commitments

So, having reviewed the objective of the UNFCCC and the Principles of how to proceed, how exactly do Parties to the UNFCCC envisage achieving the objective? The answer is in a long series of 'Commitments' contained mainly in Article 4 of the Convention (Box 3.3).

The international politics of climate change are, like several other international economic, social and environmental issues, frequently portrayed in terms of 'North versus South' (a euphemism for developed-versus-developing countries; Figure 3.8).

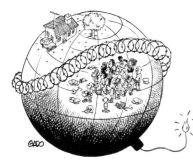

Figure 3.8 Climate change is a classic North–South battle over rights, justice and equity.

Dividing the world up into these two basic camps offers a starting point (albeit a crude one) for understanding the politics behind climate change. The 'North' is another term for developed countries, and is referred to in the UNFCCC as **Annex I** or **Annex II**, whereas the 'South' is referred to as **Non-Annex I** (Box 3.4, p. 98).

As a first approximation, the politics can be reduced to two main issues:

- How fast should developed countries demonstrate leadership in reducing their greenhouse gas emissions?
- In the meantime, what special needs and specific circumstances of developing countries need to be addressed?

Article 4 of the UNFCCC makes it clear that the developed countries should take the lead in reducing greenhouse gas emissions. Although all of them accepted the quantified emission reduction targets agreed for the Annex II countries in 1992, very few developed

Box 3.3 Overview of Article 4 — Commitments of the UNFCCC

All countries [that is, Annex I and Non-Annex I] commit to:

- the stabilization of greenhouse gas concentrations;
- publish inventories of greenhouse gas emissions;
- implement measures to mitigate and adapt to climate change;
- promote and cooperate in the development, application, diffusion (including transfer) of mitigation or adaptation technologies;
- promote sustainable management;
- cooperate in preparing for adaptation to the impacts of climate change;
- take care to minimize any adverse socio-economic or environmental effects that responding to climate change might bring about;
- promote and cooperate in relevant scientific research and technology;
- promote and cooperate in education, training and public awareness.

Developed [Annex I countries] countries commit to:

- adopt national polices to reduce greenhouse gas emissions, and return these to 1990 levels by the year 2000;
- produce national communications to periodically inform the Convention of progress;
- agree and use transparent methodologies for calculating greenhouse gas emissions;
- provide new and additional financial resources to meet the agreed full costs incurred by developing countries in meeting various commitments under the Convention;
- assist particularly vulnerable parties in meeting the costs of adaptation;
- promote, facilitate and finance the transfer of, or access to, environmentally sound technologies to developing country Parties.

Box 3.4 Making sense of the UNFCCC's classification of countries

The text of the UNFCCC reinforces the North–South dynamic by placing different commitments on developed countries (Annex II), on countries with economies in transition (EITs; countries of the former Soviet Union and other Eastern European countries), and on developing countries (everyone else; Figure 3.9).

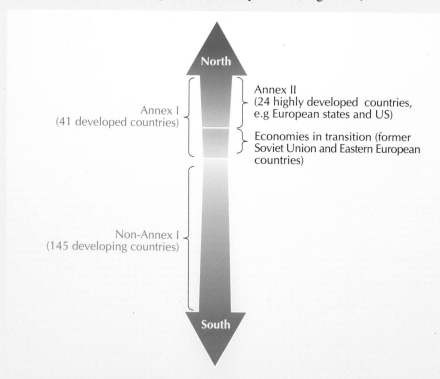

Figure 3.9   Representation of the North–South division of the world in UNFCCC terms in 2003 as a compass needle.

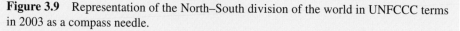

countries have shown any real progress in reducing their greenhouse gas emissions in line with their UNFCCC promises. Figure 3.10 clearly shows the reduction in Annex I emissions over the decade. Two large Annex II countries — the United Kingdom and Germany — achieved significant reductions. In the case of the UK, this is largely explained by a major shift towards gas-fired electricity generation and the ongoing decline of manufacturing industry. In the case of Germany, the statistics are significantly skewed by reunification. Its emissions reductions in the period 1990–4 were mainly due to a fall in industrial activity and the closure of inefficient, polluting factories and power stations (producing electricity from brown coal or lignite) in the former East Germany.

Developing countries have been highly critical of this failure of developed countries to meet their 1992 promise of stabilizing emissions at 1990 levels by the year 2000 contained in Articles 4.2 a and b of the Convention. On pp. 99 and 100 you can read a classic piece of the diplomatic theatre that lies at the heart of climate negotiations. (It is an extract from a statement made by a representative of the Alliance of Small Island States (Slade, 1999).)

I want to express the profound disappointment of my group in the progress made thus far by Annex I parties in meeting the Convention's commitments. The commitment under Articles 4.2 a and b, to aim to stabilize emissions of greenhouse gases at 1990 levels by the year 2000, is in force for nearly every State and the European Community listed in Annex I. The national inventories and communications required to demonstrate compliance with this obligation have been received, have been subject to in depth review and have been analysed and compiled by the Secretariat…The trends identified in this analysis suggest that the Annex I parties as a whole and the majority of individual Annex I parties are on emissions paths that overshoot their Articles 4.2 a and b commitments by substantial margins and send them into non-compliance. While these trends can be attributed to a wide range of individual factors, it is the opinion of the AOSIS countries that they reveal a fundamental failure and lack

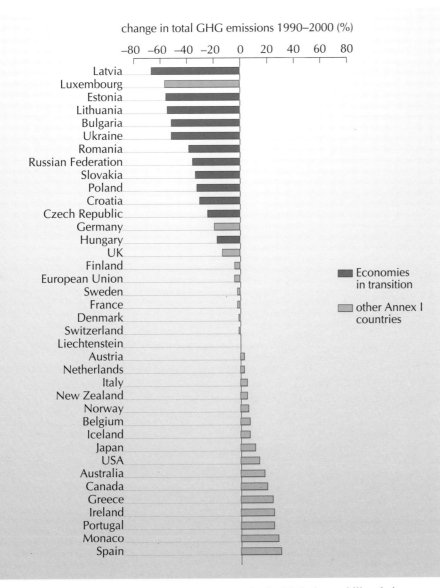

Figure 3.10 Broken promises: most Annex II countries had failed to stabilize their greenhouse gas emissions at 1990 levels by 2000 (source UNFCCC, 2002).

of action on the domestic level by the majority of Annex I parties…It is essential in the opinion of our group of countries that this lack of action and the disappointment and concern that it raises should provoke a formal response from the Convention's Institutions. We are told that public condemnation is one of the strongest tools for reminding States of their international commitments. If this is true, the opposite must also be true. Silence in the face of inaction would send a signal of complacency and neglect that neither the Convention nor the climate system could tolerate.

Ambassador Tuilome Neroni Slade (Figure 3.11) of Samoa, speaking on behalf of AOSIS, UNFCCC meeting, 1 June 1999, Bonn

'Special needs and specific circumstances' is a deliberately vague expression, but is none the less a very important one in the climate negotiations. It was introduced into the language of the Convention, and repeated in the **Kyoto Protocol** negotiations as a shorthand way of covering all the concerns held by developing countries about the impacts of climate change.

There are three very distinct types of climate change 'impacts' which concern developing countries:

- **direct climate impacts** (e.g. temperature rise, sea-level rise, floods, droughts, disease, etc.);

- **economic and social impacts** on developing countries as a result of reducing their own greenhouse gas emissions and possibly interfering with their ongoing needs for poverty eradication and the pursuit of 'sustainable' economic development;

- economic and social impacts on fossil-fuel export-dependent developing economies (e.g. the OPEC countries), brought about by any impending global shift away from fossil fuels towards cleaner, renewable sources of energy.

Figure 3.11 The distinguished face of AOSIS in the UN climate negotiations: Ambassador Slade reminds rich nations of their commitments.

All countries, but particularly some of the poorest and most vulnerable to climate variability, are concerned about the possible impacts of climate change. Many developing countries have received small amounts of bilateral and multilateral financial assistance to help them assess their vulnerability to climate change (typically of the order of a few hundred thousand US dollars per country). But even if a lot more money were spent on vulnerability assessments, future uncertainties about the nature and extent of climate change mean that it is difficult for developing countries to decide on their priorities in terms of more specific requests for assistance under the UNFCCC. Some countries, for various reasons, have not even conducted adequate vulnerability assessments. China and India — the top two most populous and powerful developing nations within the 'G77 and China' group — are particularly noteworthy in this regard. As of early 2003, they had so far failed to submit their 'First National Communications' to the UNFCCC in which they are obliged to describe their current emissions inventory, vulnerabilities to climate change and their special needs and circumstances. Developing countries frequently request assistance to help develop their capacities to adapt to actual or predicted climate change in their region. It will be some time yet before funding for actual adaptation projects (e.g. sea-walls, new genetically modified drought-resistant crops, dams, etc.) is properly underway. This is a major source of frustration for developing countries which greatly affects the politics of climate change.

There is little, if any, disagreement among nations that the first priority of developing countries is poverty eradication and economic development. The problem comes in interpreting what *kind* of economic development. All sides emphasize the need for *sustainable* economic development, but beyond the rhetoric there is no shared vision of what exactly sustainable economic development means. What has started to happen is that developed countries are paying more attention to the environmental impacts of their own ongoing development assistance programs. Developed countries are increasingly putting environmental conditions on aid for development projects (Figure 3.12).

Figure 3.12 The proposed site for the Ilisu dam in Turkey. Construction work on the dam was put 'on hold' after the withdrawal of international backing in 2001, following widespread public criticism and a sustained environmentalist campaign. However, in 2003 the Turkish authorities were still looking for other international financial support.

In order to pursue their goals of poverty eradication and economic development, developing countries emphasize their need for advanced cleaner technologies, and for developing an appropriate social infrastructure through training, education and institutional reform. However, developed countries (in particular the US and Europe) emphasize the need for developing countries to create the right sort of 'enabling conditions' for their economies to grow. Some suggest that this is simply a way for the powerful Annex II countries to try to gain access to developing country markets. Precisely how developed countries should help to build the right sort of enabling environments in developing economies is highly controversial and a major source of political disagreement. It also stimulates a great deal of interest from the development NGOs and anti-globalization movements (Figure 3.13 overleaf).

OPEC countries wield considerable power in climate negotiations. They consider the potential decline of the global petroleum industry as a 'climate impact', which is just as relevant to them as, for example, sea-level rise is to small island states. In one sense, OPEC is just an extreme example of the political sensitivities that exist in most countries around solving climate change.

Figure 3.13 'There ain't no power like the power of the people, and the power of the people won't stop'. The inspiration for the 'WTO song' (Track 9) by the folk activist band 'Seize the Day', on their album *All Hands that are Ready*, came from the chanting of the crowd outside the World Trade Organization (WTO) meeting in Seattle in 1999.

With the exception of the US, few developed countries have been open about their fears concerning the impact that taking actions to combat climate change might have on their domestic economies. George W. Bush's rejection (Box 3.5 and Figure 3.14) of the Kyoto Protocol (Section 3.4) may, however, be symptomatic of more widespread but unstated views of leaders of the developed countries. As you read the Bush letter, make a note of his main fears about the Kyoto Protocol and his hopes for a possible resolution. These issues are the focus of Activity 3.4.

Box 3.5 Text of a letter from George W. Bush to Senators Hagel, Helms, Craig and Roberts, 13 March 2001

Thank you for your letter of March 6, 2001, asking for the Administration's views on global climate change, in particular the Kyoto Protocol and efforts to regulate carbon dioxide under the Clean Air Act. My Administration takes the issue of global climate change very seriously.

As you know, I oppose the Kyoto Protocol because it exempts 80 percent of the world, including major population centers such as China and India, from compliance, and would cause serious harm to the U.S. economy. The Senate's vote, 95–0, shows that there is a clear consensus that the Kyoto Protocol is an unfair and ineffective means of addressing global climate change concerns.

As you also know, I support a comprehensive and balanced national energy policy that takes into account the importance of improving air quality. Consistent with this balanced approach, I intend to work with the Congress on a multipollutant strategy to require power plants to reduce emissions of sulfur dioxide, nitrogen oxides, and mercury. Any such strategy would include phasing in reductions over a reasonable period of time, providing regulatory certainty, and offering market-based incentives to help industry meet the targets. I do not believe, however, that the government should impose on power plants mandatory emissions reductions for carbon dioxide, which is not a 'pollutant' under the Clean Air Act.

A recently released Department of Energy Report, 'Analysis of Strategies for Reducing Multiple Emissions from Power Plants,' concluded that including caps on carbon dioxide emissions as part of a multiple emissions strategy would lead to an even more dramatic shift from coal to natural gas for electric power generation and significantly higher electricity prices compared to scenarios in which only sulfur dioxide and nitrogen oxides were reduced.

This is important new information that warrants a re-evaluation, especially at a time of rising energy prices and a serious energy shortage. Coal generates more than half of America's electricity supply. At a time when California has already experienced energy shortages, and other Western states are worried about price and availability of energy this summer, we must be very careful not to take actions that could harm consumers. This is especially true given the incomplete state of scientific knowledge of the causes of, and solutions to, global climate change and the lack of commercially available technologies for removing and storing carbon dioxide.

Consistent with these concerns, we will continue to fully examine global climate change issues — including the science, technologies, market-based systems, and innovative options for addressing concentrations of greenhouse gases in the atmosphere. I am very optimistic that, with the proper focus and working with our friends and allies, we will be able to develop technologies, market incentives, and other creative ways to address global climate change.

I look forward to working with you and others to address global climate change issues in the context of a national energy policy that protects our environment, consumers, and economy.

Sincerely,

GEORGE W. BUSH

(US Department of State, 2003)

Figure 3.14 George W. Bush controversially rejected the Kyoto Protocol on the grounds that it would harm the US economy. In March 2001 he said: 'I oppose the Kyoto Protocol because it exempts 80 per cent of the world, including major population centers, such as China and India, from compliance, and would seriously cause harm to the US economy.' How many other World leaders privately share his explicit fears and concerns?

Activity 3.4: Contours of climate politics and policy

Pick out at least *four* phrases in Bush's letter that set the pattern for the main contours of climate change politics and policy in the next 10–15 years at the international level.

Answer

The phrase 'the Kyoto Protocol is an unfair and ineffective means of addressing global climate change concerns' is a clear statement of the tensions among nations about what represents an *equitable* approach to solving the climate issue (more on this in Chapter 4). Whether or not it is ineffective remains to be seen. It certainly is ambitious.

Raw political sensitivities are revealed in the phrase 'would lead to an even more dramatic shift from coal to natural gas for electric power generation'. The implication is that a shift away from coal towards other energy sources is a bad thing. This is clearly the case if you work in the coal industry. If climate change is about stabilizing greenhouse gas concentrations, then it is about reducing the use of all types of fossil fuels in favour of renewable energy sources (and possibly nuclear). This means that under any approach we are going to have to use less fossil fuel (or does it necessarily? — see below). Climate-change politics and policy will continue to have to deal with the vested interests of the fossil fuel industries and exporting countries in the coming years.

Around the time that Bush wrote this letter, California was suffering from a series of electrical 'brown outs' that were crippling the state. Hence his comment 'at a time of rising energy prices and a serious energy shortage'. There are real fears among many stakeholders of the 'lights going out' in any shift towards a renewable energy future.

'…we must be very careful not to take actions that could harm consumers', says Bush. Here we have an example of the priority given to consumption above environmental actions or, more broadly, a strategy for sustainable development. Can we solve the climate-change issue without harming consumers? Will consumers not ultimately be harmed if no action is taken?

The two phrases 'and the lack of commercially available technologies for removing and storing carbon dioxide' and 'we will be able to develop technologies, market incentives and other creative ways to address global climate change' reveal Bush's optimism that some kind of win–win solution to climate change can be found. In fact, they suggest the possibility that the solution is to continue to use fossil fuels but to capture and store the carbon dioxide that presently goes directly into the atmosphere. Does this forecast a climate friendly fossil-fuelled economy? Perhaps! It is technologically feasible and its commercial feasibility is improving rapidly.

As we shall see in the remainder of this chapter and the next, meeting the objective of the UNFCCC implies a major shift away from the current, predominantly fossil fuel-based, global economy towards less carbon-intensive energy technologies such as renewables and, possibly, nuclear energy.

3.3.5 Three ways to respond to climate change

Within the objective, principles and commitments of the climate Convention, we can discern three basic options that countries have to respond to risks associated with climate change:

- *Option 1:* **Do little or nothing** We can choose to continue on our 'business as usual' global emissions trajectory, and simply wait and see what happens next. At any future stage, the decision can always be taken to adapt and/or mitigate.

- *Option 2:* **Adaptation** We can choose to adapt. Adaptation to climate change is any kind of adjustment in response to actual or expected climate change. The climate system is complex and highly inertial. Changes in some systems take several hundred years to work themselves through. For this reason, even if greenhouse gas emissions were to suddenly and dramatically fall today, the Earth's climate would continue to change for centuries. Greenhouse gas concentrations would continue to rise, the mean surface temperature would continue to increase, the average sea-level would continue to rise and many other climatic impacts would still occur. Examples of adaptations to climate change are shown in Figure 3.15.

(a)　　　　　　　　　　　　　(b)　　　　　　　　　　　　　(c)

(d)　　　　　　　　　　　　　(e)

Figure 3.15 Examples of adaptation technologies and options: (a) a sea wall; (b) headquarters of Munich Re, a large re-insurance company; insurance against climate damages is an adaptation option (see Chapter 4); (c) mangroves in the Eastern USA (protecting and in some case reforesting with mangroves can reduce vulnerability of fragile coastal systems to climate change); (d) building on stilts; (e) a Shanghai appartment block with lots of air-conditioning units.

(a)   (b)

(c)   (d)

Figure 3.16   Examples of greenhouse gas mitigation technologies and options:
(a) a new energy-efficient condensing gas boiler; (b) solar water heaters for sale in
Hangzhou, China; (c) a wind farm; (d) forests are a form of biological mitigation.

- *Option 3:* **Mitigation**   We can choose to mitigate (Figure 3.16). Mitigation is
  any human intervention to reduce the sources or enhance the sinks of greenhouse
  gases. Generating electricity from renewable sources of energy instead of fossil
  fuels, energy conservation and energy efficiency wherever possible, are examples
  of mitigation. Planting forests to sequester carbon in the form of woody biomass
  is another example.

3.4 One small step for the planet, one giant leap towards a global carbon economy

Once an international convention has been ratified by the participating countries, regular
Conferences of the Parties (COPs) are held to manage whatever business is necessary
to achieve the goal of the convention. At UNFCCC COP 1 held in Berlin in 1995,
a brand new round of negotiations began on an even tougher target than the 1990
stabilization target contained in the original text of the UNFCCC itself. This is the
origin of possibly the most publicly recognized international environmental agreement
to date, the Kyoto Protocol. (Any additional commitments made on climate change
under the UNFCCC are done in the form of Protocols to the Convention.)

By 1995, many developed and developing country Parties were frustrated with the
lack of progress in reducing greenhouse gas emissions in developed countries.

In the same year, the IPCC's Second Assessment Report turned up the political heat further by concluding that 'the balance of evidence suggests a discernible human influence on global climate' and predicted that, under a 'business as usual' scenario, global warming during the period 1990–2100 will be in the range 1.0 °C–3.5 °C. After two years of complex negotiations, a new legal instrument within the UNFCCC regime was adopted at UNFCCC COP 3 in Kyoto — the Kyoto Protocol (Figure 3.17).

The Kyoto Protocol added the following new features and dimensions to the international regime of climate governance:

- A new and more ambitious goal to reduce greenhouse gas emissions from Annex I countries by 5.2% by 2012 compared with 1990. Within the developed country group, countries agreed to different commitments, so that this overall target would be achieved.

- A procedure to agree new greenhouse gas reduction goals regularly into the future. The Kyoto agreement includes a process for agreeing new and more ambitious emissions cuts *ad infinitum* until the goal of the UNFCCC is declared achieved. The 5.2% reduction target is therefore the goal for what is called the **first commitment period**. Negotiations on new targets for the second commitment period (2013–18) will make headline news in the coming years.

- The target covers several greenhouse gases (those listed in Table 2.3) — not just carbon dioxide, though this is by far the biggest contributor to the problem.

- The targets are legally binding, and failure to comply with them will ultimately incur penalties, potentially in terms of fines and an increased quota of reductions.

- Annex I countries were given permission, under strict circumstances, to trade future rights to emit quantities of greenhouse gas emissions among themselves and with EITs. This is what is known as **international emissions trading**.

- Annex I countries were also granted permission to buy future rights to emit quantities of greenhouse gases from developing countries as a result of any emissions that are saved or avoided through specific projects. This is known as the **Clean Development Mechanism** (**CDM**).

The Protocol enters into force as international law once enough Annex I Parties accounting for 55% of that group's carbon dioxide emissions in 1990 have ratified it. At the time of writing, it is expected that it will enter into force in late 2003 at, or shortly after, UNFCCC COP 9.

The Kyoto Protocol introduced a number of other innovations in the climate-change regime, but the ones listed above are the main ones.

The Protocol is an example of an attempt to give the climate regime some legal teeth. Like other international treaties that provide a framework for sharing our rights to what is a global public good, the Kyoto Protocol uses the standard approach of limiting production or quantities of a particular pollutant or activity.

- What is the International Convention for the Regulation of Whaling, described in Book 1 Chapter 6, designed to limit?

- The quota for the number of whales that could be harvested.

- The Kyoto Protocol is another example of a quantity-type environmental regulation. In this instance, what is the quantity that is being limited?

- The quantity being limited is greenhouse gas emissions to within agreed levels.

The Kioto Protocol
to the Convention on Climate Change

Figure 3.17 Hot off the press: a photograph of an original from the first printed batch of Protocol texts. Can you spot the problem?

Figure 3.18 'Kyoto' is literally a household name. Here it is used as a brand for an 'eco-friendly' refrigerator.

○ Which public good is the Kyoto Protocol designed to protect?

○ The atmosphere, the climate and the services it provides us with.

The Kyoto Protocol has already had a large impact on the networks of decision-makers and stakeholders involved in climate change. The word 'Kyoto' has become practically synonymous with climate-change politics, and is now well known in the world of international business. It is even used as a marketing device to sell eco-friendly household appliances (Figure 3.18).

Although the Kyoto Protocol does serve to strengthen the global response to climate change, it adds significantly to the complexity of the regime. Developed countries did not start giving up their future rights to discharge greenhouse gases into the atmosphere without getting something in return. They insisted on a variety of 'flexibility' mechanisms to help with the economic and social withdrawal symptoms associated with their attempt to kick their fossil-fuel consumption habits; emissions trading and the Clean Development Mechanism are examples. The notion of 'flexibility' is an economic one. The basic idea was that developed countries could meet their overall 5.2% reduction on 1990 emission levels much more cheaply if they were allowed to 'buy and sell' greenhouse gas emission reduction credits. This is basic economics: markets provide a mechanism for resources to flow to those countries and activities where the cost of reducing greenhouse emissions is the lowest (see Chapter 4). The theory is that it can be much cheaper to reduce emissions in rapidly developing or transition economies, especially those that are using outdated or old technologies, rather than in developed countries that have already spent money on more efficient cars, appliances, factory equipment and power stations, for example. We shall see how this operates in Activity 3.5.

Activity 3.5: International emissions trading and the clean development mechanism

(a)   International emissions trading: 'Add these emissions to your account, subtract the same amount from my account but I'll carry on emitting and give you some money in return.'

We can use a highly simplified and hypothetical example to illustrate the basics of how international emissions trading between nations works. It's the year 2011. Germany is near to keeping its promise to reduce its emissions in line with the Kyoto Protocol. It has to find reductions of the order of another 10 million tonnes carbon equivalent (MtCe). The German Environmental Agency has worked out that all the 'low hanging fruit' in terms of quick and cheap ways of reducing emissions inside Germany have been 'picked'. People are turning off their lights, buying more-efficient cars and companies are investing a great deal in energy-saving technologies. The Agency has worked out that a further reduction of 10 MtCe 'at home' will cost the economy an average of €50/tC. Russia, by contrast, is still well below the maximum emissions it is allowed under the Protocol in this period. This is because its economy collapsed in the early 1990s, with the result that its emissions fell dramatically; in other words, Russia has emission rights to sell. It has posted 10 MtCe for sale on the international carbon market at €30/tC.

How much would Germany save by buying 10 MtCe from Russia instead of reducing its domestic emissions by an equivalent amount?

Answer

If Germany were to reduce their emissions by 10 MtCe at home, it would cost €500 million (10 MtC multiplied by €50/tC). To buy the equivalent amount from Russia would cost €300 million. Germany would therefore save €200 million by not reducing emissions at home. So the Germans save money, the Russians make money and GHG emissions are reduced. Everyone wins with emissions trading, it seems!

Can you think of any arguments why environmental NGOs and other stakeholders might not see emissions trading as such a good idea?

Answer

In theory, emissions trading is basic economic common sense, but in practice there are a few concerns about it. Firstly, there is the argument that Germany will at some stage in the future (under a continual ratcheting down of emissions across all developed countries to 60–90% of what they are now) still need to reduce the 10 MtC at home that it has just avoided addressing. Wouldn't it be cheaper and better for Germany to start sooner rather than later? This depends on how you take into account the risk of finding out that climate change is going to have greater future costs than you think at present. (Chapter 5 discusses this in more detail.)

Secondly, there is the argument that although Russia has gained some extra cash now, in the future it will have less room to grow (in emissions terms) than it would have done otherwise by giving away rights to the 10 MtCe. Perhaps then it might need to buy them back!

(b) Clean Development Mechanism: 'If I help you clean up your emissions, you keep the social, economic and environmental benefits, and I'll keep the rights to the emissions we saved together.'

Imagine now that Germany were in exactly the same position as described in part (a). However, instead of looking to Russia to buy emission credits, it decided that it would still look abroad to buy some emission entitlements, but this time would use the Clean Development Mechanism (CDM). Through an international development project, Germany decides to spend some money helping to improve coal-fired power stations in China. Now China needs a lot more power, because it is developing rapidly, and it relies heavily on coal for its electricity needs. By adding some new combustion technologies to five old Chinese power plants, the efficiency of electricity generation can be significantly improved and at the same time some of the local air pollution from the plants is also cleaned up. It also means that the electricity the plants produce is cheaper, which has benefits for the Chinese economy (ignoring the fact that one day China may well be in the same boat as Germany, and then might want higher, not lower electricity prices!). Over a period of 20 years (the life expectancy of the old power stations with new refits), this translates into a total saving of some 10 MtCe.

If it costs Germany €150 million in total to upgrade the coal plants, and China agrees to transfer the emission reduction credits generated by the project, what is the mitigation cost in Euros/tC to Germany from this project? Does it make more economic sense for Germany to spend money cleaning up Chinese power stations or to buy credits from the Russians?

Answer

Yes. The cost is €150 million/10 MtCe or €15/tCe. The cost of emissions permits from the Russians is €30/tCe. This is exactly twice the cost of the credits from the Chinese CDM project.

So what is the benefit to Germany?

Answer

Cash. Germany saves €150 million compared with emissions trading with the Russians, or €350 million compared with finding 10 MtCe of emission reductions at home.

What are the social, economic and environmental benefits to China as a result of this project?

Answer

(i) Less local pollution from the power plants, with environmental and human health benefits; (ii) cheaper electricity, which helps to boost economic and social development, particularly those suffering from energy poverty in Chinese cities and rural areas. If the electricity is used in manufacturing, it could also help reduce the cost of Chinese goods sold abroad, thereby making China more competitive.

Figure 3.19 The small print on how emissions trading and the Clean Development Mechanism will actually work began to emerge at COP 7 in Marrakesh in 2001.

Emissions trading is restricted to Annex I countries. CDM projects must involve a developing country partner. Although in theory, the CDM is a fairly simple idea, in practice it is turning into quite a complex bureaucratic headache. The system of rules began emerging at UNFCCC COP 7 in November 2001 in Marrakesh, Morocco (Figure 3.19). It had taken four-and-a-half Conferences of the Parties (COPs), around 50 technical intergovernmental workshops, several tens of millions of air miles, and the production and disposal of enough documents to deforest an area the size of which would presumably be visible with the naked eye from the International Space Station!

Activity 3.6: Quantifying Kyoto

How big a step is Kyoto? For all the column inches that Kyoto stories generate, there is one angle that seldom gets reported accurately or clearly. In this activity you will use the carbon accounting techniques we met in Chapter 2 to quantify the significance of the Kyoto agreement (first commitment period) relative to 'baseline' emissions — in other words relative to the growth in emissions that would otherwise have occurred under 'business as usual'.

The Kyoto Protocol limits the emissions of Annex I countries to within agreed limits expressed as a reduction relative to 1990 (the reference year) emission levels. The initial Kyoto targets are to reduce annual emissions of six greenhouse gases from Annex I countries to 5.2% below 1990 levels by 2012. The wording of the Kyoto agreement takes into account emissions from land-use change and forestry. Taking this into account, total emissions of the six greenhouse gases from Annex I countries in 1990 amounted to 15.93 Gt CO_2e.

Why is the Kyoto target best expressed in units of carbon dioxide equivalent?

Answer

We use this unit because the 5.2% target includes six greenhouse gases, each with very different direct global warming potentials (Table 1.3).

Express the 5.2% Annex I Kyoto reduction in units of tonnes of carbon dioxide equivalent (refer back to Activity 1.2).

Answer

828 $MtCO_2$e. In other words 5.2% of 15.93 Gt CO_2e.

What is 828 $MtCO_2$e in units of tonnes of carbon equivalent?

Answer

226 MtCe (828 multiplied by 12/44).

The current flux of carbon dioxide emissions from burning fossil fuel is 5.3 PgC per year (Book 2, Figure 1.10b). Express the 5.2% target as a percentage of the current yearly flux of carbon dioxide emissions from burning fossil fuels.

Answer

One Pg is 1×10^{15} g or 1 Gt or 1 000 Mt. The percentage is therefore $226/5300 \times 100 = 4.3$ %. The Kyoto 2012 target represents 4.3% of the global annual flux of emissions into the atmosphere due to fossil-fuel combustion.

Assuming there was no Kyoto Protocol, and total emissions from Annex I countries for the six greenhouse gases increased at previous business-as-usual rates of 0.8% per annum, what would emissions from Annex I countries be in 2012? Use the compound interest formula $F = B(1 + i)^n$ in your calculator or spreadsheet, where F is the emission rate in n years from the base year, B is the emissions rate in the base year (1990) and i is the rate of increase of carbon dioxide emissions per year.

Answer

In this instance, B = 15.93 Gt CO_2e, i = 0.008 and n = 22. The calculation gives an answer of 18.98 Gt CO_2e in 2012.

In a business-as-usual scenario, how much greater in percentage terms would emissions in 2012 be compared with 1990?

Answer

19.1% greater: (18.98/15.93 × 100) − 100.

If the Kyoto target of −5.2% is achieved by 2012, what is the real reduction in percentage terms that Kyoto represents from the baseline?

Answer

20.4%: (119.3 − 94.8)/119.3 × 100. In other words, the Kyoto targets are a great deal more ambitious than they sound at first glance. In real terms, Kyoto represents just over a 20% reduction in emissions (Figure 3.20).

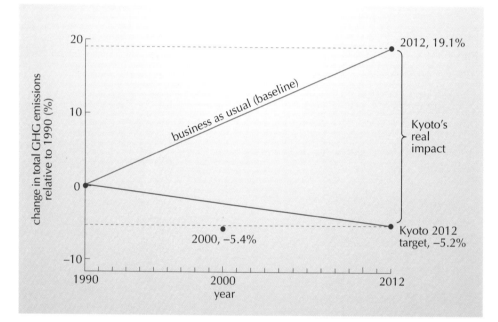

Figure 3.20 Kyoto represents a real reduction from the baseline of around 20% — an unprecedented break from historical trends.

The actual amount of greenhouse gases that the Kyoto Protocol (if successfully implemented) will have prevented from entering the atmosphere may be roughly four times bigger than the headline 5.2% target. This is because energy use and greenhouse gas emissions were rising in most developed countries at the end of the 20th century. The Kyoto targets are to be met by 2012. To reduce their emissions below 1990 levels, developed countries first have to stop the growth in their emissions from what would otherwise have been the case, and then reduce them further.

In terms of planetary management, Kyoto is a tiny step. However, in terms of changing the relationship between energy use, greenhouse gas emissions and economic growth, Kyoto is a huge leap forward. By 2000, Annex I countries as an overall group were around 5.4% below 1990 — that is, roughly where they should be by 2012 (Figure 3.21). If the group of countries as a whole didn't grow, they would have succeeded in meeting their collective Kyoto commitments. However, this is very unlikely. The headline disguises the fact that by 2000, the Annex II countries were up around 8.4%, whereas the EITs were a massive 37% down on 1990 levels. This is principally

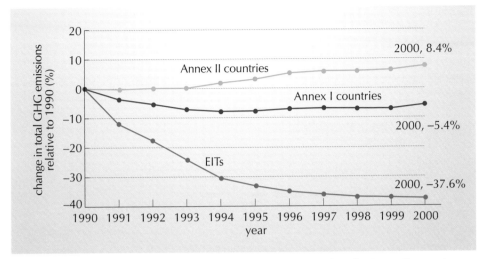

Figure 3.21 Without the decline in emissions from EIT countries, the Annex I countries would find it much harder to meet their Kyoto promise (source UNFCCC, 2002).

due to the political and economic transformation of Eastern Europe in the 1990s. Most Annex II country targets are supposed to be 8% *below* their 1990 levels by 2012.

As shown in Figure 3.21, most of the wealthier Annex I countries have actually increased their emissions over the period 1990–2000. They are moving in the opposite direction to their Kyoto targets!

So how much difference in the long term will the Kyoto Protocol's first round of emission reduction targets make to our future climate? An estimate of the difference that the Kyoto Protocol 5.2% reduction will make to the climate of the 21st century if fully implemented by 2012 is shown in Figure 3.22.

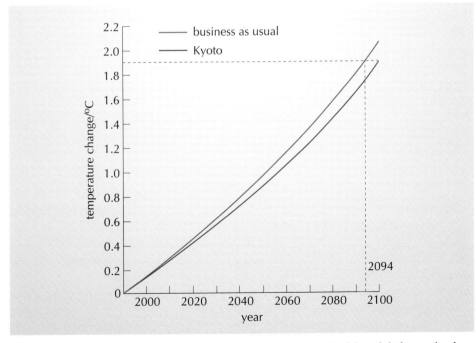

Figure 3.22 Fully implemented, the Kyoto 2012 target may only delay global warming by six years by the end of the century (adapted from Lomborg, 2001).

Figure 3.22 shows that the Kyoto Protocol (up to 2012) makes only a fraction of a °C difference to global temperatures in 2100. By itself, this first step to control GHG emissions will have had negligible impacts on GHG concentrations (all other things being equal), and therefore temperature increases. But it does represent the start of the international environmental governance system applying its hand to 'planetary management'.

The Protocol added a new level to the politics of international climate change. The politics flow around the following key questions:

- How flexible is 'flexible'? In practice, how much cheap carbon will Annex II countries be permitted to trade with EITs or gain through CDM credits from developing countries?

- Which technologies and activities would be allowed? Could nations invest in forests and nuclear power (Figure 3.23) and claim credits?

- Who would be allowed to participate in Kyoto mechanisms? Does it include everyone, or just those who had met their promises, and which promises and how would those promises be measured?

- In practice, how much cheap carbon will Annex II countries be permitted to trade with EITs or gain through CDM credits from developing countries?

- How do we accurately account for greenhouse gas transactions? Who's going to keep track of all those transactions?

- What would be the consequences of non-compliance? At the end of the day, won't developed countries just abandon their promises, as they failed to meet their original stabilization commitment in the UNFCCC?

Some legal observers have labelled the Kyoto compliance regime as 'unprecedented in international law'. The agreement establishes consequences for non-compliance, along with a new Compliance Committee and Enforcement Branch to monitor non-compliance. The real teeth in the Kyoto Protocol are in the form of an instant penalty (e.g. 30%) on any amount a country emits above its target for a given period. In other words if you are 10 MtCe overdrawn in your carbon account, it will be increased by an extra 30% (in this case to 13 MtCe). Though it may not be strictly legally binding, the emerging compliance regime looks like one of the toughest environmental multilateral agreements yet. Kyoto gave birth to a complex organism of global environmental governance. We haven't seen this organizational species before, and really have no idea what it is going to look like when it is fully developed. Some have speculated that when mature it will be the environmental counterbalance to the World Trade Organization (Figure 3.24). Rumours of the establishment of a possible 'World Environment Organization' have been circulating for years.

Scientifically, and from a global perspective, each and every tonne of carbon (or other greenhouse gas) reduced, from whatever technology or process, and wherever in the world, is equally important. At some stage within the next few years or so, total greenhouse gas emissions from developing countries will for the first time overtake those from developed countries. The Kyoto Protocol therefore only addresses just over half the climate-change problem. Over time, that fraction will fall even further. Herein lies a major political stumbling block in the ongoing climate negotiations. Developed countries, quite reasonably, point out that developing countries also need to honour their own commitments in the UNFCCC (Articles 3 and 4) by reducing their

(a)   (b)

Figure 3.23 (a) Monocultured forest plantation; (b) Sizewell B nuclear power station. These options could provide carbon credits, but are not everyone's idea of sustainable development.

future greenhouse gas emissions. Countries like India and China recognize the scientific basis of this perspective, but argue that they are only at the start of their fossil-fuel based industrial transformations. They cry 'double standards' and point out that developed nations have combusted their way to their current living standards.

On the bright side, some optimists point out that new technologies — like living species — can and do transcend political borders. They point to the potential 'spill-over effects' of radical actions to curb greenhouse gas emissions in developed countries. The idea is that new carbon-efficient technologies, and practices that developed countries invent and adopt to meet their Kyoto targets, will find their way into developing economies. In other words, developing nations will emit less in the future as a result of

Figure 3.24 Riots outside the 1999 WTO meeting in Genoa. Does the emerging climate governance regime represent the beginning of a counterbalance to the WTO?

the development and transfer of cleaner technologies from the developed world. Developing nations may leapfrog over fossil-fuel powered industrialization, and develop on the basis of more sustainable technologies and practices. New cars sold in China today have nearly the same level of technological efficiency that new cars sold in Europe have.

However, the clearest political way out of this dilemma for the foreseeable future would seem to be for developed countries to accelerate the implementation of their domestic climate-change action plans, and for developing countries to declare some sort of time-frame for reducing their emissions.

The UNFCCC is the most advanced example of a global environmental response to date in terms of the sophistication of its subsidiary instruments and processes. Climate negotiations have come a long way in a relatively short time. As the true nature of the compliance regime around the Kyoto Protocol unfolds, Kyoto may prove to be an unprecedented turning point in the evolution of international legal systems. However, there are clear signs that there are some turbulent years ahead for such treaties. The chief reason is that very few, if any, governments spend their time thinking mainly about environmental issues. On the whole, all governments are united in their pursuit of economic and social development as the primary objective. When climate change has to take its place in a competing list of aims and objectives, conflicts begin to arise around decisions.

You should now go to the Web and do the activities associated with Chapter 3.

3.5 Summary of Chapter 3

3.1   The global political response to climate change is relatively recent. Formally beginning in 1994 with the establishment of the UNFCCC, it was triggered by two decades of scientific assessment.

3.2   The UNFCCC is the centre piece of the global political response to climate change. The core of the UNFCCC is a framework of a central Objective, some guiding Principles and a series of Commitments. The objective of the convention is clear in one sense, but open to considerable scientific and political uncertainty in other ways. The guiding Principles are littered with potential sources of political uncertainty. The Commitments contained in Article 4 distinguish between those that apply to all countries, and those that apply to developed countries (Annex I countries).

3.3   Developing countries distinguish three distinct types of 'climate impact': actual impacts (e.g. sea-level rise), economic and social impacts (e.g. cost of adaptation and mitigation), and economic and social impacts on fossil-fuel-exporting countries as a result of switching to renewable energy sources.

3.4   The Kyoto Protocol significantly strengthens the UNFCCC regime. It adds legal teeth to the climate negotiations. Its main innovations are quantified targets for greenhouse gas reduction for developed countries that can be extended *ad infinitum*, the possibility of emissions trading among Annex I countries and the opportunity for developed countries to embark on clean development projects with developing country partners.

3.5   In terms of planetary management, the Kyoto Protocol is only a small step. However, in terms of changing the relationship between economic growth, energy use and greenhouse gas emissions, it is a significant step. These two different perspectives on the same Treaty provide some insight into different views of the significance of the Kyoto climate regime.

3.6   Even if Kyoto (in its first commitment period, 2008–12) is implemented fully, it will have a very limited impact on future increases in GMST. Much tougher reduction targets will be required in the future to stabilize the climate.

Learning Outcomes for Chapter 3

When you have completed this chapter, you should be able to:

3.1   Define and use, or recognize definitions and applications of, the terms given in **bold** in the text.

3.2   Describe the key elements of the Framework of the United Nations Framework Convention on Climate Change (UNFCCC) in terms of its Objective, main Principles and Commitments. (Questions 3.1, 3.2, 3.3 and 3.4)

3.3   Describe three types of climate-change impact that nations are concerned about and three response options. (Questions 3.5 and 3.6)

3.4   Describe the main features of the Kyoto Protocol, and give practical examples of the principles of international emissions trading and the Clean Development Mechanism. (Question 3.7)

3.5   Explain the significance of the Kyoto Protocol in its first commitment period (to 2012) in relation to (a) the achievement of climate stabilization and (b) the relationship between the energy and economic systems of developed countries. (Question 3.8)

Chapter 4   Tuning in: integrated assessments of climate futures

Prepared for the course team by Stephen Peake

4.1 Introduction

Even if we manage to reach a political agreement on a 'safe' greenhouse gas stabilization level, how exactly are we going to get there? The UNFCCC does not specify *how* greenhouse gas concentrations can be stabilized at safe levels. The Kyoto Protocol is a step in the right direction — but only a step. In Activity 3.6, we saw that in order to stabilize greenhouse gas concentrations, global emissions must be constrained at a fraction of their current levels. In fact, the industrialized countries need to reduce their emissions by 60–90% of their 1990 levels during the course of this century. The process has only just begun, and the Kyoto 2012 targets are, from a long-term perspective, relatively easy to achieve.

- Kyoto represents a 5% decrease in greenhouse gas emissions relative to 1990. How many more 'Kyotos' would we need to reduce greenhouse gas emissions from industrialized countries to 40% of 1990 levels (that is, a 60% reduction)?

- We would need another eleven 'Kyotos' to achieve a 60% reduction from 1990 levels (twelve steps of 5% reduction = 60%).

As the political temperature rises in developed and developing country capitals, world leaders will have to establish the facts and start to take serious decisions about allocating limited resources to tackle climate change and assess the political risks of different courses of action. There is a lot to think about, and many choices to be made. What stabilization level? How much to reduce emissions? How fast? Who needs to reduce their emissions? How much will it all cost in economic, social and political terms? What happens if we don't do anything? Climate change is just one of a number of pressing global problems. Where can we best direct the limited money our governments are prepared to spend on climate change?

The goal of this chapter is to help you tune in to the sort of issues that these questions raise. We hope to give you a longer-term view of the problem of climate change, and prepare you to think through (in Chapter 5) fundamental philosophical questions that climate change raises about fairness and the future.

4.2 An integrated approach to thinking climate change through

Responding to climate change requires decision-making in the context of extreme scientific complexity and uncertainty. This demands an overview of the three possible options available to respond to climate change: business as usual (doing little or nothing); adaptation; mitigation. In other words, **integrated assessments** of climate change are required to take into account the costs and benefits of all three options.

- Give two examples for each of the three climate-change response options.

○ Examples of doing little or nothing include: disaster assistance and relief following a major tropical storm; food aid to drought-stricken African regions. Examples of adaptation include: investment in irrigation technologies to cope with extended dry seasons; building of sea walls to protect valuable infrastructure. Examples of mitigation responses include: any kind of technology with improved energy efficiency; substituting fossil-fuel consumption with renewable energy.

So far, the UNFCCC process has been almost entirely focused on mitigation. This seems quite natural. Quick, turn off the tap! But as you saw in Chapter 2 (Figure 2.9), we have started to see that even under different scenarios where the tap is turned down a bit (and ultimately a lot in the course of this century), we may well be facing serious risks from unavoidable climate change due to past emissions of greenhouse gases. In some cases, there may be things we can do to limit or prevent damage from climate change. Just as there is a wide menu of options for mitigation, there is also a range of adaptation measures that can be taken across different sectors. Some of this will happen anyway (we call this **reactive adaptation**, for example when farmers compensate as a matter of course for natural variability in climate), some of it we can anticipate (we call this **anticipatory adaptation** — for example, building better and higher sea walls). In other cases, there may be no choice, or it simply may be less costly, to sit back and suffer climate consequences as they unfold. You will be reasonably familiar with various mitigation options. Adaptation options are probably less familiar to you, and in some cases are less obvious (Table 4.1).

In some cases there are examples of so-called **no regrets** mitigation and adaptation options. 'No regrets' mitigation options are those that actually don't cost you anything: they are zero cost or even *pay you* to implement them. Similarly, a no regrets adaptation option has zero costs because it helps limit or prevent damage from climate change, but at the same time delivers some other benefits — for example, more secure water supplies — which, in turn, benefit local development and human health.

Figure 4.1 The growth in the value of insured losses and total losses for catastrophic weather events in the years 1950–98.

But there are only so many no regrets options. It is a common truth that there is generally no such thing as a free lunch. This means that quite soon, the task of reducing emissions and making adjustments to avoid or insure against future climate-change damages is going to start costing real people real money. It may well already be doing so (Figure 4.1).

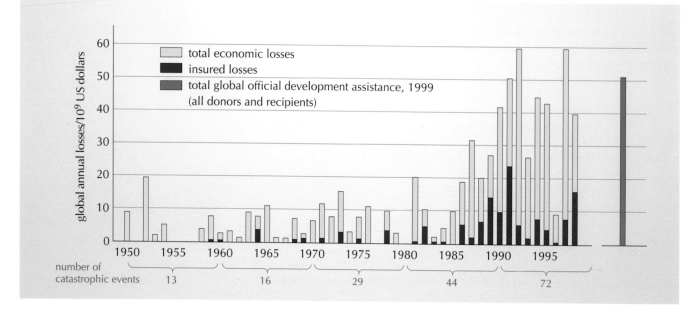

Table 4.1 Examples of adaptation options in different sectors (based on Fankhauser, 1998)

Sector	Adaptation options
agriculture	Change farming practices: e.g. fertilizer use, heat/drought-resistant plants; improve irrigation systems; change land topography; insurance/disaster relief; emergency plans for famines; crop insurance.
forestry	Protection of existing forests: e.g. fire prevention; suppress impacts of diseases, droughts, etc.; introduction of new species; forest management options e.g. change in cutting practice; sustainable forest use; conserve gene pools (install seed banks); efficient forest management (e.g. abolish subsidies).
health/ air pollution	Health care options: improve health/sanitary standards; precautionary policies such as vaccination; air pollution policy options e.g. impose air quality standards; emission taxes/permits; training and information (e.g. training of medical staff; informing vulnerable groups); research in improved prevention (e.g. vaccines); encourage structural adaptation (e.g. implement planning/building guidelines/ recommended air quality levels).
coastal zones	Options to protect against effects of sea-level rise: e.g. sea-walls dykes, coastal afforestation, beach nourishment; options to retreat from sea-level rise e.g. restrict development (set back zones, resettlement of affected people); options to accommodate sea-level rise e.g. adjust economic activities such as convert farms to fish ponds; insurance; implement Integrated Coastal Zone Management: e.g. make new institutional arrangements, build technological capacity, provide information to public, market-based instruments, design regulatory measures, set standards such as water quality; plan physical structures, ongoing monitoring of coastal processes; and storm forecasting.
water	Supply management options: e.g. investment in reservoirs and infrastructure; system optimization (e.g. interregional water transfers); recycling water for lower quality use; demand-side management options e.g. investment in water-saving technologies; change in water-use practices; drought management plans; formulate water quality standards; remove market distortions like subsidies; create institutions and train staff: e.g. create water supply agencies; develop hydrological models; R&D on desalination and water recycling schemes; education/information for households.

One explicitly rational approach to the challenge of integrated assessment is to put all this into the words of economists. They would think of the challenge in terms of minimizing the overall human welfare loss from climate change (Fankhauser, 1998). In other words, we can apply one of the most widely used weapons in the economists' armoury — cost–benefit analysis. This approach is applicable to all the three response options. The climate-change welfare problem can then be expressed as finding the level of mitigation m and adaptation a which minimizes the combined sum of mitigation costs MC, adaptation costs AC and damage costs D. The challenge is to find a balance among the three options which minimizes total welfare costs. Mitigation costs rise with the level of mitigation achieved (we say MC is a function of m, or $MC(m)$). Similarly, the cost of adaptation is a function of the achieved level of adaptation ($MA(a)$). Damage costs depend on the levels of *both* mitigation and adaptation. Mitigation reduces damages independent of adaptation. Adaptation also reduces damages, independent of mitigation. D is therefore a function of m and a, or $D(m, a)$.

In the language of economics, this rational approach to integration can be expressed as:

$$\text{minimize } [MC(m) + AC(a) + D(m, a)]$$

There are trade-offs between the costs of mitigation and adaptation, and those of damage. A global cost–benefit approach to decision-making about climate change therefore involves comparing marginal mitigation and adaptation costs with the marginal benefits of avoiding damage. A full exploration of the costs of climate change would fill a whole book, so we'll leave the formal economics there! The important point is that you recognize that however uncertain and complex the climate-change conundrum may appear, there *are* rational tools available for thinking the problem through. Policy analysts, and economists in particular, are already using them, and politicians have begun listening.

Kyoto is ostensibly about negotiating a minimum acceptable long-term rate of mitigation of greenhouse gas emissions. For large greenhouse gas emitters (for example, the US, China, Europe, India), this makes much sense. They will all eventually benefit from lower damage costs. Less future climate damage means that mitigation also benefits developed countries by reducing their future responsibilities under the UNFCCC to assist vulnerable, less-developed countries to adapt to climate change or compensate them for any damages. From a small-emitter perspective (e.g. small island developing states, and, in fact, the vast majority of the 191 UN member states), the problem of climate change becomes one of finding the amount of adaptation that minimizes the sum of damage and adaptation costs for a given amount of climate change. This is because these countries account for a relatively small proportion of total greenhouse gas emissions, many for a fraction of a single per cent. Whatever they do individually will make little difference to the future global climate. Essentially, when not acting as part of a larger political group, small emitters are primarily interested in limiting the amount of residual climate damage they will suffer.

The global outlook for CO_2 emissions is certainly upwards for a good while yet. Current emissions trends, population growth and the expectation of significant economic development in all countries over this century all point to growing emissions.

There is a great deal of uncertainty about the potential costs of climate change. We are still in the very early days of rational cost–benefit integrated assessments of climate change. As a result of numerous global energy crises, our climate modelling heritage is dominated by energy–economy systems dynamics models.

Integrated assessment models that can deal with the costs of mitigation, adaptation and climate damages are, however, evolving rapidly. Five important factors that affect mitigation/stabilization costs are:

- *Baseline emissions*   A great deal depends on what assumptions are made about the future baseline (see Activity 3.6, p. 110). If we think the baseline emissions are likely to be high, then the costs of stabilization are going to be high, and vice versa. For example, how rapidly will the introduction of renewable energy and energy-efficiency technologies develop, and how competitive will they be relative to future oil and natural gas prices?

- *Stabilization level*   The political choice of the stabilization level for Article 2 will critically influence costs. Clearly, the lower the level of stabilization sought, the more costly it is going to be, since this is working against the prevailing rising trend. Stabilization at 450 p.p.m. would be more expensive than at 550 p.p.m. or 650 p.p.m.

- *Speed of stabilization*   The political choice of when we achieve stabilization also critically affects costs. The cost of stabilization rises the sooner the target year for achieving it. This is because of (i) the way economists treat the notion of cost (in particular, future costs; see Chapter 5), and (ii) how the economy functions in terms of replacing technologies in the economic system (economists call this 'capital stock turnover').

- *Burden sharing*   A problem shared is a problem halved. The number of players working together 'inside' the climate-control regime is very important. The sooner developing countries avoid going down the same fossil-fuel development route as developed countries have done, the lower the overall costs of stabilization will be. This is another way of saying 'the sooner that developing countries change their baseline, the less costly stabilization will be'.

- *Rules and the cost of red tape*   The rules governing international emissions trading and the Clean Development Mechanism also affect costs. If rich nations are allowed to buy more of their emissions reductions abroad rather than cleaning up at home, the costs will be much lower (and vice versa). Which technologies and practices are allowed is also important; not all the possible technical solutions to climate change are welcomed by everybody (Figure 4.2 overleaf). The sustainability of some climate-change solutions is hotly contested. Forests, nuclear power and carbon capture and storage all have vociferous champions and opponents. Renewable energies such as wind, biomass and solar power tend to have the widest support, but there are even objections to these most benign of our non-fossil-fuel energy options.

The remainder of this chapter introduces you to integrated assessment models, to some basic issues around models and policymaking, and then to some of the issues underlying each of the above five cost factors in turn. The chapter does not go further into issues related to rules and red tape. This is a particularly complex area, and it is only necessary for our purposes to note that small print does matter!

Figure 4.2 The possibility that the Clean Development Mechanism will encourage developing countries to implement forestry activities (sinks projects), or adopt nuclear and certain renewable energy technologies has generated considerable concern among environmental NGOs and other stakeholders.

4.3 From emissions to decisions: integrated assessment models

Policymakers in the real world have to juggle with all the various dimensions of climate change — emissions, climate variables, impacts and costs. Only when we think the problem of climate change through in a rational structured way, can we make sense of the global, regional, national and local political dynamics that climate change is unleashing. Scientists have developed a range of models designed to help policymakers think through the implications of climate change — from emissions to decisions. They are called **integrated assessment models** (**IAMs**), and they are a critical tool for policymakers deliberating answers to complex climate questions.

Integrated assessment modelling involves the use of sub-models to undertake four steps of analysis (Figure 4.3).

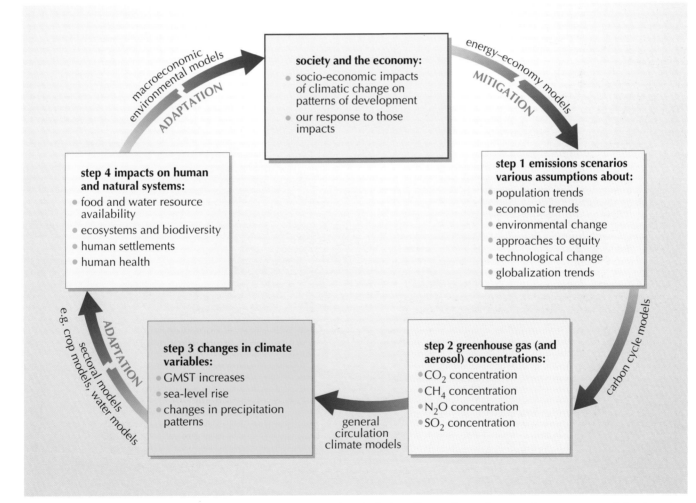

Figure 4.3 Schematic representation of the four main steps of analysis that climate-change integrated assessment models attempt to incorporate. The Figure indicates where results from specific sub-models are used from one step to the next. Full versions of these models cannot be easily combined into one giant IAM. In practice, IAMs take short cuts sacrificing detail to simulate a more comprehensive analysis.

1   Firstly, different scenarios about possible future emissions profiles of developed and developing countries must be generated. In turn, this step requires energy–emissions–economy models be used to explore the various plausible emissions pathways for different countries or regions, and then to estimate their costs.

2   Secondly, models of the interaction between the atmosphere, land surface, oceans and the carbon cycle (and other greenhouse gas cycles; see Figure 2.2) are then needed to translate the various emissions scenarios into various scenarios of greenhouse gas emissions and their atmospheric concentrations.

3   Thirdly, various scenarios of greenhouse gas concentrations must be translated into projections for GMST change and the associated regional impacts on climate variables (sea-level rise, precipitation, cloud cover, etc.).

4   Fourthly, the social and economic impacts of such changes in climate variables must be assessed.

Any single stage of the above cascade of estimation and modelling is extremely complex, and uncertainties are amplified at each stage (Figure 4.4). Already many thousands of person years of effort have gone into integrated assessment modelling. Nevertheless, understanding of the uncertainties within IAMs is likely to improve and be better characterized. The use of such models is likely to be critical in developing comprehensive response strategies as an aid to decision-making.

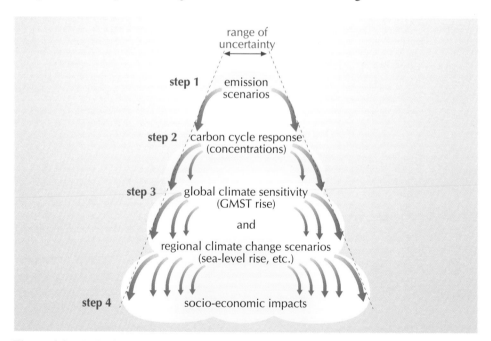

Figure 4.4   Each of the analytical steps involved in integrated assessment modelling introduces uncertainties that feed through to the next stage. The range of uncertainty therefore 'cascades' around the modelling loop.

Some of the IAMs cited in the IPCC TAR are capable of providing insights into the possible future costs of climate change, taking into account, among others, the following positive and negative costs: the costs of mitigation, secondary benefits for sustainable development in general, adaptation and residual damage costs. They are starting to provide indications of the pros and cons of different policy choices in dealing with climate change. This is because IAMs include both a climate system and an economic system. The economic system of these models is capable of modelling the costs of mitigation and adaptation, and of residual climate damage.

Integrated assessment modelling is still very young, and the results so far can only be treated at best as rough indications of relative costs, and a chance to allow more informed political questioning of the pros and cons of different strategies for responding to climate change. Ultimately, the outputs of IAMs rely on assumptions about human values and human behaviour, both of which are complex and dynamic.

Indeed the whole business of IAMs is inevitably political, such that the IPCC in 1998 took a policy decision not to look at the economics of climate change in the context of the TAR.

IAMs have been used to work through various IPCC scenarios, and have begun providing some early results. Estimates of the total annual cost of climate change in the range 1.5–4.0% of global GDP, spread more or less evenly between developed and developing countries by 2100. However, this is an uneven world, where the industrialized nations are many times richer than their developing neighbours.

Such models have also been used to estimate the cost of implementing the Kyoto Protocol in its first commitment period (2008–2012). One estimate puts total costs in the range in the $75 billion to $350 billion, depending on assumptions about the nature of future rules governing global emissions trading (Weyant and Hill, 1999).

In its TAR, the IPCC refers to managing our approach to climate change as 'sequential decision-making under uncertainty'. What does that mean? It means that you act (or not), then learn from your actions as new information is received, then act (or not), then learn, etc. The adoption of the UNFCCC in 1992 and the Kyoto Protocol in 1997 are examples of sequential decision-making under uncertainty: we knew there was a great deal of scientific uncertainty, but nevertheless decided to act. In the coming years, as climate modelling improves and political debates mature, we shall learn and then act again, etc.; that is, it is an iterative process.

The history of the evolution of the scientific case for global warming is itself an example of sequential opinion formation under changing uncertainty. We can't really say 'decision-making under uncertainty' — that only really began at the international level in 1992.

The full-scale scientific assault of every nook and cranny of climate science was unleashed by the establishment of the IPCC in 1988. However, although this has helped reduce uncertainty around some information, it has also, perhaps temporarily, increased the uncertainty in others. Simple and obvious questions about the behaviour of the Earth's climate system have only complex, uncertain answers at present. The evolving field of integrated assessment modelling can already provide some useful insights into decision-making on climate. However, IAMs compound scientific and other uncertainties (see Figure 4.4). In some senses, it is a case of the more you know, the less certain you are. Nevertheless, in the years to come, IAMs are likely to provide a key decision tool as governments deliberate how best to respond to climate change. They provide a rational complement to the burgeoning political discourse on climate change and equity. It is helpful in approaching IAMs to think about the context and priorities of those constructing them.

4.4 Models and policymakers

Recall the last time you were spending lots of money on something — say, a new appliance, camera, car or computer. Have you ever noticed when you are in the process of choosing something that you suddenly find yourself surrounded by 'facts and figures'. Statistics, charts, schematic graphics are all part of the sales pitch. It's no different if you are a policy expert trying to sell your ideas to politicians. Negotiating and making decisions is often only the tip of an iceberg that is part of a far more complex decision-making process. The defining moments in any decision process are when emotions come together with facts and figures to deliver a moment of clarity. This is why, when we are being sold a new car or other gadget, the marketing is a careful blend of emotion and fact. All of a sudden, we make up our minds and that's it — it's time to hand over the cash.

If you were passionate about global environmental change, and you had an ability to deal with numbers, graphics and computers, it is quite easy to imagine that you might bring these skills together. One day, while you are playing around with numbers, you might open a spreadsheet, or put pen to paper, and manage to see your feelings or your philosophical ideas about climate change, expressed there. You might have arrived at a quantitative description of your thinking. No matter how trivial your back-of-the-envelope questions might be, you would essentially be constructing a 'model'.

Expert policy analysts regularly draw upon computer models as a form of persuasion (though they usually think of this work as neutral and value-free analysis). Of course, facts and figures are not the only things that capture people's attention. These are just some of several factors that bring us to the point of a decision. When computers are used to provide facts and figures in environmental policy-making — they are referred to as **decision support tools** — they support the process of making decisions where there is contention and complexity. Buying the services of a computer model is often the first resort of those charged with thinking through a policy problem. Just like the marketing slogan 'no one ever got fired for buying IBM' in the early days of personal computers, we might say that 'no civil servant ever got fired for consulting a computer model'.

This is not to say that policymakers believe everything a model forecasts. The great majority of people using such models lack the technical background required to look behind the model to see the workings of it. They are not in a position to interrogate the assumptions and data sources, and hence may approach them with a mix of fear, faith and scepticism. So computer models and modellers occupy a strange but important place in the world of international climate-change diplomacy.

It's amazing what a few numbers, indicators, graphics, etc., can do to transform a discussion or negotiation. At the very least, we should appreciate that computer models are sometimes generated by concerned people whose way of understanding is particularly informed by numbers — by quantitative analysis (Figure 4.5).

Good decision-making on environmental issues requires appropriate information. Frequently, this information needs to be evaluated and manipulated. Indeed, the data are often transformed into new indicators by the decision-making process itself. Building quantitative models of different aspects of environmental systems is a critical tool in environmental policy analysis. Different stakeholders (e.g. governments, business, NGOs and civil society) all rely on modelling. Groups involved in environmental decision-making share — or in the case of conflict, fire — the results of modelling at each other. 'This policy will cost the tax payer £5.5 million in the next 2 years', 'That technology will make little difference to air quality in Europe in the next decade'. These statements are only deemed credible if they are supported by models. Frequently, all that is required is that some model — any model — produced an answer. Policymakers have little time to scrutinize how the models were put together. The absence of close scrutiny of the models can reflect very poor analysis. One well-known example of the limitations of modelling comes from the field of energy modelling. The International Institute of Applied Systems Analysis (IIASA) study of the global energy system began in 1973 and took eight years, $10m (of the day) and 225 person years to complete. Keepin and Wynne describe a major shortcoming with IIASA's approach:

> The completely dominant structure underlying the lack of any degrees of freedom in the modelling is that, given IIASA's primary assumptions about global population, demographic shifts and economic growth, the total primary energy demand always threatens to far outstrip any feasible supply scenarios from what is assumed can only be more capital-intensive, centrally managed supply systems.
>
> (Keepin and Wynne, 1987)

In other words, IIASA's $10m 'story' didn't add up.

Quantitative models are sets of mathematical relationships. The simplest models have few equations and use simple mathematical functions (multiplication, addition, etc.). Usually, models are far more complex and contain many interlinked sets of simultaneous equations incorporating complex functions (exponentials, integrals, differentials) and often involve uncertainties. Climate models, for example, use hundreds of mathematical equations to describe various parts of the climate system and provide impressive, colourful and graphic outputs (Figure 4.6 overleaf).

In general, models are only as good as: (a) the quality of the input assumptions; (b) the realism of the mathematical relationships used to describe the system being modelled; (c) their treatment of uncertainty; and (d) the cautious and sensible interpretation overlaid on a model by its end user.

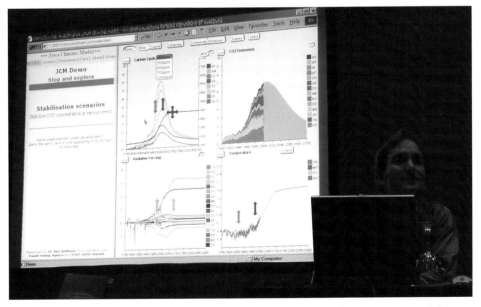

Figure 4.5   According to Dr Ben Matthews, the ultimate integrated assessment model is a human brain. Here he is shown presenting his Java Climate Model at COP 7 in Marrakesh in 2001. He's passionate about opening up and communicating the results of climate modelling to decision makers and the public via his website (Matthews, 2003).

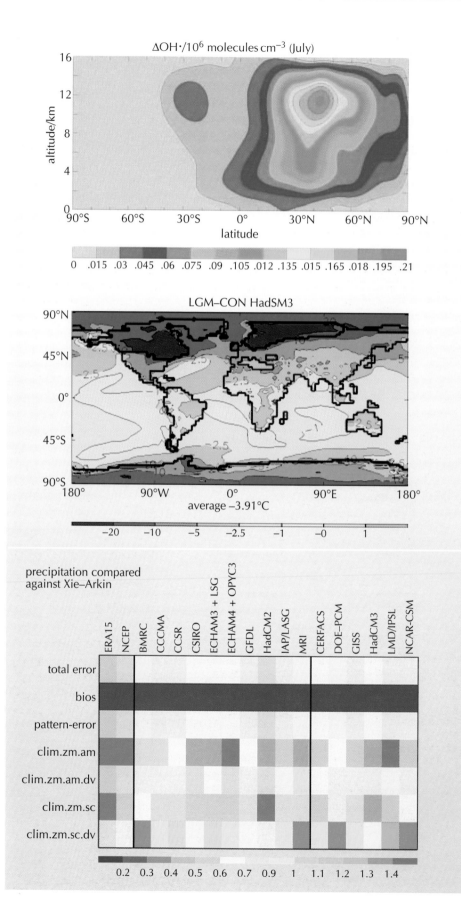

Figure 4.6 The art of climate modelling? These images from the IPCC TAR would not look out of place in a modern art gallery. (a) This splodge shows the tell-tale signature of aircraft emissions on the hydroxyl radical (OH·) concentration 12 km up in the Northern Hemisphere. (b) The HADSM3 models produce some outputs in the form of global maps of future climates. (c) A Mondrian-esque comparison of different climate models.

Thinking climate change through means predicting the behaviour of humans — a complex sub-system in the overall web of biogeochemical systems that make up the climate system. Forecasting population trends is a whole specialized field in itself. Predicting incomes and economic growth again is another. Thinking through technological, social and cultural change requires a range of interdisciplinary perspectives and tools.

We live in a world of predictions, targets, indicators and models. How many times have you been aware of forecasters of one sort or another being wrong? Weather forecasters are an obvious case in point, but what about the other forecasts and predictions that we regularly meet? Examples include: economic growth, house prices, interest and employment rates, manufacturing outputs, high street spending, savings rates, traffic levels, mobile phone ownership rates, car ownership use and traffic levels, etc.

Something as outwardly simple and important as predicting economic growth for one country, for just three years into the future, is, in fact, an incredibly complex forecasting exercise. Apart from asking experts to give their best guess (a perfectly legitimate and well-used technique), forecasts also rely extensively on models of one sort or another.

Take any simple economic or social trend, and think about it in a structured way, deconstructing its driving forces. Before you know it, you can arrive at a very complex 'systems map' or even mathematical model. Block 4 will develop your systems mapping skills around the theme of water.

Even predicting the behaviour of a simple system, can get very complicated very quickly. For a short time at the turn of the last century, there was a growing fear that London was facing a dramatic horse dung 'crisis' (Figure 4.7). Imagine a very simple 'model' for calculating the amount of horse dung and urine generated in a city such as London at the beginning of the 20th century. The model boils down to one equation. The total amount of waste deposited on London's streets is equal to the number of horses times the amount of dung and urine they each produce over a year. In fact, there were around 300 000 horses in London at the turn of the century, each producing on average of 5 t of dung and urine per year.

Figure 4.7 The streets of London in the early 1900s were paved with more than gold! An army of road sweepers were employed to keep the streets free of horse dung.

How much horse dung and urine was dumped each year on London's streets in 1900?

1.5 Mt.

Such was the problem with horse dung in London around 1900 that there was speculation at the time that the city would soon be several metres deep in it. This was based on the assumption that the number of horses would continue to rise as it had — at exponential rates. In fact, this did not happen. The simple assumption about the horse population introduced considerable uncertainty. How fast was the horse population in London expected to grow in the period 1900–1910? This was not a trivial question to answer, and as it turned out depended on a complex set of social, economic and technological interactions. Of course, London never became submerged in horse dung; instead it has become gridlocked with vehicles. Much the same sort of basic assumptions underpinned the *Limits to Growth* analysis referred to in Chapter 1 and other dynamic systems modelling exercises in the mid-1970s (e.g. IIASA's energy study).

4.5 Future emissions: exploring the uncertainties

Emissions for 1900–2000 from various regions are shown in Figure 4.8. The image is taken from the simple climate model depicted in Figure 4.5. Annual emissions from Annex I countries are shown in the slices of colours from red at the bottom up to dark

Figure 4.8 Historical CO_2 emissions from fossil fuels and land-use change 1900–2000 for various countries and regions. (This Figure just deals with one greenhouse gas, namely carbon dioxide. We don't have reliable historical data for the other greenhouse gases, though increases in concentrations of these gases (Table 1.2) are also primarily due to human activity in industrialized countries.)

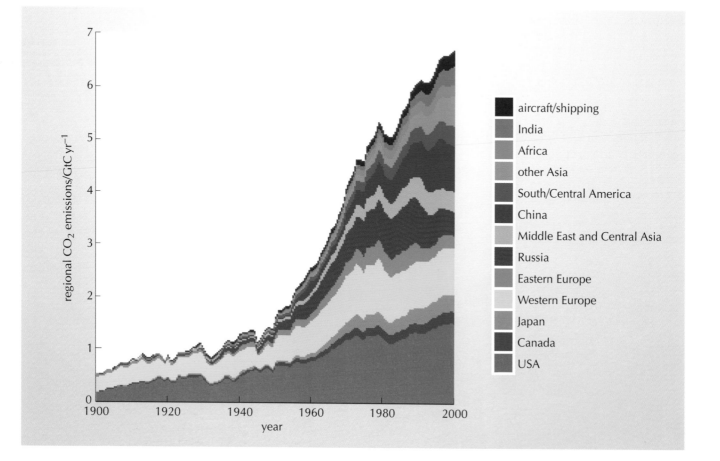

red around the middle. Emissions from the developing world are shown in the remainder of the colours. The area under the curve is the total cumulative historical CO_2 emissions from burning fossil fuel and land-use change. Clearly, for much of the last century Annex I countries have been responsible for the vast majority of emissions. However, from around the 1950s onwards, emissions from developing countries have been growing rapidly.

The high rate of growth of greenhouse gas emissions in developing economies is due to a combination of factors including population trends, economic growth and technological change. There is nothing new in this story. Historically, as economies develop, they use more and more energy. Wood, coal, oil and gas fuelled the Industrial Revolution in Europe and North America. Historically, therefore, there has been a direct link between industrialization and the growth of greenhouse gas emissions in the industrialized world. The link is complex, but has changed over time. We can track the linkage between the two by observing changes in **emissions intensity**, which is simply the ratio of carbon emissions to economic activity. Emissions intensity is often used as a measure of the 'efficiency' with which an economy is 'using' the climate (as a free dumping ground for waste greenhouse gases).

Trends in emissions intensities for various regions and countries are shown in Figure 4.9. Overall, this depicts the world (black line) becoming steadily and gradually more efficient (measured by the ratio of emissions/$US) by some 20–30% over the period 1971–1999. This is a huge change, and if the trends to date continue into the future, this would significantly reduce greenhouse gas emissions per unit GDP. This overall improvement in world emissions intensity is evidence of a gradual decoupling of emissions from economic growth.

The trend in rich developed countries (the OECD) closely follows that of the world. Latin America, Asia and Africa are all shown as having small increases in emissions intensity, whereas non-OECD Europe and China experienced dramatic falls. The Chinese data are astonishing, and reflect massive economic and social changes. They are also controversial, with some analysts disputing the figures either because they overstate economic growth for China or understate CO_2 emissions or both.

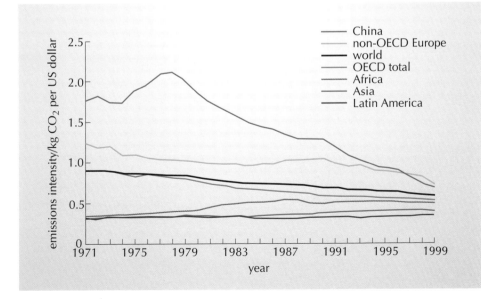

Figure 4.9 Evidence of the decoupling of energy consumption (measured by CO_2 emissions) from economic growth, 1971–1999, for various countries and regions. (Source: IEA 2001.)

Figure 4.10 uses US data to show a variety of other ways in which emission intensity indicators can be used to explore changes in the energy-economy system. Intensity indicators are a very crude but useful way to measure changes in the ratio (such as emissions intensity) of system variables. Over the decade 1990–9 the various emissions intensity indicators tell different stories. If the efficiency parameter used is emissions per capita, then you see that the US became less efficient over the period (reflecting record consumption levels). However, at the other extreme, if the measure of efficiency is emissions/$GDP, Figure 4.10 shows a dramatic improvement in efficiency (reflecting the economic boom that led to record consumption levels).

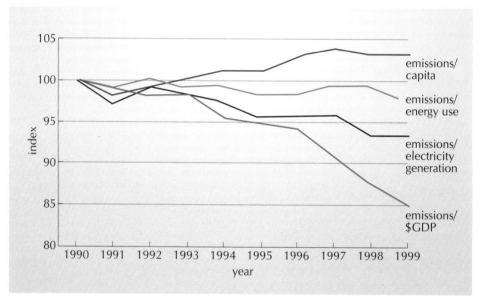

Figure 4.10 Various emissions intensity indicators for the United States in the period 1990–9. (Source: US EPA, 2001)

When we think about the future trend in greenhouse gas emissions, it is tools such as emissions intensity that can help us cross-check our logic to see if our thoughts are plausible.

Activity 4.1: Future emissions — over to you

(a)   Look again at Figure 4.8. Imagine the year axis continued on for another 100 years. If the trend of the latter part of the 20th century continues for the rest of this century, what will the rate of annual emissions be in 2100?

Answer

A simple extrapolation of recent historical trends (using a ruler) indicates an annual rate of emissions in 2100 of around 20 GtC yr^{-1}, which is roughly three times today's emissions level of 6.7 GtC yr^{-1}.

(b)   In 2001, global GDP was $31.2 trillion ($10^{12}$) and the global population was 6.1 billion. Calculate the economic and population emissions intensities (emissions/GDP and emissions/capita) as they stood in 2001. Express economic emissions intensity in the unit kgC/$ and population emissions intensity in tC/capita.

Answer

To work out economic emissions intensity in kgC/\$ we need to convert 6.7 GtC into kilograms. A gigatonne is 10^9 tonnes, and $1\,t \equiv 10^3\,kg$. Hence, $1\,GtC \equiv 10^{12}\,kg$.

In 2001, the world economic emissions intensity was

$6.7 \times 10^{12}\,kgC/\$31.2 \times 10^{12} = 0.21\,kgC/\$$

In 2001, the world population emissions intensity was

$6.7 \times 10^9\,tC/6.1 \times 10^9 = 1.1\,tC\,capita^{-1}$

(c)   Assuming economic and population intensities remain constant at 2001 levels up to 2100, calculate the implied values of global GDP and global population if global emissions in 2100 are $20\,GtC\,yr^{-1}$.

Answer

If emissions are $20\,GtC\,yr^{-1}$ in 2100, this represents a threefold increase in emissions from 2001. If economic emissions intensities remain constant, this would imply global GDP of US\$ 93.6 trillion (\$31.2 trillion $\times$ 3) and a world population of 18.3 billion people (6.1 $\times$ 3).

Comment

A trebling of world GDP in 100 years is modest compared with the 19-fold increase experienced in the period 1900–2000. Higher assumptions about economic growth imply that emissions intensity will fall. However, as you saw in Figure 1.8, world population is expected to peak in 2050 at around 9 billion. The implied population in 2100 (at 2001 population intensity) is double this. Assuming population remains below 9 billion for the rest of the century, total emissions of some 20 Gt (our simple guess based on historical trends) by the end of the century implies a doubling in population emissions intensity. How likely do you think it is that by the end of the century 9 billion of us will be emitting twice the amount we do now? It is *plausible*. Constructing ratios of two model variables — intensities — is a useful way of cross-checking results.

Predicting future greenhouse gas emissions essentially means thinking through human activity into the future. In turn, we need to think about the underlying forces that drive human production of greenhouse gas emissions. These include:

- Human population dynamics — how many will we be?

- Regional income trends — how rich or poor will we be, and what sorts of lifestyles will we lead?

- The transfer and diffusion of new technologies — what kinds of cars will we drive (will we drive cars?!), and where will our electricity come from?

These three driving forces together are the basis of how global models and scenarios are constructed to explore future emissions levels. The three factors are related in the analysis through the 'IPRT' formula (Reddish, 2003), the general version of which is expressed as:

$I = P \times R \times T$

or

impact = population $\times$ resource use per head $\times$ technology used

In the case of modelling greenhouse gas emissions, the identity becomes:

emissions = population × energy use/head × carbon emissions/unit energy

Imagine then being faced with the task of accurately modelling future CO_2 emissions for the whole globe and for the next 100 years! There are a million ways to get it wrong (and only one way to get it right). And yet if we are to predict, assess and respond to the impacts of climate change, we need to have a better understanding of what the future might be under different circumstances. Because of inertias in the climate system, what we think might be happening in 2050, 2080 and 2100 *ought* to affect decisions we make today. Despite the complexities and the uncertainties, we can't avoid thinking seriously about the future. The way that the IPCC has tried to overcome the complexities is to use 'scenario analysis'.

4.6 Emissions scenarios as a way of thinking about an uncertain future

According to the Oxford English Dictionary, the word 'scenario' has several meanings including:

1   A sketch or outline of the plot of a play, ballet, novel, opera, story, etc., giving particulars of the scenes, situations, etc. A film script with all the details of scenes, appearances of characters, stage directions, etc., necessary for shooting the film.

2   A sketch, outline, or description of an imagined situation or sequence of events; esp. (a) a synopsis of the development of a hypothetical future world war, and hence an outline of any possible sequence of future events; (b) an outline of an intended course of action; (c) a scientific model or description intended to account for observable facts.

At one level, good books and movies are those that manage to suspend our disbelief in the story being told. They are credible and compelling. Often this means that they have to be well researched, and characters, plots, facts and contexts must all hang convincingly together.

In the world of forecasting, modelling and environmental planning, **scenario** analysis clearly doesn't mean writing alternative screenplays for different environmental futures, but it does usually mean thinking about how a set of different and uncertain variables (inputs/outputs) might change and/or interact. The IPCC uses scenarios as images of the future, or alternative futures. They can be viewed as a linking tool that integrates qualitative narratives or storylines with formal quantitative modelling (Figure 4.11). Variables are measures of different aspects of a system that change over time. Models use a variety of input variables in order to compute output variables. When changes in one variable affect another, they are said to be *determinants*. Examples of input variables for climate models might include population, average incomes, number of cars, etc. These are the determinants of emission levels.

Storytellers, scenario builders and modellers are all human. Computers are used in modelling, but it is humans who formulate the models and ask questions of them. Humans think; computers number crunch. It's a simple fact that scientists and policy analysts cannot help but introduce subjective and very human preconceptions, values and feelings into their models. This is one reason why different models give rise to

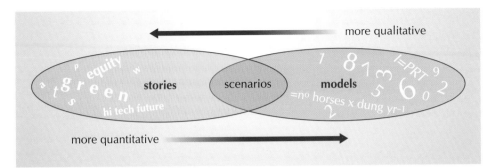

Figure 4.11 Scenarios lie between storylines and models in terms of their quantitative and qualitative characteristics.

different answers to the same questions. One way in which the IPCC has used scenarios in the TAR is as a way of posing the same question to lots of different models and then comparing the answers — 'what does your model say if you run it with this scenario?'.

Scenarios can be either *normative* (prescriptive) or *descriptive*. Normative scenarios are explicitly value based, exploring paths to problems (dystopias) or solutions (utopias). Stories leading to a sustainable future are inherently normative — a picture of where we might need to get in order to meet certain criteria deemed to be 'sustainable' (more on this in Chapter 6). Descriptive scenarios have no particular destination — good or bad, high or low; they are descriptions of possible (rather than preferred) futures.

Activity 4.2: Scenario analysis in practice

(a)   Give a range of factors that may influence the growth in the number of UK passenger vehicles in the next 20 years. In each case, explain possible sources of uncertainty in the prediction of each of the factors.

Answer

There are lots of possible answers to this question. Hopefully, you may have considered some of the factors that we give in the following response.

Total UK human population. Some uncertainty creeps in here. Population has been relatively stable, and if anything is predicted to decline. Will the birth rate in the next few years remain unchanged — or could there be a sudden change that would feed through to those coming of age (in driving terms) in around 17 years from now?

Number of people/households who currently do not own a car and who want to in the future. Just as the boom in demand for housing has been linked to social changes (more people choosing to live alone), this may affect car ownership patterns — one household, one car. Will the trend towards single living continue? Overall ownership levels are fairly high and over time are rising less and less (the market saturates, just like the mobile phone market). However the number of households owning more than one car has been steadily growing. Will that trend continue?

There are numerous underlying influences on car ownership decisions. Economic factors are important. How fast will the UK economy grow over the period? How much disposable income will people have to spend on additional cars? How much more will the government choose to tax car purchases, car ownership, fuel or congestion? How will alternatives to the car evolve such as buses and trains?

(b) Make up a few lines for the normative scenario 'Reclaim the streets', which halves current UK car population in the UK by 2020.

Answer

One possible answer is the following:

> Following a successful experiment in central London, congestion charging is introduced in all major UK towns and cities, and pedestrianization is expanded. In 2008, the new Green Party-led coalition government increases car purchase taxes to 100% [equivalent to the 2003 situation in Denmark] and quadruples fuel prices to reflect a $50/tC carbon tax. No money is available for road building or even repair. The government launches a roads closure programme, and adopts a policy target of reducing car ownership by half by 2020. The government announces the end of the car society and launches a national reclaim the streets programme. The additional revenues are pumped into renewing the UK's bus system and upgrading its train system.

(c) Make up a few lines for a descriptive scenario ('Jam today; jam tomorrow') showing how UK car population might evolve.

Answer

One possible answer is the following:

> Current patterns of car ownership continue, slowly evolving in a business as usual manner. As the number of new households rise (through social change) car ownership rises at the same rate. The government continues to spend similar amounts (in real terms) on road investment and on public transport. Political appetite for major increases in the cost of car ownership and use is low, reflecting public opinion. Various new congestion charging schemes are introduced throughout the country. Some work, others not. Overall there is no significant move towards congestion charging that affects car ownership decisions.

The IPCC TAR assessed 128 emissions scenarios from 48 different sources. The answer to what global CO_2 emissions might be over the course of the 21st century plotted as a graph, looks a bit like some computer flex, stripped to reveal a myriad coloured wires, and splayed out as if run over by a car tyre. Figure 4.12 shows the full range of emissions paths for 40 scenarios.

In addition to reviewing the range of scenarios in the literature, the IPCC TAR also defined four scenario families. Two of the scenario families (coded A) focus on economic development and two on environmental development (coded B). In each case, the stories are further subdivided depending on whether the scenarios are globally orientated (suffix 1) or regionally orientated (suffix 2). The A1 (economic/global) is further divided into three separate scenarios — A1F (fossil fuels), A1T (transition to non-fossil fuels) and A1B (balance*) .

* Balanced is defined as not relying too heavily on one particular energy source,on the assumption that similar improvement rates apply to all energy supply and end-use technologies.

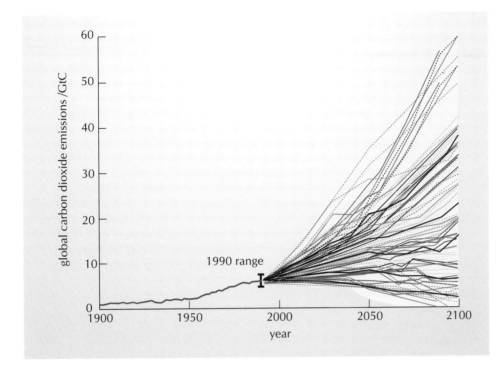

Figure 4.12 Spaghetti futures: 256 emission scenarios identified in the IPCC's literature review. The shaded boundaries signify the maximum and minimum scenarios. Our guess at global emissions in 2100 from Activity 4.1 (20 GtC) is roughly in the middle! Rulers are simple models.

The IPCC summarizes the four main scenario families as follows:

- The A1 storyline and scenario family describes a future world of very rapid economic growth, global population that peaks in mid-century and declines thereafter, and the rapid introduction of new and more efficient technologies. Major underlying themes are convergence among regions, capacity building, and increased cultural and social interactions, with a substantial reduction in regional differences in per capita income. The A1 scenario family develops into three groups that describe alternative directions of technological change in the energy system. The three A1 groups are distinguished by their technological emphasis: fossil-fuel intensive (A1F), non-fossil fuel sources (A1T), or a balance across all energy sources (A1B).

- The A2 storyline and scenario family describes a very heterogeneous world. The underlying theme is self-reliance and preservation of local identities. Fertility patterns across regions converge very slowly, which results in continuously increasing global population. Economic development is primarily regionally oriented and per capita economic growth, and technological change is more fragmented and slower than in other storylines.

- The B1 storyline and scenario family describes a convergent world with the same global population that peaks in mid-century and declines thereafter, as in the A1 storyline, but with rapid changes in economic structures toward a service and information economy, with reductions in material intensity, and the introduction of clean and resource-efficient technologies. The emphasis is on global solutions to economic, social and environmental sustainability, including improved equity, without additional climate initiatives.

- The B2 storyline and its scenario family describes a world in which the emphasis is on regional solutions to economic, social and environmental sustainability. It is a world with continuously increasing global population at a rate lower than A2, intermediate levels of economic development, and less rapid and more diverse technological change than in the B1 and A1 storylines. Although the scenario is also orientated toward environmental protection and social equity, it focuses on local and regional levels.

The IPCC makes three important assumptions regarding the four scenario families:

- The scenarios are descriptive.
- No one scenario is more likely than any other.
- All scenarios assume no new climate policies in the future.

A schematic comparison of the difference in the scenarios is shown in Figure 4.13, and the underlying trends used to construct each of the four families of IPCC scenarios are shown in Figure 4.14. What the scenario family descriptions and Figure 4.14 do not tell us is exactly how the driving forces in each case take the shape they do. All we know is that they are definitely not the result of explicit climate policies on the part of governments and other stakeholders. In this way, these scenarios are all a bit like alternative outlines of story plots and endings. The detail is missing.

⬤ According to which scenario in Figure 4.14 is the world becoming less equitable?

⬤ A2.

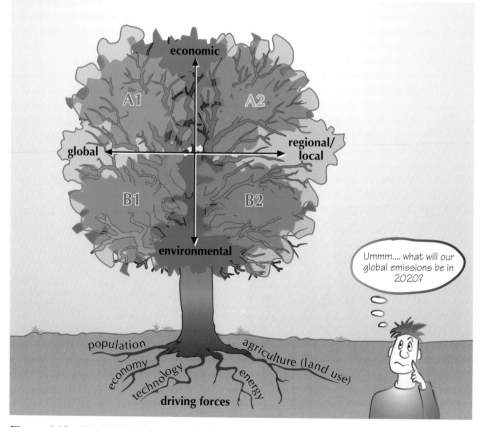

Figure 4.13 The IPCC's four scenario families and driving forces schematically represented as a tree and its roots.

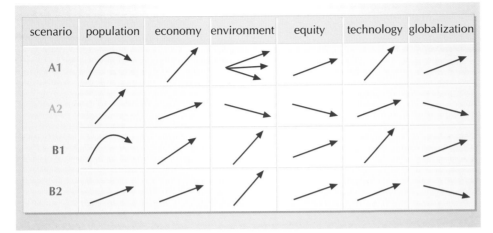

Figure 4.14 Simple qualitative arrow descriptions of drivers behind different IPCC TAR emissions scenario families. Upward-pointing arrows mean increasing, and vice versa. Each column covers the time period 1990–2100 (Source: IPCC, 2000).

● According to which scenario in Figure 4.14 is the environment improving *and* globalization weakening?

● B2.

The evolution of total global CO_2 emissions from fossil-fuel combustion and land-use change for each of the four scenario families is shown in Figure 4.15. These emissions can be translated into changes in climate variables (temperature, sea-level rise)

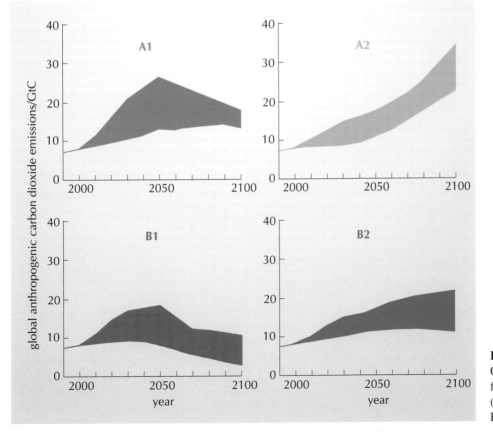

Figure 4.15 The evolution of total CO_2 emissions for the IPCC TAR's four scenario families, 1990–2100 (Adapted from IPCC, 2001c, Fig. 2-14, p. 151).

associated with each of the scenarios. Look again at the plots in Figure 2.9 (p. 70), and in each case you will see that the various scenarios are represented.

- In Figure 2.9, which of the scenarios gives the lowest temperature increase and lowest sea-level rise?

- B1. Indeed, this makes sense from the scenario description above.

The last of the three assumptions concerning the IPCC's four scenario families is particularly hard to make sense of. Climate change is a real concern, at the global and national levels we have already begun to introduce climate policies. The idea that it is useful or even possible to create future scenarios in which no new climate policies are introduced is quite hard to fathom.

Nevertheless, the IPCC TAR is the basis of global debate on climate change, and the four emissions scenario families are a central part of the analysis. Several integrated assessment models incorporate these scenarios and they have become a useful communication tool for investigating uncertainties surrounding our climate future.

4.7 Quantifying the challenge: baselines and target stabilization levels

Now let's consider the first two factors that affect the size of the mitigation challenge we face. An extremely important and quite subtle point to understand in the way that the IPCC science is informing political discussions about climate change is the notion of an emissions 'baseline'. This is sometimes also referred to as a 'business as usual case', or sometimes 'no (climate policy) intervention' scenario.

Intervention in this case means actions by governments and other stakeholders to try to manage climate change. Some scenarios are built without assumptions of action on the part of governments, and some with an assumption of action. The Kyoto Protocol is an example of a policy intervention on the part of governments, which if achieved will affect emissions trends from industrialized countries. In the grand scheme of things we have seen that the Kyoto 2012 targets are just a small step compared to the size of the challenge of stabilizing the climate.

- Why is Kyoto a small step?

- Because it involves only the developed nations, and requires them to make only an initial, relatively modest first step towards the significant greenhouse gas reductions necessary to stabilize the climate.

With or without action, the net balance of mitigation, adaptation and damage costs (and the distribution of winners and losers therein) is at the hub of political debates about the best (such as least costly, or more ethical) course of action to take.

The costs associated with climate change are highly uncertain and dependent on assumptions about the future. Yet, climate costs can only be expressed relative to a baseline. If you believe that in the future the drivers of emissions are going to change naturally in a way that results in lower emissions (lower population growth, less economic growth, cleaner technologies), then the costs of achieving a particular climate stabilization target are going to be relatively low (Table 4.2). However, if you believe that future emissions are going to be very high without intervention (in other words, high population growth, high economic growth, slower transition to cleaner technologies, human behaviour as usual), then the cost of that intervention is going to be very high.

Table 4.2 Factors associated with changing GHG emissions in global futures scenarios (Source IPCC, 2001c, Table 2.4 p. 141)

Factor	Rising GHGs emissions	Falling GHGs emissions
economy	Growing, post-industrial economy with globalization (mostly) low government intervention, and generally high level of competition.	Level of economic activity limited to lower or ecologically sustainable levels; generally high level of government intervention.
population	Growing population with high level of migration.	Growing population that stabilizes at relatively low level; migration at low level.
governance	No clear pattern in governance.	Improvements in citizen participation in governance, community vitality, and responsiveness of institutions.
equity	Generally declining income equality within nations, and no clear pattern in social equity or international income equality.	Increasing social equity and income equality within and among nations.
conflict/ security	High level of conflict and security activity (mostly), deteriorating conflict resolution capability.	Low level of conflict and security activity; improved conflict resolution capability.
technology	High level of technological development, innovation, and technological diffusion.	High level of technological development, innovation, and technological diffusion.
resource availability	Declining renewable resource and water availability; no clear pattern for non-renewable resource and food availability	Increasing availability of renewable resources, food and water; no clear pattern for non-renewable resources.
environment	Declining environmental quality.	Improving environmental quality.

Political disagreements about climate change are in large measure about different perspectives on future **baselines**. In simple terms, this means whether you are an optimist or a pessimist. Table 4.3 (overleaf) shows a different categorization of scenarios into different groups, emphasizing pessimism, current trends, high tech optimist and sustainable development.

The gap between climate goals (climate stabilization targets) and the baseline (whatever future you think is more likely) is a measure of the size of the challenge of stabilizing greenhouse gas concentrations. Figure 4.16 graphically shows four examples of the possible size of the challenge using the IPCC A1, A2, B1 and B2 scenario families as baselines. The difference between baseline and target indicates the size of the challenge as baselines. In all cases the target stabilization is 550 p.p.m. You can see that in one case the gap is as high as 27 GtC (A2) to 0 — a vast difference, and all as a result of the choice of baseline. Obviously, if a higher stabilization level were chosen as the policy goal, then the gap between baseline and target would be less.

The third factor that greatly affects the nature of the climate challenge is the speed at which emissions are reduced. There are no clear answers here for policymakers as to how fast they should be going. Table 4.4 (p. 147) summarizes the arguments for and against early mitigation in terms of a variety of factors. These can be used as a basis for developing your own thoughts about the future.

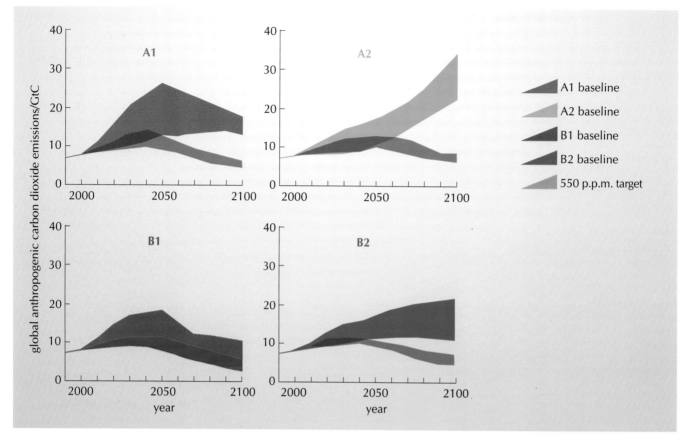

Figure 4.16   Assumptions about future global GHG emissions baselines dramatically affect the size of the climate stabilization challenge. (Source: adapted from IPCC, 2001c)

Table 4.3   Examples of factors underlying pessimistic, current trends, optimistic and sustainable development scenarios (Source: IPCC, 2001c)

Scenario group	Storylines
pessimistic	Breakdown: collapse of human society.
	Fractured world: deterioration into antagonistic regional blocs.
	Chaos: instability and disorder.
	Conservative: world economic crash is succeeded by conservative and risk-averse regimes.
current trends	Conventional: no significant change from current and/or continuation of present-day trends.
	High growth: government facilitates business, leading to prosperity.
	Asia shift: economic power shifts from the West to Asia.
	Economy paramount: emphasis on economic values leads to deterioration in social and environmental conditions.
high tech optimist	Cybertopia: information and communication technologies facilitate individualistic, diverse and innovative world.
	Technotopia: technology solves all or most of humanity's problems.
sustainable development	Our common future: increased economic activity is made to be consistent with improved equity and environmental quality.
	Low consumption: conscious shift from consumerism.

Table 4.4   How fast should nations be mitigating greenhouse gas emissions?

Issue	Arguments favouring modest early mitigation	Arguments favouring stringent early mitigation
Technological development	Energy technologies are changing and improved versions of existing technologies are becoming available, even without policy intervention. Modest early deployment of rapidly improving technologies allows 'quick start' cost reductions, without premature lock-in to existing, low-productivity technology. The development of radically advanced technologies will require investment in basic research.	Availability of low-cost measures may have substantial impact on emissions trajectories. Endogenous (market-induced) change could accelerate development of low-cost solutions (learning-by-doing). Clustering effects highlight the importance of moving to lower emission trajectories. Induces early switch of corporate-funded energy R&D from fossil frontier developments to low carbon technologies.
Capital stock and inertia	Beginning with initially modest emissions avoids premature retirement of existing capital stocks and takes advantage of the natural rate of capital stock turnover. It also reduces the switching cost of existing capital and prevents rising prices of investments caused by crowding out effects.	Exploit more fully natural stock turnover by influencing new investments. By limiting emissions to levels consistent with low CO_2 concentrations, preserves an option to limit CO_2 concentrations to low levels using current technology. Reduces the risks from uncertainties in stabilization constraints and hence the risk of being forced into very rapid reductions that would require premature capital retirement later.
Social effects and inertia	Gradual emissions reduction reduces the extent of induced sectoral unemployment by giving more time to retrain the workforce and for structural shifts in the labour market and education. Reduces welfare losses associated with the need for fast changes in people's lifestyles and living arrangements.	Especially if lower stabilization targets would be required; ultimately, stronger early action reduces the maximum rate of emissions reduction required subsequently and reduces associated transitional problems, disruption and the welfare losses associated with the need for faster later changes in people's lifestyles and living arrangements.
Discounting and intergenerational equity	Reduces the present value (see Chapter 5 for discussion of 'discounting' in this context) of future abatement costs, but possibly reduces future relative costs by furnishing cheap technologies and increasing future income levels.	Reduces impacts and reduces their present value.
Carbon cycle and radiative change	Small increase in short-term CO_2 concentration. More early emissions absorbed, thus enabling higher total carbon emissions this century under a given stabilization constraint (to be compensated by lower emissions thereafter).	Small decrease in short-term CO_2 concentration. Reduces peak rates in temperature change.
Climate-change impacts	Little evidence on damages from multi-decade episodes of relatively rapid change in the past.	Avoids possibly higher damages caused by faster rates of climate change.

Activity 4.3: Writing your own pessimistic and optimistic baseline scenarios

Use Tables 4.2, 4.3 and 4.4 to write down elements of a story and consequences associated with (a) a high (pessimistic) baseline and (b) a low (optimistic) baseline. (Pick and mix elements from the three tables to form a logical argument.)

Answer

(a)   If we are heading for high CO_2 emissions, we can expect greater climate change and therefore potentially high risks. This could lead to a world economic crash or even the collapse of human society. The driving forces include: high economic growth fuelled by high levels of competition and minimum government intervention; a growing population and high level of migration; no clear pattern of global governance, and declining renewable energy resources and water availability. A higher baseline means that the problem of stabilizing greenhouse gas emissions is greater for everyone — not just developed countries, but developing countries too. It also means that failure to act now will make it harder for the global economy to break its carbon habit in the future. Many opportunities to accelerate a transition to lower emissions trajectories are missed: low-cost alternatives to fossil fuels are developed later rather than sooner; normal chances in the economy to improve energy efficiency and switch to renewable energy sources are missed.

(b)   If the future is for lower CO_2 emissions, we face fewer risks, and the challenge of stabilizing the climate is not as great. Information and communication technologies greatly accelerate a transition to greater sustainability. They also transform systems of governance to be more democratic and reduce environmental conflicts around equity issues. Technology is used to solve many problems. Failure to act now will not have the same climate consequences as in the high baseline case. There are economic and political benefits associated with a smoother transition towards lower emissions — reduced welfare losses caused by rapid changes in lifestyles, less upfront investment in new technologies is needed, etc.

Comment

There are several ways to construct an answer to this activity. The key point is to see for yourself how storylines and scenarios can be constructed from different sets of alternative and, in this case, opposing building blocks.

4.8 Sharing the burden: equity and climate change

Finally, let's consider the fourth factor that dramatically alters the nature of the climate stabilization challenge — the number of players sharing the burden of mitigation. This, in turn, raises the issue of **equity**. Predicted rapid rates of climate change are linked to and caused directly by human activity. In both developed and developing worlds, lives, livelihoods and economies are changing at an incredible pace as a result of social, cultural, economic and technological forces that are constantly transforming the way we live (Figure 4.17).

Figure 4.17 Boom! China's population of over 1.3 billion is the largest single market in the world.

The current global distribution of income is heavily skewed towards a lucky 15% of the world's population (Figure 4.18). If, as is widely anticipated, global incomes continue to grow significantly over the century, we can expect to see the shape of Figure 4.18 change. As you saw at the beginning of the chapter, in any economy at whatever stage of development, there are direct links between income, energy consumption and

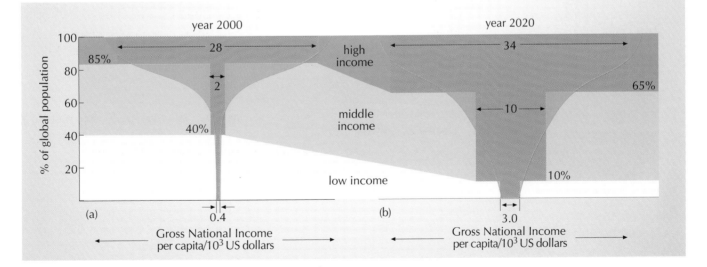

Figure 4.18 The much used 'wine glass' representation of the distribution of global income. The turquoise bands represent average income within a group. The orange 'glass' outline represents the distribution of incomes as a continuum. (a) According to the World Bank, in the year 2000, the top 15% of the world's population received on average $28k per year (80% of global income). (b) By 2020, the distribution of incomes among the lower, middle and upper groups could become more equitable (see Chapter 5) with incomes in each group rising and higher proportions of global population in the upper and middle income groups. In this scenario the richest 35% now receive $34k per year (67% of global income).

greenhouse gas emissions trends. Those links change over time, becoming stronger or weaker depending on the stage of development and other factors. If we look at a plot of income per capita against carbon emissions per capita (Figure 4.19), we see some evidence of a correlation between them. The data in Figure 4.19 generally support the idea that rising income is associated with rising greenhouse gas emissions.

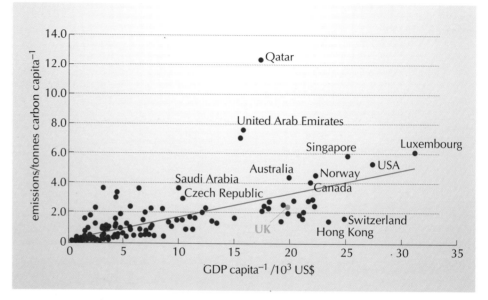

Figure 4.19 Have money, will emit carbon?

Reducing global emissions can only come about as a result of changes in the fundamental driving forces behind greenhouse gas emissions. But which forces? Is climate change important enough for politicians to consider population control as part of the answer (Figure 4.20)? This option would be highly controversial, and is not being discussed seriously at present. Is climate change sufficiently important for politicians to adopt an explicit global agreement on lower economic growth rates perhaps? Few people (and certainly no leading politicians) wish for lower, rather than higher, rates of economic growth.

- So which other driving force behind human impacts on the climate does that leave us with?

- The answer is technology.

Climate policies use a mixture of regulatory and market mechanisms to affect energy prices, consumer behaviour and technological markets. Changes away from the baseline arise as a result of a combination of international and national policies, autonomous changes in behaviour of business and citizens, and technological developments. Two aspects here are the source of a great deal of uncertainty, confusion and conflict among experts and activists — the rate of technological improvement and the efficiency of international and national climate policies.

- Under the UNFCCC/Kyoto Protocol, which nations are legally 'burdened' with the task of reducing their greenhouse gas emissions?

- The Annex I countries, which includes OECD nations as well as the group of countries with economies in transition (Eastern Europe and the former Soviet Union).

Figure 4.20 Baby 6 billion! Kofi Annan welcomes baby Adnan into the world. The Sarajevo boy, born on 11 October 1999, officially pushed the human population over the 6 billion mark.

Activity 4.4: The changing balance between the CO_2 emissions from developed (Annex I) and developing countries (Non-Annex I)

(a)   Use Figure 4.8 to make a rough estimate of how rapidly emissions from developed and developing countries have risen in the period 1960 to present. How much faster are emissions growing in developing countries compared with developed?

Answer

In 1960, emissions from the industrialized world were running at an annual rate of $2 \, \text{GtC yr}^{-1}$ and from the developing world at $0.6 \, \text{GtC yr}^{-1}$. In 2000, these figures rose to $3.6 \, \text{GtC yr}^{-1}$ for the industrialized countries and $3.0 \, \text{GtC yr}^{-1}$ for developing countries. This represents growth rates over the period of 80% and 400%, respectively. In other words, in the period 1960–2000, greenhouse gas emissions from developing countries grew five times as fast as they did in the industrialized world.

You have seen that future climate change will be the result of emissions from developed countries as well as today's developing countries. What are the various possibilities of sharing the burden of stabilizing the climate among developed and developing countries? To begin thinking this through, let's first consider why developing countries are currently not included in the Kyoto Protocol.

(b)   Use the Principles in Box 3.2 to identify reasons why developing countries are not currently legally bound to share the burden of reducing greenhouse gas emissions.

Answer

Principle 1 establishes that developed countries should take the lead.

Principle 3 notes that precautionary responses to climate change 'should take into account different socio-economic contexts'.

Principle 4 refers to a nation's right to 'promote sustainable development', and that actions should be 'integrated with national development programmes, taking into account that economic development is essential for adopting measures to address climate change'.

Principle 5 refers to 'a supportive and open international economic system that would lead to sustainable economic growth and development in all Parties, particularly developing country Parties'.

The rights of developing countries to develop economically above all else are clearly central to the framework of the regime of international climate governance. What chance do industrialized countries have of achieving the goals of the UNFCCC without greater participation from developing countries? This is a good question for an integrated assessment model. The answer according to one integrated climate assessment model is shown in Figure 4.21 (overleaf). The developers of the FAIR (Framework to Assess International Regimes for Burden-sharing) model have been asked to work out what would happen if emissions from Non-Annex I countries followed a medium-growth baseline. The model then assumes that the only countries involved in sharing the burden of stabilization are the Annex I countries. The model assumes that the industrialized countries decide to go it alone and attempt to stabilize CO_2 emissions at 650 p.p.m.

Issues of equity have always been a major driver of political debate and action. The extension of the right to vote to working-class men, and later to women, or the rapid development of welfare states in Western Europe in the mid-20th century are examples. In these cases, direct political pressure by specific groups achieved progress towards their equity goals. Climate change is different; equity is driving climate change politics, but the 'losers' who will feel the negative effects of future climate change are not, on the whole, the direct source of pressure. Policy debate is attempting to anticipate who the losers are — now and in the future; human and non-human — and trying to find ways to represent them. To decide about actions on climate change is to anticipate and weigh-up consequences. But as we've seen, understanding climate change requires us to splice together insights from all kinds of intellectual endeavour, from analysing sea-bed sediments to the political economy of development; from the cycling of carbon in a forest to the sociology of consumption.

It should come as no surprise to you that, given the uncertainties in our knowledge in some key areas, and the sheer ambition of the interdisciplinary exercise, there are going to be more than a few fuzzy edges. But there is little doubt about the need to try to bring this range of knowledge to bear on a discussion of sustainability, equity and the future. One influential way in which this has happened to date has been in the efforts of integrated assessment modellers, who have sought to create tools that use numbers and graphics to make choices about climate change tangible.

There are, in fact, surprisingly few decision tools in the field of climate change. Most modelling expertise has been engaged in attempting to construct more and more accurate (and complex and uncertain) models of how the climate system works. In the years to come, we are likely to see quite a few more climate policy decision support tools. You are now going to work intensively with one such tool. The activity will see you using it much as a senior politician or civil servant would. But you will also take time to look inside the box of computational tricks in order to better understand the ways in which the complexities and uncertainties of climate change are presented and managed within modelling.

You should now go to the Web and do the activities associated with Chapter 4.

4.9 Summary of Chapter 4

4.1   The UNFCCC and its Kyoto Protocol are 'living' agreements at the heart of the global political response to climate change. The Kyoto 2012 targets are the first small steps of many more that will be necessary if we are to stabilize the climate by cutting emissions by up to 60–90% compared with their present levels.

4.2   An integrated approach to thinking through climate change takes into account the balance of costs (however defined) between (a) business as usual (doing little or nothing), (b) adaptation and (c) mitigation. There are costs, risks and trade-offs associated with all three response options. Different nations view these differently. For large emitters, such as the US, China, Europe and India, all three costs are important. For small emitters, such as small island states, the balancing act is much simpler: they must balance the cost of climate damage against the cost of adaptation to climate change.

4.3   Five key factors determine the cost of climate stabilization: baseline assumptions; the climate stabilization level; speed of stabilization; the burden-sharing regime; and rules governing the use of Kyoto mechanisms.

4.4   Integrated assessment models help decision-makers think through the implications of different courses of action in responding to climate change. They link biogeochemical changes in the climate to socio-economic impacts in four steps: emissions scenarios; atmospheric concentrations; changes in climate; and socio-economic impacts. There are uncertainties in each step and these cascade from one step to the next.

4.5   The use of quantitative models as decision support tools is a critical part of environmental policy-making. Uncertainties abound in environmental modelling, pervading even the simplest models. Modelling future global emissions is a highly complex task, as there are considerable uncertainties in the prediction of all three key driving forces of global emissions models (population, income trends and technological change).

4.6   Good scenarios comprise a plausible set of quantified variables, allied to a convincing story line. The IPCC uses scenario analysis extensively in its assessments of possible future climate change as a way of overcoming issues about complexity and uncertainty. The IPCC TAR identifies four families of scenarios — two centred on economic development and two on environmental improvements. The scenarios are not predictions or forecasts, and none is more likely than another. They all also assume 'no new climate policies' in the future, but some of them also represent very low carbon futures.

4.7   The concept of emissions baselines is pivotal to the understanding of different perspectives on the nature of the climate stabilization challenge. A 'baseline' is a non-climate intervention scenario. There is no single baseline: different studies, scientists, policymakers and analysts all make different judgements about the future baseline depending on how optimistic or pessimistic, normative or descriptive, they are about changes in key driving forces (population, income and technological change).

4.8   The difference between the baseline and future climate stabilization targets (e.g. 450, 550 or 650 p.p.m.) is a proxy measure of the political, economic and social challenge of managing climate change. The economic and social costs of stabilization are greater, the higher the baseline or the lower the stabilization levels. Conversely, the cost of stabilization is lower for lower baselines or higher stabilization levels.

4.9   Emissions from developing countries are growing five times faster than in the industrialized world, and will very shortly make up the lion's share of global emissions. Climate change is a global problem, which requires a global response. It is unlikely that developed countries will continue to act alone without the cooperation of developing countries. However, we are right at the start of establishing exactly on what basis — and by which rules — developed and developing countries should share the burden of emission reduction. In the next decades we are likely to witness intense and controversial negotiations of how all nations can move forward together as a global community in the search for an equitable approach to achieving Article 2 of the UNFCCC.

Learning Outcomes for Chapter 4

When you have completed this chapter, you should be able to:

4.1 Define and use, or recognize definitions and applications of, the terms given in **bold** in the text.

4.2 Use the concepts of damage costs, adaptation costs and mitigation costs to explain how different nations view the challenge of responding to climate change differently. Describe the basic elements and function of integrated assessment modelling as tools to support climate decisions. (Questions 4.1 and 4.2)

4.3 List the three key driving forces behind the future growth of greenhouse gas emissions, and describe five factors that affect the cost of greenhouse gas mitigation. (Question 4.3).

4.4 Explain the relationships between stories, models and scenarios. Briefly describe the four scenario families used in the IPCC TAR to explore alternative global emissions pathways for the 21st century. (Question 4.4)

4.5 Explain why the concept of 'baseline' is important in explaining the size of the challenge of stabilizing greenhouse gas concentrations in the atmosphere. Illustrate alternative pessimistic and optimistic views of the future baseline in terms of the key driving forces behind greenhouse gas emission scenarios. (Question 4.5)

4.6 Explain why the challenge of meeting Article 2 of the UNFCCC raises questions about equity. Describe four perspectives on equity and climate change. (Question 4.6)

Questions for Chapter 4

Question 4.1

Rational approaches to thinking climate change through seek to minimize the net total of mitigation, adaptation and residual damage costs. Describe how each of the following stakeholders might see the problem:

(a) a small island state;

(b) the European Union.

Question 4.2

(a) Briefly outline the main steps involved in integrated assessment modelling.

(b) Outline two arguments in support of the IPCC's 1998 policy decision not to look at the economics of climate change in the context of the TAR.

Question 4.3

(a) Which three forces are the key drivers of global emissions trends?

(b) List five factors that affect the cost of mitigation/stabilization.

Question 4.4

(a)   Which of the four IPCC TAR scenario families (A1, A2, B1, B2) assume that global population peaks around 2050, declining thereafter, *and* optimistic rates of technological change?

(b)   Which two scenarios are most technologically optimistic?

(c)   Which assumption made in the IPCC TAR to some extent undermines the credibility of scenario analysis?

Question 4.5

Which of the following combinations of baselines and targets is clearly the most challenging (produces the largest global emissions reduction burden)? Briefly explain why.

(a)   Medium global emissions baseline, 650 p.p.m. atmospheric stabilization target.

(b)   High global emissions baseline, 450 p.p.m. atmospheric stabilization target.

(c)   Medium global emissions baseline, 750 p.p.m. atmospheric stabilization target.

Question 4.6

Complete the table below by matching the following key phrases to each of the four approaches to equity:

- actions of others
- global commons
- protection against climate impacts
- standards of living

Approach to equity	Key phrases
opportunity-based	
poverty-based	
liability-based	
rights-based	

References

Fankhauser, S. (1998) The cost of adapting to climate change, Working Paper 16. Washington DC: Global Environment Facility.

IEA (2001) *Emissions from Fuel Combustion 1971–1999*. International Energy Agency, Paris, France.

IPCC (2000) *Emissions Scenarios 2000* IPCC Special Report. Cambridge: Cambridge University Press.

IPCC (2001a) *Climate Change 2001: The Scientific Basis. Contribution of Working Group I to the Third Assessment Report of the Intergovernmental Panel on Climate Change*. Cambridge: Cambridge University Press.

IPCC (2001b) *Climate Change 2001: Impacts, Adaptation and Vulnerability. Contribution of Working Group II to the Third Assessment Report of the Intergovernmental Panel on Climate Change*. Cambridge: Cambridge University Press.

IPCC (2001c) *Climate Change 2001: Mitigation. Contribution of Working Group III to the Third Assessment Report of the Intergovernmental Panel on Climate Change*. Cambridge: Cambridge University Press.

IPCC (2001d) *Climate Change 2001: Synthesis Report. Contribution of Working Groups I, II and III to the Third Assessment Report of the Intergovernmental Panel on Climate Change*. Cambridge: Cambridge University Press.

Keepin, B., and Wynne, B. (1987) The roles of models — what can we expect from science? A study of the IIASA World Energy Model. In Baumgartner, T. and Midttun, A. (eds) *The Politics of Energy Forecasting,* pp. 33–57. Oxford: Clarendon Press.

Matthews, B. (2003) [online] Available at: http://www.chooseclimate.org. [Accessed 14 February 2003]

Reddish, A. (2003) Dynamic Earth: human impacts. In Morris, R. et al. (eds) *Changing Environments* Chichester: Wiley in association with The Open University.

US Environmental Protection Agency (2001), 'Inventory of US Greenhouse Gas Emissions and Sinks: 1990–1999', April 2001, EPA 236-R-01–001, p. 1–11 [online]. Available from: http://www.ott.doe.gov/facts/archives/fotw207.shtml [Accessed 14 December 2002]

Weyant, J. P., and Hill, J. N. (1999) Introduction and overview. In Weyant, J. P. (ed.) *Energy Journal Special Issue on the Costs of the Kyoto Protocol: a Multi-Model Evaluation*, pp. vii–xliv.

Chapter 5 Listening out: climate, politics, philosophy

Prepared for the course team by Joe Smith

5.1 Bringing strangers into the equation

Take some time to ponder the two images of the Earth shown on this page. You will recognize the 'blue marble' image of the globe taken from space (Figure 5.1). It seems very familiar to us now, but it is a perspective that has only been available since the first space flights. This global perspective is reflected in both the science and politics of climate change. The second image, 'Earth lights' (Figure 5.2), is a visual shorthand giving an indication of where the most intensive use of energy is going on. These are some of the 'hotspots' of climate-change politics around mitigating greenhouse gas emissions.

Figure 5.1 The 'blue marble' image of the globe from space.

Making decisions about climate change presents some of the biggest political and ethical questions we face in coming years. The first part of this chapter will introduce contrasting approaches to thinking about **equity** (literally meaning being equal, fair or even-handed) in the context of climate-change politics. In the later sections of the chapter we'll set these within a more philosophical setting, and separate out (quite artificially perhaps) discussion of how distant others in the present, future generations and the non-human world are represented in climate-change politics. We want this chapter to help you to connect the science and policy issues that you've covered to a discussion of how we might think about justice and obligation in relation to the still relatively novel issue of climate change.

Figure 5.2 'Earth lights': an image of city lights from space.

Activity 5.1: Climate change politics: reviewing what you know

To prepare yourself to consider some of the political and philosophical questions raised here, you will need to refer back to the preceding chapters to try to sketch out brief answers to the following questions. Don't spend more than a few minutes on each question, and write just a couple of sentences or notes on each. Any of these questions could result in very long answers, but this short review activity is simply meant to help you tune in to the kinds of material you have already met that is relevant to this chapter:

1 Which countries are more responsible for the rise in atmospheric GHG concentrations, and which less responsible?

2 Which countries have the fastest growing GHG emissions?

3 Which groups of people and countries are most vulnerable to the impacts of climate change?

4 What costs and benefits will fall on different social groups, industries and countries as we develop policies to adapt to and mitigate climate change?

Comment

There is a danger when anyone begins to set a major issue such as climate change within a wider context of discussion of politics and philosophy: in trying to analyse and account for events, we become distanced from them and lose track of the concerns that drove us to study a subject more closely. Your answers to this activity will remind you that there are some winners but probably many losers, as we adapt to climate change, attempt to mitigate it and learn to live with its consequences.

1 Developed countries are the originators of most current and historical GHG emissions, and hence are seen by the environmentalists from these countries and negotiators and environmentalists (Figure 5.3) from the less-developed countries as being primarily responsible for meeting the costs of emissions reductions.

2 Less-developed countries are rapidly increasing their emissions of greenhouse gases, particularly India and China. The US and others argue that climate-change policies have to take this fact into account from the start (recall Box 3.5). But it's worth thinking about who precisely is causing the rise. The rapid growth of middle classes is the main cause, allied to industrialization along the Western model of fossil-fuel intensive development. The benefits of this form of development are not being spread evenly across the whole of these societies.

3 There are different kinds of vulnerability. Vulnerability to the physical impacts of climate change is highest in arid or coastal delta regions. The limited infrastructure (housing, healthcare, transport, etc.) of the world's poorest ensures that they will suffer most from impacts. However, impacts are also anticipated in the developed world (changing land uses in coastal areas; homeowners on floodplains finding houses unsaleable; higher insurance premiums in the wake of storm damage, etc.). Although these are modest by comparison, they matter to those affected, and they do capture public interest in the topic. OPEC countries also consider themselves vulnerable (Chapter 3, p. 100).

4 The costs and benefits will fall very unevenly. Protests against fuel price rises, disputes about decisions regarding changing land uses and restructuring of greenhouse gas-intensive industrial sectors (with job losses and shifts of location of investment often implied) are examples of the politics of 'bearing the costs' in developed and, increasingly, also in less-developed countries. If climate change policies work, there is the promise of some rapid growth in industries such as renewable energy. Carbon trading is a potentially huge new financial sector. Climate change threatens to hit poor people dependent on cities and agriculture in low-lying areas in less-developed countries hardest. However, it may deliver better growing conditions and boost agriculture in areas of the former Soviet Union and Canada.

Figure 5.3 Thai environmentalists demand a low carbon path to development.

These questions bring into focus the fact that the climate change losers, and occasional winners, are unevenly spread, among current generations, and between current and future generations, as well as across habitats and species. (Although, of course, you saw in Chapter 1 that for increases in GMST above 3–4 °C everyone and every system becomes a loser.) Not only are there winners and losers when it comes to the impacts of climate change, but also when we consider the effects of policies aimed at mitigating climate change. This fact hasn't been lost on those involved in debating climate change policies. Indeed working out the distribution of costs of the physical impacts of adaptation and mitigation strategies has been a keystone of political debates. This section gives a brief summary of two influential ways of bringing distant others (and, by extension, future generations) into debates about equity and climate change — the contraction and convergence approach and the opportunity-based approach.

Contraction and convergence approach to climate equity

One way of ensuring **climate equity** or justice assumes equal rights to the **global commons** — that is, the oceans, Antarctica, space and the atmosphere. One influential example of this way of thinking is the **contraction and convergence approach** mentioned on p. 154. In this case, the goal is to see net aggregate emissions decline over time below some maximum threshold level that stabilizes greenhouse gas concentrations, with per capita emissions of Annex I and non-Annex I countries arriving at equality. A key assumption within this approach is that international climate-change agreements should be based on equitable distribution of rights to emit greenhouse gases.

In other words, everybody carries around an imaginary budget of carbon emissions. There is something about this per capita approach that has immediately struck the right note with many people engaged with this problem. It is interesting to note then, that the idea did not come from a well-resourced international NGO, or one of the

Figure 5.4 Determined individuals make a difference: Meyer and colleagues could be seen as the Robin Hoods of climate negotiations in the 1990s.

international agencies, but was forced on climate-change negotiations by the determination of a small number of campaigners. One of the most audible was Aubrey Meyer (Figure 5.4), a former classical musician. With some savings, a suitcase, a laptop computer and some supportive friends he toured the climate-change negotiations to press his arguments.

The contraction and convergence JAVA climate model that you have worked with earlier in the block was designed to promote support for this fairness approach. There are variations within this camp, and most have developed beyond the initial goal of allocation of equal rights to emit greenhouse gases to the global commons. There are now proposals for other routes to equitable allocation. Some of these are based on geographical area, some on historical responsibility for emissions, on the level of economic activity, or a combination of all of these.

In all these approaches, countries with 'surplus' **emissions entitlements** — in other words, those with per capita emissions well below their entitlement (currently likely to be less-developed countries) — would be able to enter a marketplace and sell those surpluses to countries (almost certainly developed) with a deficit of permits. In addition to structuring a flow of resources from rich to poor countries, this approach encourages emissions reductions or avoidance among all parties.

- What are the political/philosophical origins of this approach?

- This kind of thinking wears its intellectual heritage on its sleeve: it is a direct descendant of emancipatory/liberation struggles of the left.

- It is easy to see what is fair about this approach, but what are the weaknesses?

- The weaknesses are those of Robin Hood himself, a folk hero that many people can identify with. However right his actions might seem to be to most people, he was nevertheless a romantic figure, thinking and working outside the framework of political norms of the time. The huge flow of resources (read money) from rich to poor countries implied in this argument might be seen as impossibly idealistic. US negotiators would just lean against the bar, roll their eyes and say 'get real'!

We're now going to look at arguments that seek to allow current and future generations to enjoy the fruits of current patterns of economic development while still protecting the environment.

Opportunity-based approach to climate equity

The **opportunity-based approach** that frames equity in terms of the right to achieve a desired standard of living was touched upon at the end of Chapter 4. The aim of this way of approaching climate change is to deliver the environmental goals of reducing and averting emissions, while at the same time allowing economic progress in the less-developed world. Where contraction and convergence has as its 'base unit' per capita emissions, this contrasting approach seeks to find a way to achieve stabilization of CO_2 emissions while permitting developed countries to maintain their current development path, and also allowing less-developed countries to follow the same route. This approach assumes that technology (including rapid transfer of environment-friendly technologies to less-developed countries) provides the magic bullet that facilitates economic development alongside mitigation of climate change.

There are some basic assumptions that go with this approach:

- minimal transfers of wealth from developed to less-developed countries (i.e. the rich stay rich and the poor become less poor, e.g. see Figure 4.18);
- gradual progress on emissions reductions in line with improving technical capacity;
- a wide range of development paths open to less-developed countries;
- no restrictions on development (but assumes this will be 'sustainable').

Given that international environmental negotiations are carried out by representatives of nation states, rather than radical environmental NGOs, we should not be surprised to find that it is this approach that has dominated the thinking of climate-change negotiators. The last bullet point links this position with the term 'sustainable development'. You have met this term before and the final chapters of this book will interrogate it more closely. For the moment, you should simply note how (dangerously?) flexible the term can be.

Does the political realism implied in the opportunity-based option make this the only realistic approach in current circumstances, or does it doom international climate-change policy agreements to achieving no more than trivial tinkering with global greenhouse gas emissions, with the inevitable environmental consequences?

Critics would, of course, argue that the opportunity-based perspective is really a charter for continuing business as usual (Figure 5.5). According to this argument, the pace of reductions in CO_2 emissions that might be delivered will be far outstripped by the increased emissions that come with economic development in less-developed countries, and sustained high consumption in the developed world. Defenders of this approach would insist that this is the only route available at the moment; that if you have a long journey to make you have to take a few first steps rather than stand still debating which route to take.

Figure 5.5   European second hand cars on the beach in Benin, West Africa: one of the more tangible ways in which the West exports a fossil-fuel intensive model of development and progress.

This takes us back to the difficult questions laid out in Chapter 4. Can we decarbonize the global economy without stifling it? Can we decouple economic growth from emissions? In other words, can we achieve very low greenhouse gas emission intensities?

Whereas the contraction and convergence approach is founded in philosophical debates about justice, the opportunity-based approach sits more comfortably in the context of established practices of international relations and 'real-world' politics. Indeed, this approach arises out of, and hence goes with the grain of, trends in mainstream economics and politics. Both approaches would insist, however, that equity is a driving concern. But the enormous complexity of human–environment interactions, overlain with intensely difficult philosophical questions about winners and losers of climate-change adaptation and mitigation, make it difficult to order our thinking about equity and climate change.

Activity 5.2: Bringing the consequences home...

The talk above of per capita emissions and CO_2 stabilization may seem rather abstract. We need to bring home the implications of all this. For some, the penny dropped a while back, and their conclusion was not heartening: in 1992, US President George Bush (senior) stated that 'the American lifestyle is non-negotiable'. Bush junior took a similar stand on the issue from the day he took office. Below we have listed a few common features of daily lives in the developed world that are treasured and/or envied, but are also generally identified as 'unsustainable' in terms of climate change (Table 5.1).

State why they are associated with climate change, and the kinds of solutions on offer. Keep your answers very brief: this activity is just to help you identify the kinds of political battlegrounds to which global environmental change issues direct us.

Table 5.1 Bringing climate change home to the public.

Lifestyle feature	Global problem	Possible solutions
My own car outside my door whenever I want it		
Well-travelled food — that is, a shopping basket of goods from around the world		
A warm house and plenty of gadgets		
A rubbish bin full of waste		
Tourism — flying is freedom		

Comment

One of the course team (Figure 5.6!, p. 166) offered the following responses to the five lifestyle features (Table 5.2). They are all features that most people in the developed world enjoy the benefit of, but we know they cannot be sustainable if they are taken up by a large portion of the global population in coming decades.

Table 5.2   Bringing climate change home to the public (worked example)

Lifestyle feature	Global problem	Possible solutions
My own car outside my door whenever I want it	Climate change — cars are the fastest growing source of CO_2 emissions in the UK; they also cause resource depletion (fossil fuels, steel, aluminium, etc.).	Reduce need to travel through land-use planning; prioritize walking and cycling; invest in public transport; energy-efficient engine technology; materials recycling; increase taxes on fossil fuels/price use of congested roads.
Well-travelled food	Climate change as a result of the energy demands of pesticide and fertilizer production, and the transport and processing of food; diminished habitats and biodiversity through monocropping and extension of cultivated land; pressure on water resources.	Environmentally orientated farming practices; linking local production and consumption.
A warm house and plenty of gadgets	Biggest source of greenhouse gas emissions in the developed world. Appliance production and disposal are also a source of landfill and toxic waste.	Investments in energy conservation and efficient boiler technologies; renewable energy production; repair and upgrading of appliances rather than disposal.
A rubbish bin full of waste	Source of greenhouse gases (CO_2 produced in transport of waste; methane given off at landfill sites).	Reduction of waste through regulation and consumer action: greater re-use of packaging; composting of appropriate waste; recycling of remaining waste to maximum.
Tourism — flying is freedom	CO_2 emissions; land use and intensive resource consumption to support short-stay tourist populations; new airport construction.	More local tourism; fewer but longer 'sabbatical' exchanges with distant places; more efficient transport technologies; more use of lower impact travel e.g. bikes and trains; ecologically and socially sustainable tourism practices.

Take some time now to think through the political implications of the possible solutions listed in Table 5.2. It has taken relatively little time to sketch out a range of policies and actions needed to make developed-world lifestyles more sustainable (and more globally equitable). But the kinds of action required by every layer of government, and the life choices required by individuals and communities, seem at first sight to be demanding more than we can reasonably expect. It suggests that the whole menu of policy options will need to come into play: regulation and taxation by governments, voluntary agreements by businesses, and more. Chapters 6 and 7, and the other activities in the block will look at progress in some of these areas. But Table 5.2 also suggests that we shall have to let policymakers reshape our daily lives. The next section goes beyond the thinking about strangers, or distant others, that has been central to Section 5.1 to consider what climate change means for our relationship with future generations and the non-human world.

Figure 5.6 Thinking about climate change… Once you start, you can't stop: it links to many aspects of our lives.

5.2 Being fair to the future

Section 5.1 sketched two ways of deciding what equity is, and how we might implement it for people living today. However, the contraction and convergence approach often refers out into the future, and this is where we will now look. This section explores another set of philosophical discussions that go beyond current human societies to consider the place that future generations and the non-human natural world hold in our ethical debates. There is a big and difficult question sitting behind the remainder of this chapter: just how far can we stretch our ethical and political frameworks to include parties other than humans alive today? Specifically, the final section looks at the implications of thinking of humans as one part of a dynamic Earth system. In short, it asks: does climate change mean that we need to develop wholly new ways of thinking and acting?

5.2.1 Future generations: a price on their lives

What kinds of ethical question do climate change pose? Those underlying Section 5.1 are the stuff of long-standing political debates: what resources are available to whom, and where? How are rights and responsibilities divided up? How are the interests of different parties represented? In other words, who defines what is 'fair', and how do they do it? However, there is one feature of the ethics of global environmental change (including both climate change and biodiversity loss) that is distinctly new, and that is its relation to the future.

Future generations are vulnerable to our decisions. At the simplest level, even their very existence is dependent on current generations (think about it…). Their welfare cannot be left to them to look after because they are downstream in time; their choices and life chances are limited by the decisions of those upstream (Figure 5.7).

Human economic activity has reached a scale that has the potential not only to boost but also to threaten the welfare, and possibly even the existence, of future generations.

The combination of population growth, technological and economic change and resultant environmental change brings human societies face to face with the startling fact that they have the capacity to limit, and possibly erase, the prospects of future generations. Unlike the threat of devastation through nuclear war, this potential does not arise out of the presence of competing centralized military powers, but out of the everyday actions of ordinary people. Almost all our framework of ethical debate is focused on questions about how we should behave in relation to humans alive today. The long shadows that our present-day actions throw on the life chances of future human generations present novel ethical questions. How should these be framed?

You don't have to listen to a conversation about environmental issues for very long — whether it's about global climate change, or a local Site of Special Scientific Interest threatened by a new development — to hear reference to the interests of 'future generations'. Paradoxically they are an entirely silent, but very potent voice in environmental policy discussions. But everyone that brings these imagined future generations into the debate is guessing at the state of their environment, and their needs and wants. Although the problems that are bringing these issues onto the agenda are new, there are some resources to draw on and in this section we look at ways of framing our thinking about future generations at the point where economics and philosophy meet.

Thinking about the future can take many forms — including day-dreaming, guessing and betting. In fact, the future takes up quite a lot of our time already. Personal finances — constructed as they are around interest rates, mortgages and credit cards — are all permeated by assumptions about the future. If we borrow money, interest rates are a reflection of how much we are prepared to pay for something later, which we don't have but want now. If we save money, interest accrues to our savings because we are willing to give up certain things now to be rewarded for our patience later. Economists work to throw light on the behaviour we will follow (and assumptions we make), whether at the scale of the household or society, and hence they cannot avoid including the future in their deliberations.

Figure 5.7 The ambitions and choices of our children will cast a long shadow into the future. How can we introduce the future into their thinking?

Discounting is the main way that economists have sought to integrate the future into present-day thinking. As you've seen in Section 5.1, their efforts tend to concentrate on the present to the detriment of future generations and the environment. It is, in practice, a procedure whereby future gains and losses are seen as being less important than an equivalent gain or loss in the present. This practice has led to economists being singled out for sustained heavy criticism from environmentalists for their failure to recognize that future generations will experience the worst of climate change or biodiversity loss caused in the present (Box 5.1). A letter to the leading scientific journal *Nature* makes the point clearly:

> Who but an economist could imagine that future generations would owe us an impossible debt for not damaging their environment? Isn't it we who owe future generations a sound environment?

Box 5.1   Discounting the future

When economists try to think about assessing the costs and benefits of taking a particular course of action, they work to express them in as complete a way as possible. If you consider that every decision to invest or spend a particular resource cuts down the options to use that resource in other ways (known as **opportunity costs**), it becomes clear why economists want to put figures on the value of things in the future relative to the present (Figure 5.8). In other words, they discount the future in calculating the value of things in the present.

For example: if you could get an 8% interest rate return by putting your money into a particular savings account you are likely to choose this option above an investment in a slow-growing hardwood forest which will increase in value at only 3% a year. The rate of interest impacts on how people think about natural resources. With an interest rate at 10%, £1 a year from now is worth 91p today. The same sum ten years from now is only worth 34p today; £1 twenty years from now will be worth just 11p today. Hence a resource or species has to have a very high value to be considered worth saving. With a lower interest rate, that resource would be discounted less and, therefore, worth more to us. With the kinds of interest rates sought by commercial and international banks (around 15% for the World Bank), the short-term exploitation of natural resources becomes an integral feature of investment and economic growth (Costanza et al., 1997, p. 44). Hence the practice of 'discounting the future' — a standard feature of mainstream economic practice —promotes environmentally unsustainable decisions.

Figure 5.8 Discounting: the economic equivalent of what makes an elephant seem small in the distance. Costs (and benefits) look smaller as we look to the future.

In their defence, economists point out problems caused by not discounting. In the case of climate change it may be that without discounting we would not amass capital or develop technology that will benefit future generations. On a different tack, the economists point to the exceptionally difficult logical problems that have been thrown up by global environmental change issues, and suggest that at least they are trying to tackle them. Above all, they want us to be frank about why the relationship we have with the future is heavily, inevitably, weighted in our own favour.

Current generations are in a position of power because future generations have no voice in our politics, markets or civil society, yet we continue to shape and limit the possibilities of theirs. Also, the harm that future generations may suffer as a consequence of our actions (or inactions) will not touch those of us alive today. Furthermore, much of the harm that our actions in the present do to future generations cannot be undone. These people of the future cannot speak to, or impact on our lives, and fictionalized representations of possible futures can often tend towards the optimistic (Figure 5.9).

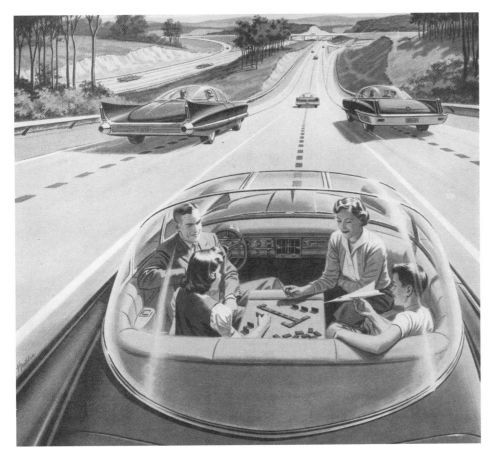

Figure 5.9 We struggle to imagine how society and technology will be in the future.

Activity 5.3: Islands in a stream of time

Imagine generations as different populations living on islands in a stream of time with a one-way current. Upstream are previous generations; downstream are future generations. What kinds of things (ranging from physical things to institutions and ideas — both good and bad) can the stream carry to us from the past and from us into the future? You might want to organize your thoughts as a diagram with the islands sketched in this stream of time.

Comment

One approach to this question is illustrated in Figure 5.10. We know something of previous generations by the things that come bobbing along to us in the current (some good stuff, some bad — for example, some great inventions and an inherited stock of capital; some pollution, landfill sites and imperfect institutions). Although we can be sure that the rubbish we throw into the stream will be carried away into a future that we won't experience (or hear from…), we also know that we can't put a message in a bottle and expect it to go upstream. At the same time, future generations downstream will know who to blame for the problems washed up on the shore (whether landfill or climate change), but we won't hear them in the present. On the plus side, you could say that we *can* send a message in a bottle to the future, in the sense of lessons learnt, new products and technologies and successfully implemented policies. Economists often stress these benefits to the future that can accrue from economic development in the present.

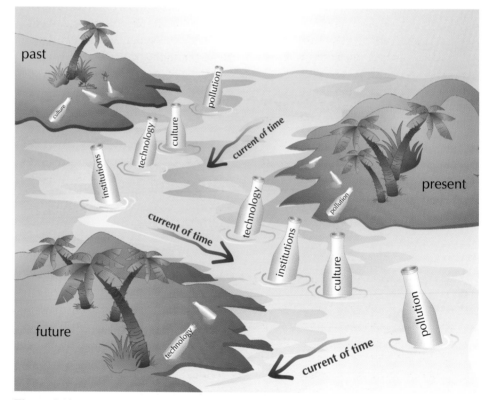

Figure 5.10 We know what the past has sent towards us. But we are deaf to the future's thanks or blame, and don't think too much about them, as we throw both 'good' and 'bad' their way.

Some economists have been known to ask why we don't simply pursue economic development that rewards many in present generations but only *may* be creating hazards and harm in the future.

- Which country's political position in international environmental negotiations aims to maximize benefits to present generations, ignoring potential harm to those in the future?

● The United States has consistently done so. George W. Bush made precisely this argument in 2001 when he refused to sign up to the Kyoto Protocol and sacrifice what he saw as US economic interests and the American way of life (Box 3.5).

One intuitive answer to this argument is that many people have children, nephews and nieces, grandchildren, and so on, and they extend the concern they feel for them into their thinking about future generations. It has been suggested that this argument breaks down when pushed; most people with families want to maximize their economic security and share that security with their close relations. Ties with distant future generations, whether kin or not, are altogether less compelling, and are unlikely to distract people from the goal of maximizing their own (and their kin's) welfare in the present and near-future. Economists Wilfred Beckermann and Joanna Pasek (2001) make a provocative and clear call to societies to focus solely on bequeathing more just and decent societies. In pursuit of this they propose that we should attempt to maximize welfare (implying economic growth) in the short term. They may be being provocative, but make an important point when they urge us to disregard the environmental consequences of today's actions on the assumption that future generations will have to devise solutions to whatever problems we bestow on them. Beckermann and Pasek are posing some difficult questions of those NGOs and politicians who make emotive pleas to us to change the way we act in the interests of future generations.

● Do Beckermann and Pasek believe that individuals today *should* care for the environmental security of future generations?

● 'Should' is an inappropriate word: economists such as these propose that the best we can do for future generations is to maximize our welfare today, and hence expand the wealth and technological potential that will be available to future generations. They might add that even if we try to help future generations, technological developments may make our sacrifice seem absurd. This is illustrated by the call in Victorian times to conserve coal for the future.

5.2.2 'Full' environmental costs

If we were to leave this very brief account of economic approaches to future generations and their environment there, we would leave a good number of economists frustrated and angry. Many environmental economists would argue that their efforts to ensure that the full environmental costs are integrated into any decision are, among other things, about making the environmental quality of future generations a part of decision-making in the present. What can we do about the negative environmental impacts that head downstream to future generations in our islands-in-time thought experiment?

These economists put the pollution into a category. They consider it an **externality**. Externalities are costs or benefits that are (or might be) considered somewhere or somehow, but are not included in the calculation of the internal costs of a good or service. Environmental economists have invested a great deal of energy in arguing why and how these externalities might be internalized. In other words, they have worked to put prices on, for example, the greenhouse gas emissions and biodiversity lost as a result of a new road scheme. Hence the price of such a scheme will need to increase to include not just the costs of materials, labour and land purchase, but also the social and environmental costs, such as increased local and global pollution, communities being severed and so on. The cash price of such a scheme would always have been passed on

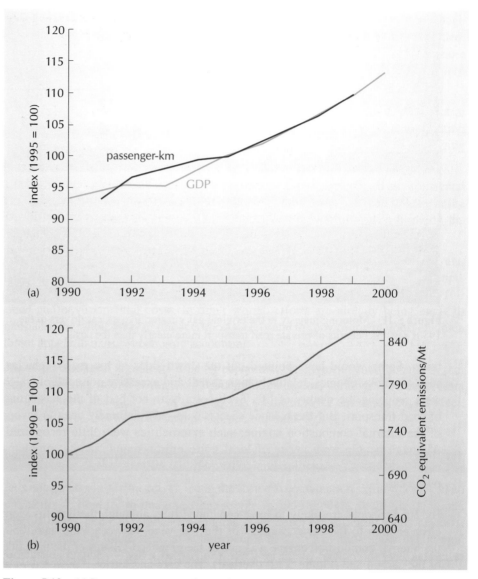

Figure 5.12 (a) Passenger transport demand (passenger-km) remains closely linked to economic growth in the European Union (EU). (b) EU transport greenhouse gas emissions 1990–2000. Cars are likely to contribute a third of CO_2 emissions in the 21st century and are the fastest growing source in recent years.

Figure 5.13 Futuristic traffic solutions: technological optimism isn't always the best way of planning for the future. But much of road transport policy has, quite literally, fixed our mobility patterns in concrete.

The scenario described in Activity 5.4 for 2055 is in some ways an optimistic one, but it does serve to illustrate one of the central points in debates about economics, the environment and the future, namely that the way we value things can change. But economists restrict themselves to monetary values, and they do not have a defence against one of the most fundamental criticisms they face. Their attempts to enumerate environmental problems, or to express them in terms of 'maximizing welfare', fail to plumb the ethical and philosophical depths that these issues inhabit. The next section will introduce an approach that offers a solution to the failures of economic approaches that starts out from an acceptance of James Lovelock's Gaia hypothesis. We don't intend you to elevate this above other responses to global environmental change (and there are plenty). Nevertheless, it does address our course themes in interesting ways, and will start you thinking about systems in a way that will lay the ground nicely for your work on Block 4.

5.3 People in place: connecting environmental change, philosophy and politics

Your work on the course to date will have left you in no doubt as to the capacity of humans to effect dramatic global environmental changes. We carry enormous responsibility for the environmental security of distant others, future generations and the non-human natural world both now and in the future. However, it is very difficult for us to imagine future people and their environments, and to integrate them into our decision-making. Our framework of ethical systems is formed around behaviour towards people and, to some degree, places that we are in one way or another close to.

Climate change more than any other issue prompts us to question the currently narrow boundaries of what has been called our **moral community** (those beings who have moral duties, rights, or in general deserve moral consideration). The response of much environmental philosophy and politics has been to suggest that we should extend this community towards future generations and the non-human world. Figure 5.14 shows just such a widening scope, moving, for example, from the ending of slavery and recognition of equal rights for women and men, to animal rights in the present and near future, and an anticipated extension into the non-animate natural world. Heady stuff!

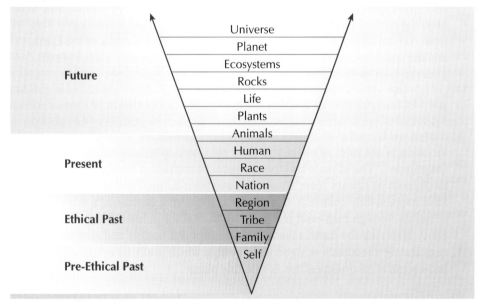

Figure 5.14   The evolution of ethics (Nash, 1989).

Publications concerned with this argument have filled several bookshelves, and we don't propose to delve into that literature. It is enough to note at this point that many critics have noted that there is little evidence to suggest that we are making swift progress along even the lower rungs of this ladder towards a wider conception of moral community.

Figure 5.15 Three pages from Diderot and D'Alembert's extensive Encyclopédie, showing mining, mechanized egg production and a sugar plantation. Many view the Enlightenment as the period when knowledge of the natural world allowed humans to claim dominion over it — and view themselves as apart from it.

Midgley uses Lovelock's arguments to rectify this overemphasis on competition as a natural force above all others. She suggests that this exaggerated extension of Darwin's theory of natural selection is myth-making passed off as objective fact. The problems with such myth-making really begin when the economic realm, and particularly business, is understood purely in terms of a socio-biology of competition — in other words, 'what can we do about inequality, greed and selfishness? It's human nature' (Figure 5.16).

Drawing on Gaia, she argues that cooperation is at least as important a force in human societies as competition. Midgley's view is one in a long line of critiques of the Western scientific tradition. She asserts that much of science tends to focus on individual elements as their subject of study, and fail to see these elements as parts of dynamic systems.

- According to Midgley, when did the dominant ways of thinking in modern science emerge, and what are the consequences of this?

- The intense period of intellectual development in the 17th and 18th centuries known as the Enlightenment is often viewed as the point at which human societies regarded themselves as separate from the natural world. From this point on, natural sciences developed into highly refined and distinct disciplines which pursued discrete objects of study. Holistic accounts that attempt to describe whole systems hence became rare, though the last few decades have seen ecology and environmental science, with precisely these goals, rise in prominence.

Figure 5.16 Naturally competitive or cooperative? This is a question we've struggled with since Darwin revealed our place in the evolutionary development of the primates.

This chapter's survey of some of the ethical dimensions of climate change has led to some very fundamental questions about equity, the future and our relations with the non-human natural world. Midgley leaves us in no doubt as to the scale of the challenge. She feels that the culture of individualism has expanded to the point where we are resigned to the rule of historical forces and are powerless to effect change. Her goal is no less than to see environmentalism move from being a fringe interest to being central to the way society thinks and works.

Nobody would claim that the Gaia hypothesis has made much headway in becoming the starting point for mainstream political decision-making, although the next chapter will chart how the parallel concept of sustainability has gradually risen to prominence.

However, there are some signs that, where Lovelock and Margulis's theory has been taken up outside science, their intentions have been misunderstood or deployed in ways that they themselves would not support or recognize. Initially, Lovelock used the term Gaia to help communicate his scientific hypothesis. He saw the reference to the Greek word for mother Earth as an approachable way into what he was saying. More recently, he relabelled it as 'Earth systems science', partly in response to the way some people in the green movement have adapted the term and approached it as a mystical quasi-religion. It's not difficult to see how this has happened. The idea inherent in the Gaia hypothesis — that the Earth *seeks* an optimum physical and chemical environment for life on this planet — implies purposeful activity. This view takes the debate way outside the comfort zone of most people engaged in contemporary environmental policy and politics debates. Many drawing on Gaia to inform their worldview use spiritual/mystical and often sentimental language and images (Figure 5.17) that contrast sharply with Midgley's demand for an academically robust integration of science and philosophy. This led to her plea for the Gaia hypothesis to be shaped as a powerful political tool for interpreting and responding to anthropogenic global environmental change; at present, this is little more than a distant hope. Indeed the language of Gaia is shared with parties that are a long way from scientific and political debate. A quick web search on 'Gaia' offers up witches spells, sportswear, meditation courses and pagan music among thousands of other sites capitalizing on the word.

Figure 5.17 Compassion or cloying sentiment? Either way 'Gaia' means something other than Earth systems science to many.

The *science* of climate change, with its promise of dramatic impacts, has to some extent become lodged in the public imagination. However, it has not yet catalysed widespread action. It does not yet appear to reach into our cultural or ethical conversations in the modern world in a way that has the power to reorientate the way we design, produce or consume goods, or live our everyday lives. What Midgley is working to do is to see the consequences of viewing our environment as a whole Earth system worked through in the way we debate politics. Her arguments might be considered a modest almost inaudible voice by contrast with the mainstream views of narrow specialist science and human-centred political philosophy.

Nevertheless, if you consider her arguments as one among many theories being put — whether it be by ecologists, climate scientists, political philosophers or radical environmental economists — that complement each other, it may be that we can see in these arguments the basis of a very different kind of 'mainstream view' of the future.

Bound together by the climate question

One aspect that may have occurred to you while reading the last two sections is that the notion of **obligations** (although the word hasn't been used) has been a consistent thread throughout. Book 1 Chapter 3 noted that the word's root lies in the Latin *ligare*, meaning 'to bind'. The point was made there that we are becoming more aware of our lives being bound to those of distant others. Section 5.1 showed how climate change emphasizes those bonds or links. Later sections went beyond distant others in the present to acknowledge that climate change binds our actions and thinking to future generations. The Gaia hypothesis is one of several that take us further, demanding that we place ourselves in a causal web of interconnections within the natural world.

This huge extension of ethical thinking from its basis in our community in the present, to the global environment and the future is a big challenge, and the consequences are far reaching. But the practical outcomes of this extension of obligations won't be played out on paper by philosophers, but rather in the political and social worlds. Hence the question of what climate change means for politics is one we're going to approach from a different angle in Chapter 6, where we look at the intersection between climate change and sustainable development. None would claim that Midgley's goal of seeing holistic ecological thinking becoming the hub of politics has been reached. However, Chapter 6 will show that something surprising has been happening. Climate change has promoted environmentalism's concept of sustainability to centre stage in the mainstream debate of environmental problems. Our understanding of the issue is pressing a huge question on society: must we bring the 'carbon age' of human development to a rapid close (Figure 5.18)?

Figure 5.18   Carhenge, Nebraska: how close are we to the end of the carbon age?

Activity 5.5: Environmental economics and 'Gaian' approaches: constructing a balance sheet

By way of a conclusion to this chapter, look back over the last two sections and try to draw up a balance sheet of the strengths and weaknesses of both environmental economics and the 'Gaian' approaches to representing future generations and the non-human natural world in our thinking today. You might want to do this as a table of pros and cons that speak to each other. Some appear in the text, but you may want to add in your own.

Comment

One approach to the challenge set is outlined in Tables 5.3 and 5.4.

Table 5.3 Environmental economics — a balance sheet.

Pros	Cons
Environmental economics is a realistic solution to environmentalist naivety: it starts from where we are today, and writes from the dominant intellectual paradigm. We price so many of the other things in daily life, why not bring the environment into the equation?	For all its apparently neutral rationality, economics incorporates a deep-seated ideological vein. It is one of the bigger cogs in the engine room of capitalism. It is precisely the fact that the economic paradigm dominates that has left us in such a mess: you could say that economics knows the price of everything and the value of nothing. Trying to price something like the value of a human life or a beautiful landscape inevitably ends in absurdity.
No other field of intellectual activity has come anywhere near economics in giving a meaningful voice to the interests of the future in the decisions of the present in a logical and transparent way.	Economics cannot claim to offer anything more than abstract guesses when it comes to putting a price on the value of environmental quality or protection for future generations.
The practice of discounting is a helpful reminder of the simple fact that present generations have enough on their mind in creating and dividing up welfare among themselves: it's only natural that future generations come second. Furthermore, by creating wealth today we are expanding the potential for technological advance, further wealth creation and a fairer distribution of the growing 'wealth cake' in the future. Indeed, wealth today is the greatest guarantee of solving the environmental problems of the future	Discounting is strongly biased in favour of present generations, but this fact is often disguised in the whirl of number crunching. Dickens' character Mr Micawber is famous for hurtling through his chaotic life repeating that 'something will turn up'. As Barry points out, this isn't desirable in an individual, let alone as a society's way of thinking about future generations (Barry, 1999)

Table 5.4 The Gaian approach — a balance sheet.

Pros	Cons
The Gaian approach redresses three centuries of separation of humans from the natural world in scientific methodology: it places us within its systemsand feedbacks rather than outside, observing its components.	It is no more than a populist restatement of a mainstream perspective in ecology and other disciplines. There is no scientific justification for singling out Lovelock's work.
It offers a timely means of linking insights from ecology, Earth sciences and climate research to the way we think about human society.	The hypothesis has attracted attention from very marginal groups that overlay it with quasi-mystical language but has not registered any serious attention from mainstream media or politics.
It gives us a language and a powerful metaphor for expressing the fact that humans belong to, and are reliant on, the natural world rather than sovereign over it.	It's implicitly a conservative worldview. In talking about a single Earth system, within which humans are a small part, there's a danger of coming to the conclusion that humans have no power over their own destiny, and that we must fatalistically accept environmental, social or economic change.

5.4 Summary of Chapter 5

5.1 Debates on action on climate change relate to every scale of human activity, and require us to look at questions of equity, vulnerability and responsibility across time and space.

5.2 Developed world lifestyles and consumption patterns are the source of major global problems — climate change above all. Solutions do exist but they demand both investment and commitment — from individuals and government at all scales.

5.3 Economics presents both opportunities and problems in the search for environmental and social security and quality in the future. Methods such as discounting can be contentious, but the internalizing of externalities can be fruitful.

5.4 Alternative ways of thinking about environmental problems are numerous. Lovelock's Gaia hypothesis is one that offers a different starting point, based on the drawing together of geological, atmospheric and biological sciences. It argues for thinking of the Earth in terms of Gaia — a single living organism.

5.5 The Gaia hypothesis has inspired one political philosopher to propose a political system reliant on cooperation correcting the over-extension of Darwinist understanding of competition and evolution into social and political philosophy.

5.6 A balance sheet of both environmental economics and Gaian approaches suggests that there is no single store of practical or philosophical answers to guide our responses to climate change. Rather, we shall need to take a critical and open-minded approach to a range of disciplines.

Learning Outcomes for Chapter 5

When you have completed this chapter, you should be able to:

5.1 Define and use, or recognize definitions and applications of, each of the terms given in **bold** in the text. (Question 5.1)

5.2 Explain the main differences between contraction and convergence and opportunity-based positions in climate politics. (Questions 5.1 and 5.2)

5.3 Explain economic approaches to the future and the possible consequences of these approaches for current and future environments. (Questions 5.3 and 5.4)

5.4 Briefly describe James Lovelock's Gaia hypothesis and efforts to apply the Gaia hypothesis to produce a political philosophy. (Questions 5.5 and 5.6)

5.5 Summarize the pros and cons of environmental economics and Gaian approaches as alternative responses to global environmental change issues. (Questions 5.7 and 5.8)

Questions for Chapter 5

Question 5.1

Explain, in no more than 80 words, which of the main positions outlined in this chapter — opportunity-based and contraction and convergence — characterizes the mainstream of climate-change negotiations.

Question 5.2

State four aspects of the opportunity-based approach.

Question 5.3

Why do rates of discounting impact on natural resources? Answer in around 100 words.

Question 5.4

In a paragraph of around 150 words, give an example of an environmental externality linked to climate change, and explain how it might be internalized in economics calculations.

Question 5.5

In one short sentence, outline the argument and foundation of Lovelock's Gaia hypothesis.

Question 5.6

What philosophical fallacy based in science is Mary Midgley seeking to correct with her arguments based in Lovelock's Gaia science? Answer in no more than 80 words.

Question 5.7

List three pros and three cons of the environmental economics approach to global environmental change issues.

Question 5.8

List three pros and three cons of the Gaian approach to global environmental change issues.

References

Barry, B. (1999) Justice between generations: power and knowledge. In Smith, M. (ed), *Thinking through the Environment: A Reader*. London: Routledge.

Beckermann, W. and Pasek, J. (2001) *Justice, Posterity and the Environment*. Oxford: Oxford University Press.

Charlton, N. (2002) *Guide to Philosophy and the Environment*, University of Lancaster, Department of Philosophy and Environment [online]. Available from: http://www.lancs.ac.uk/users/philosophy/mave/guide/gaiath~1.htm [Accessed 27 March 2003]

Costanza, R. et al. (1997) *An Introduction to Ecological Economics*. Boca Raton, Florida: St Lucie Press.

Letter to *Nature*, **420**, p. 605.

Lovelock, J. (1979) *Gaia: A New Look at Life on Earth*. Oxford: Oxford University Press.

Midgley, M. (2001) *Gaia: the Next Big Idea*. London: Demos.

Nash, R. T. (1989) *The Rights of Nature: A history of environmental ethics*. Wisconsin: University of Wisconsin Press.

Chapter 6 Climate change and sustainability — inseparable

Prepared for the course team by Joe Smith

6.1 Career of the concept of sustainable development

Climate change is the most demanding of all policy integration challenges: it is likely to touch most people's lives on the planet, and is as much about development as it is about environment (Figure 6.1). Any attempt by policymakers to mitigate or adapt to climate change requires that they keep the 'big picture' visible in their work at all times. Neither is it simply a matter of integrating policy across different sectors. It is also essential to integrate thinking across scales, meaning inter-linkages across local, regional, national, supranational (meaning literally 'above' national, e.g. EU) and international levels — that is, integrated assessement (Figure 6.2). Also, you can't leave anybody out of the discussion: the political context within which it is being addressed demands unprecedented breadth of participation. As Chapter 4 showed, climate change also demands 'sequential decision-making under uncertainty' — a very tall order.

Figure 6.1 Tuvalu's seat at COP 7. How long will it be required? The island is vulnerable to climate change, and needs global sustainability.

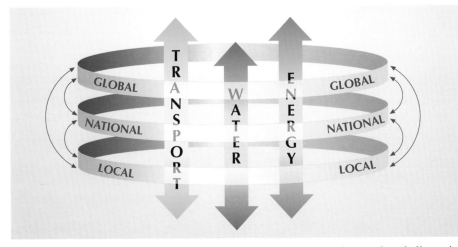

Figure 6.2 Adapting to and mitigating climate change — a huge integration challenge in sectors such as transport, water and energy.

Furthermore, local and global environmental issues such as climate change, loss of biodiversity, stratospheric ozone depletion, desertification, freshwater availability and air quality are often interlinked in complex ways. In all these cases, local actions and processes have global social and/or environmental consequences. The first half of the block stressed that there is a great deal of uncertainty surrounding the consequences of climate change, but one thing we do know for sure is that vulnerabilities to climate changes, whether social or ecological, now or in the future, are unevenly distributed.

Figure 6.3 Not long before a hurricane struck this forest, it provided the means of shelter, fuel and food to human societies near and far.

'Building in resilience' is one answer to this vulnerability, but this simple expression carries huge implications: are our societies ready to hear them (Figure 6.3)?

There have been many points in the course up to this point where we have demonstrated that the relationship between environmental and social change is a result of a complex web of economic growth, broad technological changes, lifestyle patterns, demographic shifts and environmental feedbacks. At the hub of the concept of sustainable development is the assumption that there are opportunities to address environmental problems that enhance benefits, reduce costs and meet human needs at the same time.

For all the hot air talked, forests felled for publications and air miles flown for international meetings, sustainable development is about putting this thought into action. To prepare you to play a role in making this happen, this chapter looks deeper into the concept of sustainability. It will sketch its rise to prominence and intellectual underpinnings, and consider ways in which some people are trying to weave it into mainstream decision-making.

Activity 6.1: How climate change hits the poorest

What are the needs of the poor, and what are their chances of meeting these through development? What does climate change mean for the poorest in the world? How do the answers to these two questions come together to promote the concept of sustainable development? Draw on Table 6.1 and Figure 6.4 (opposite) to write a paragraph of between 100 and 200 words.

Table 6.1 The poor are often vulnerable (and vice versa) — and climate change makes them more so

	Facts of life for the world's poorest	The poor's vulnerability to climate change
food	Food production needs to double to meet the needs of an additional 3 billion people by 2030.	Climate change is projected to lead to a decrease in agricultural productivity in the tropics and sub-tropics for almost any amount of warming.
forests	Wood only source of fuel for one-third of the world's population, which is expected to double by 2050.	Climate change is likely to increase forest productivity, but forest management will become more difficult due to an increase in pests and fires.
freshwater	One-third of the world's population is now subject to water scarcity.	Climate change is projected to decrease water availability in many arid- and semi-arid regions. Number of people facing water scarcity will more than double by 2030.
biodiversity	Estimated 10–15% of the world's species could become extinct by 2030. Biodiversity underlies goods and services on which human societies depend.	Climate change will exacerbate the loss of biodiversity.

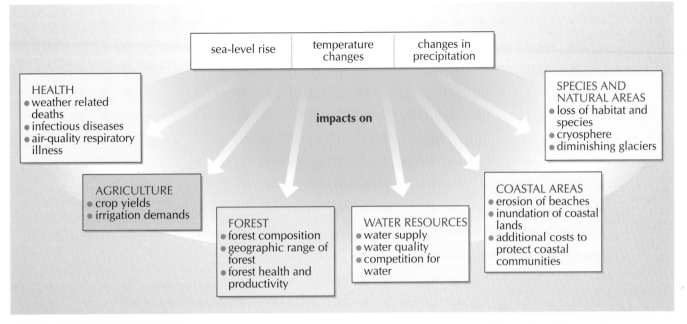

Figure 6.4 Climate-change impacts hit the poorest hardest.

Answer

Many people in the world lack access to some of their basic life needs. The poor and their environment are the most vulnerable to climate change: it will exacerbate what are already enormous problems. In addition to the depletion of the basic human needs of food, fuel and water, the extinction of the fundamental source of all the things that human societies rely on — biodiversity — is likely to be accelerated. Climate change limits the poor's chances of development. Together, these factors have done much to promote sustainability to a central role in our local and global responses to the challenges of the 21st century.

This section charts the emergence of the concept of sustainable development, and goes on to look at some of its theoretical foundations. For a concept that is proclaimed by world leaders as the only viable framework for society in the coming century, it is surprising how little agreement there is about what it actually means, or how it might inform action. Put another way, if sustainability were a bus, you couldn't be sure the engine was going to work, let alone where it was going to take you. Is anyone willing to buy a ticket?

Looking closely at criticism of an idea is often the best way to understand it. The roots of sustainability thinking are found in the 'first wave' of environmentalism in the early 1970s. This first wave ebbed after it was realized that doom-laden predictions such as those in *Limits to Growth* (Chapter 1) were not being fulfilled. Other apparently more urgent political priorities also served to limit the influence of environmentalists. Three criticisms had banished them to the sidelines of debate. All are relevant today, and here we have picked out some of the threads of continuity with the arguments of present-day sceptics of climate change and/or sustainable development. The sceptics' view of environmentalism can be represented as:

- Over-confidence in computer-based projections of interactions between human societies and economies on the one hand, and environmental change on the other. Human–environment interactions are simply too complex to be modelled in this way. Many assumptions are made which could be presented differently by someone with different political intentions.

- Many feel that Western environmentalists want to 'pull the ladder up' behind them. In other words, they believe that those who have already enjoyed the benefits of economic growth in the developed world wish to deny those benefits to others for fear of the environmental consequences.

- Environmentalists fail to recognize the adaptability of human systems and the ingenuity of technology. Capitalism is at its most dynamic and adaptable in the face of economic or environmental challenges, whether in seeking new oilfields, or new ways of extracting oil, or in moving towards more environmentally orientated industrial production (known among other things as 'clean production').

These criticisms served to limit environmentalism's capacity to influence mainstream thinking in the 1970s and early 1980s, and continue to be difficult to answer in the present. However, the mid-to-late 1980s saw environmental issues return to prominence in public and political debate. This time they were not going to go away. The surge in the membership and visibility of environmental NGOs in that period has been dubbed the 'second wave' of modern environmentalism. The origin of this wave is difficult to pin down, but the following were all contributory factors:

1   *A body of evidence*   There was a steady flow of proclamations of continuing loss of biological diversity, deforestation and desertification from NGOs, and UN and scientific bodies. The fate of specific habitats, notably the Amazon rainforest, attracted widespread media interest.

2   *Transboundary pollution*   In the first half of the 1980s, scientific and policy debates about acid rain demonstrated that industrial and domestic processes in one region resulted in environmental degradation in another. Dramatic images of lakes devoid of life and dying forests captured the public imagination in Europe and North America.

3   *Local acts — global impacts*   In the early 1980s, scientists discovered a hole in the ozone layer (Figure 6.5c; vital for absorbing high-energy ultraviolet radiation, which can lead to skin cancer) over the Antarctic, and were able to attribute it to the release into the atmosphere of chlorofluorocarbons (CFCs). These chemicals had been widely used as, for example, refrigerants and fire retardants. As a result, there was widespread publicity about the threats this carried, particularly to human health in terms of skin cancers from the higher level of UV radiation in sunlight. This pollution was again the result of industrial and domestic processes, but this time local actions (as simple as using underarm deodorant containing CFC-based aerosol propellants) had global impacts that could be made graphic on maps on the screens of the ozone depletion researchers.

4   *Rich enough to worry*   Developed societies enjoyed a sustained period of growth in the 1980s. Sociological studies of environmentalism suggests that as people are more secure in terms of meeting immediate economic needs, there is a greater likelihood of them developing concerns for issues beyond their own material needs. In other words, having satisfied their need for basic economic security, they are able to consider a wider range of concerns, including their local and global environment.

5   *Environmental pain with no gain*   The promise of a sustained progression towards Western standards of living made to leaders of less-developed countries by developed country governments and the development institutions was simply not being delivered in practice. Against a background of immense and growing debts of less-developed countries to banks in the developed world, regulatory and technological changes meant that the world's largest companies were enjoying increasing mobility and global reach (a process summarized as 'economic globalization', discussed in more depth in Chapter 7). The environment was being degraded, but with no development gains.

Environmentalism has always understood that pictures can often speak more loudly than words. The images in Figure 6.5 link with points 1–5 above, but work on us at a different level. Using these images as a starting point, consider why images have been particularly important for NGOs in establishing widespread public support, and, in turn, official support for integrating environmental and economic concerns.

(a)   (b)   (c)

(d)   (e)

Figure 6.5   Environmentalism lives in our minds as images at least as much as words: (a) the Amazon; (b) tree death caused by acid rain; (c) ozone hole over Antarctica; (d) media-friendly environmental campaigners; (e) reforestation work in response to poverty and environmental degradation in Africa.

● People communicate at a range of levels, and images have proved to be one of the most powerful means by which the environmental movement has come to represent both arguments and feelings.

All five of these factors fed into the development of a new, and more tangible, critique of what conventional growth delivers in terms of increased poverty and environmental degradation. They ensured that this second wave of environmentalism would be more politically potent than the first. The fact that local actions could aggregate to cause global environmental changes (and vice versa) contrasted with the fact that global companies reach high environmental standards in one part of the world while dumping in another. Pressures were building behind demands for an urgent rethink about the pattern of development.

These pressures were expressed in the politically deft Brundtland report that you have already come across in Book 1 Chapter 1. Gro Harlem Brundtland, a former Norwegian prime minister, was chair of the World Commission on Environment and Development (WCED), which was searching for a development model that would sustain economies in the developed world, enable (equitable) development, yet avert environmental damage. Convened in 1984 at a time of intense cold war tension, the WCED achieved a remarkable political feat in gaining consensus support for its final report *Our Common Future*. All 24 Commission members signed, including the representatives from China, the Soviet Union, the United States, Brazil, India, Japan, Indonesia, Saudi Arabia and Nigeria. This was only possible because the Commission entertained the need for change not just in less-developed countries, but also in the way developed economies worked and charted the outline of a new relationship between North and South.

The magic words were 'sustainable development', and by now you will be very familiar with the definition offered in the report. Its definitive statement of: '... development that meets the needs of the present without compromising the ability of future generations to meet their own needs' (Brundtland, 1987) has become a mantra of the environmental policy community. But like many such mantras, incantations, prayers and promises, people settle into the rhythm of the words, while often forgetting to explore their content, or likelihood of their being put into practice.

● Why did the Brundtland report become the widely accepted definition of sustainable development and have such an impact on mainstream politics?

● The report was politically astute — giving everyone around the table something (the promise of development, the protection of biodiversity and so on) — but did not specify who would take action or when. Its timing was fortuitous in that it was published during (and contributed to) an upswing in environmentalist support in developed countries.

The Brundtland report was not the first time that the goals and means of development in the less-developed countries had been considered. The literature on development evolved over time beyond a concern purely with economic growth to include concepts such as human development, equitable development, poverty eradication and alternative development. *Our Common Future* could have been just another in the flow of worthy documents that occupied themselves with this question if another major issue in international environmental politics had not come to prominence. That issue was, of course, the central subject of this book — climate change.

By the late 1980s, climate-change science, and the policy debates it generated, had arrived at a point at which political leaders had to pay some attention. The context was of a rapidly growing and increasingly professional environmental movement, an upswing in wider public concern about environmental issues, and attendant media interest. Public and politicians had in recent years become aware of links between local actions and global environmental impacts. 'Sustainable development' was the driving purpose behind 1992's Rio (Figure 6.6) or 'Earth Summit' (or UNCED; see Chapter 3). The outcomes, among other things, included Agenda 21 — a hugely ambitious set of goals for sustainable development — and UN Conventions on Climate Change, Biodiversity and Desertification.

Figure 6.6 'Too little too late' was the environmentalists view in 1992, but with hindsight UNCED is seen as a key milestone.

These outcomes forced a number of issues into the spotlight, including questions about: how to intervene in increasingly global economic processes that threaten the environment; what 'good governance' might mean and the changing nature of citizenship. These are all terms that will be explored further in the last chapter in the book. Climate change gave UNCED a political potency and apparent urgency. In turn, UNCED promoted sustainable development to the status of dominant **discourse** in environment and development policy debate. The consensus was that sustainable development would have to sit at the heart of any response to climate change.

There is a chorus of commentators that charge the term 'sustainable development' with being at best elusive and at worst a sham. In an attempt to answer them, we have gathered together six strands — most of which you have come across already in this block — that run through most accounts of sustainable development. In Table 6.2 we have also tried to illustrate ways in which the environmental policy community has worked to implement or represent these strands. In other words, the second column tries to show exactly how practitioners are trying to put notions of sustainability into practice.

Table 6.2 Six strands of the concept of sustainability and six ways of delivering them

Issue or underlying theme	Action or response
Integration of environmental, social and economic interests in decision-making	Environmental taxes; **sustainable development indicators** (more on these in Section 6.3).
Futurity Binding the interests of future generations into decisions made today, which might impact upon their life chances	Sustainability stated as a goal in planning guidance and other regulations, where 'projects, policies and plans' may impact on future generations or the non-human natural world now or in the future.
Limits There are limits to the capacity of ecological systems to sustain (human) life (either in terms of resource depletion, or degradation through pollution or other human practices)	Climate science is working to understand these limits; whether at the level of botanists tracking the 'movement' of mosses in response to changing climate, or modellers trying to capture the dynamics of the global system.
Equity In making decisions about the environment and the economy, we must represent the interests of the most vulnerable now living on the planet, and future generations	It's early days, but the goal of many of the practical outcomes of climate negotiations is to achieve equitable 'win–win' outcomes that deliver development in less-developed countries without damaging the environment of future generations.
Precaution The **precautionary principle** shifts the burden of proof such that those undertaking an activity that might be environmentally damaging must prove it to be harmless.	Climate-change politics is driven in large part by the anticipation of, and desire to avoid, environmental changes brought about by current patterns of human activity. Regulation of some chemicals, particularly in Scandinavian countries, reflects the precautionary principle. Some would point to the EU's handling of genetically modified food in the late 1990s and early 2000s as an example (though anti-GM campaigners would question this).
Participation Sustainability can only be implemented through the active engagement of the full range of **stakeholders** (that is, government, NGOs, business and academia).	**Local Agenda 21** processes and sustainable development roundtables; participatory decision-making processes.

Sustainable development is a fluid concept, and is constantly being renegotiated by its stakeholders. NGOs, business interests and governments are constantly working to make their own reading of the concept dominant. At the same time, the concepts and components outlined above would be accepted by most of the players. This is not to say that independent commentators (including this course team) would consider it complete.

Box 6.1 Anything missing? What about redundancy?

Although you have met some of these terms before in this course, here they are bundled together as components of a 'regulation-issue sustainable development toolkit'. One thing missing from the table that you will have picked up in references to sustainability in Blocks 1 and 2 is the notion of **redundancy**. How might it be important to the issues discussed in this block?

The idea that sustainability, or resilience, of ecosystems requires a considerable and committed potential for change (or redundancy) is not acknowledged in most accounts of sustainable development. The notion that there are ecological limits to human development, which will intervene to constrain human action, is a parallel argument, and the arrival at these limits implies a depletion of this potential. However, this powerful (and subversive) notion of the need to keep up a 'stock' of ecological resilience in response to ecological vulnerability has been overlooked in policy debate. This may be because it breathes life back into uncomfortable arguments that there are ecological limits to development. In other words, sustainability may require the reduction and in some cases stopping of some activities that claim to be able to achieve sustainability (sustainable mobility; sustainable tourism, etc.).

The course of the 2002 World Summit on Sustainable Development in Johannesburg confirmed a feeling that these components of sustainability had not made their way off the drawing board (Figure 6.7) and into meaningful implementation. This is why it is difficult to fill in some of boxes in the Action column of Table 6.2. Indeed, one of the apparent outcomes of the summit was that there may not be another summit of this nature until there is some solid evidence that countries have begun to implement previous commitments.

Figure 6.7 How many world leaders does it take to change a light bulb? If it relies on leadership, you'd better get used to the dark.

Activity 6.2: Who are the 'stakeholders' in sustainable development?

Summarize the main stakeholders in sustainable development conferences at national and international levels. In other words, who do you need to get around the table to bring sustainable development into the mainstream of decision-making?

Answer

The cast list is usually the same, and usually includes the following at international, national and regional levels:

Government   Usually represented by civil servants. They are the voice of democratically elected politics (interestingly, until the closing stages of major conferences, politicians themselves are rarely visible in these debates). Officials often become impassioned by the issues, and a big distance can open up between them and more 'mainstream' colleagues working with well-established transport, economics or development portfolios.

NGOs   Environmental campaigners are some of the main drivers of interest in the concept of sustainable development, but, in their diversity, can appear wracked with indecision. Some are reformist (that is, 'let's take some little steps along a long road'), others could be called revolutionary (for example, 'we must walk out of these greenwash talkshops and demand some real action' — *greenwash* is the term given to industry or governments' use of environmentalist images or rhetoric to disguise the absence or inefficacy of action being undertaken). Note that business associations are officially considered to be NGOs in the context of international associations; they are known as 'BINGOs' (Business Initiated NGOs).

Business   There are two main reasons for business involvement. The most well established is fear of being targeted by NGO campaigns against businesses seen as major polluters or destroyers of communities. Hence, the major fossil fuel companies, Shell and BP, which were accused on charges of social and environmental misdemeanours in the 1990s, have been prominent players on sustainability issues in the 2000s. The other reason is when a business has a particular commitment to environmental or social issues. The Body Shop and Co-operative Bank in the UK, or Interface carpets in the US, are some of the best-known examples.

Others   There are other players: independent commentators and experts (including specialist journalists and academics) play background roles. The international bodies that manage these processes (such as the UNFCCC) also have a stake and an influence. A great deal of the pressure on all these parties for action is coming from environmental concern expressed by ordinary people. New ways are being sought to connect grassroots opinion with national and international decision-making (Figure 6.8).

Figure 6.8   The road to sustainability is paved with talk shops. The New Economics Foundation is one body that is working to connect grassroots thinking to national policies.

6.2 Intellectual foundations of sustainable development

6.2.1 Three journeys to sustainability thinking

What do you think when you see the word 'sustaining'? Dictionaries would offer 'to support' or 'to keep in a state of being', but we should look a little deeper to consider the thinking behind its now widespread usage. Here we are going to touch on three fields of academic study that have contributed to our thinking on sustainable development: ecology, thermodynamics and economics. There are many other important contributions, but these three chart the interdisciplinary scope of discussions about sustainability. Indeed, as you read them, you'll notice that there is a lot of continuity of approach. As you look at the brief paragraphs summarizing their contribution, bear in mind where we shall be going in Chapter 7: the following chapter aims to place sustainability within the context of the two major course themes of *globalization* and *governance*. What you are about to read offers a lens through which you can look at these themes. Not all these contributions are particularly visible in current debates: that's why we are making some of them explicit here.

Ecology — living metaphor for sustainability

Ecology as a modern academic discipline had emerged as a way of looking at relationships between plants, animals and environmental conditions in a complete and systematic way, rather than focusing on one species. In the context of the 1970s, this complete (sometimes called **holistic**) approach led to commentaries on the sustainability or otherwise of particular places and human practices.

The term 'sustainable' has long been applied in fisheries ecology, where it was part of the concept of 'maximum sustainable yield' (MSY), and refers to particular species that are subject to harvesting. You have already encountered this idea in the context of Antarctic fisheries in Block 1. The term is now sometimes used by ecologists in a much larger sense, as illustrated by the 'Sustainable Biosphere Initiative', which is an ongoing agenda for ecological research promulgated by the Ecological Society of America, the learned society that represents ecological scientists in North America.

The discussion of Antarctic ecology in Block 1 and the more in-depth exploration of biodiversity that you've undertaken in Block 2 have given you a sound understanding of the science of biodiversity, and in the later stages of that block, the steps from knowledge of a system to its management. Our purpose here is to draw your attention to the fact that ecological notions of systemic collapse have been a forceful backdrop to the emergence of the concept of sustainable development.

Thermodynamics: sustainability and physics

Early 1970s environmentalists concerned with natural resources were looking for ways of talking with authority about the consequences of rapid rates of depletion of natural resouces. There are no more authoritative reference points than the laws of physics. Hence, we shouldn't be surprised that influential environmental authors such as Fritz Schumacher and Hermann Daly identified the laws of thermodynamics as both the basis of a theoretical argument and as a pressing metaphor for their catastrophic view of the contemporary economy of natural resources.

The first law of thermodynamics states that 'we do not produce or consume anything, we merely rearrange it'. In other words resources cannot be made afresh; hence there is the threat of them running out. The second law — that of entropy — has it that 'our rearrangement implies a continual reduction in potential for further use within the system as a whole'.

(Daly, 1977)

In this view, waste (high entropy) is an inevitable result of the extraction and use of resources (low entropy). They had already applied these ideas to economics, but the context of the 1970s oil crises gave their arguments added urgency and weight. This way of thinking sits in the background of any discussion of sustainability, represented as a concern with 'limits' and 'capacities'.

Economics for sustainability

There are parallels between the insights from thermodynamics and environmental economists' understanding of sustainable development. David Pearce and colleagues demand that economists expand their standard definition of capital to set human economies within their environmental context:

What is capital? Capital comprises the stock of man-made capital — machines and infrastructure such as housing and roads — together with the stock of knowledge and skills, or human capital. But it also comprises the stock of natural capital including natural resources (oil, gas, and coal), biological diversity, habitat, clean air and water and so on. Together, these capital stocks comprise the aggregate capital stock of a nation.

(Pearce *et al.*, 1993)

These economists argued that such features of 'natural capital', which had rarely been considered in conventional economics, should be brought into every economic equation. This **natural capital** is defined as the stock of natural assets that continually yield goods and services. It provides us with resources (e.g. fish, timber and cereals), takes up wastes (via, for example, CO_2 absorption and sewage decomposition), and offers life support services (stability of climate, protection from ultraviolet radiation, water cleansing, and so on). Environmental economists argue that these should be fully considered within any economics that is concerned to promote sustainability.

Note that a new branch of economics called 'ecological economics', has sought to overcome what they see as inherent contradictions in mainstream environmental economics (see, for example, Costanza *et al.*, 1997).

Ecologists, physicists and economists are among the most prominent intellectual resources at the root of the concept of 'sustainable development'. However, whatever the quality of the intellectual debate, the concept has failed to capture the public imagination. Maybe it would have been better if advertising executives and journalists had been involved earlier. Activity 6.3 invites you to confront the fact that sustainable development has not yet struck a chord with the general public.

Activity 6.3: 'Sustainable development'—catchy phrase urgently required

In the charts of impossibly obscure and off-putting phrases, 'sustainable development' belongs with terms like 'exogenous growth theory' and 'anti-disestablishmentarianism'. Try to put the Brundtland definition, '… development that meets the needs of the present without compromising the ability of future generations to meet their own needs' (WCED, 1987), into your own words. You will have already done a similar exercise in Block 2 but this time use words that could be understood by friends and family who are not in the middle of studying an Open University environment course!). You only need to write a sentence or two.

Answer

Almost all the numerous definitions of sustainable development work to integrate economic, social and environmental considerations, although they often place one above another (revealing the priorities of those offering the definition). You may not have chosen to spell these out; the breakthrough definition may imply rather than state the range of ambitions of sustainable development, or it may use a pop-philosophy homily to suggest these. Catch phrases like 'eating the seed corn' or the South American 'don't eat tomorrow's potatoes' suggest that you can destroy future security by irresponsibly using up available resources today. In the early 1990s, the British environment minister, John Gummer, ran a competition within his department. He offered a bottle of champagne to anyone who could find a phrase that would strike a chord with the public. His ultimate test was a phrase that might make its way onto a T-shirt: his own offering was 'Don't Cheat On Your Children'. They haven't sold any T-shirts yet, and the champagne bottle is ageing nicely (Figure 6.9).

Figure 6.9 Children learning about renewable energy; by the end of the day they'll know more about sustainability than some of John Gummer's former colleagues.

We described the achievements of the WCED in promoting a vision of sustained, equitable, capitalist development as 'politically deft' above. This is because it skilfully achieved consensus around the insight that economic growth could only continue in the context of environmental protection. This was achieved despite a long history of tensions between the aspirations of less-developed country elites' for development, and developed country civil society's goals of environmental clean-up and protection. But the skill was exercised in creating a consensus document, not in drawing diverse interests to the same way of thinking. The costs of such a compromise are being felt later. The Brundtland report had only served to paper over the cracks; it didn't resolve issues at the heart of the vexed question of what 'good development' really meant. This became evident at the UNCED in Rio in 1992, and in the negotiations and institutions (including the UNFCCC, and ten years on the WSSD in Johannesburg in 2002) that flowed from that meeting.

6.2.2 Some questions that won't go away

Now that we've looked at both the political background and some of the fundamental thinking that underpins the concept of sustainable development, we return to some critical problems that emerged in Chapter 5:

- How can we represent the interests of distant others and future generations in the here-and-now of developed world economic and social life?

- How do we integrate environment and development in the context of everyday debates and decisions?

- How do we represent the non-human natural world in our decisions?

- How do we interpret and decide on conflicting proposals that both claim to be pursuing 'sustainable development'?

Chapter 7 will help to give some depth to your answers to these questions. You should also keep them in mind as you progress through Block 4. However, to conclude this chapter we're going to spend some time looking at the methodology and purpose of sustainable development indicators. These indicators have been developed by international bodies, NGOs, local and national governments with the aim of measuring progress on sustainable development. In effect they are trying to answer the questions laid out above by means of some well-chosen statistics.

6.3 Making sustainability count

'We measure things we value and we value things we measure.'

Whether it's a Ferrari owner glancing down at the speedometer on the dashboard or a heart patient having a check-up, there's no doubt that simple clear measurements play a big role in our lives and our perception of wellbeing. One of the most influential measurements in political and economic life is gross domestic product (GDP). The rapidly growing community of experts concerned with **sustainable development indicators** view GDP as exerting a tyrannical influence over politics, resulting in economics being viewed as an end rather than a means of human existence. Sustainability indicators are intended to find an integrated way of measuring all the things we value: economic, environmental and social. By measuring sustainable development, the authors of indicators hope that politicians, civil servants and the public will come to value it more highly as a social goal. This is achieved in the publication of sets of sustainable development indicators. As you start to look at this set of indicators, you may want to refer back to the simpler indicator 'emissions intensity' in Chapter 4.

The most ambitious attempts at sustainability indicators aim for just one number — an index — that can replace GDP as the be-all-and-end-all of measurements of progress. Indices are aggregate (overall indicator) measures, combining a range of indicators that can serve to summarize the performance of a sector of an economy, a local region or a nation state. GDP aims to tell the story of a complex economic system with just one number. Of course, this can be useful, but at the same time can be deceptive. It all depends on the ingredients and the steps in the recipe: which data were chosen, and how were they handled and presented? Critiques of GDP have been produced by environment and development specialists and campaigners since the 1970s. Some of the most influential alternative indices include the concept of **ecological footprinting** (Rees and Wackernagel, 1994) and the Index of Sustainable Economic Welfare (Daly and Cobb, 1994).

However politically desirable an index of sustainability might be, these approaches have not yet had a significant impact. These exploratory efforts have failed to produce one robust and compelling index of sustainability, although they have moved thinking about sustainability forward. Exponents of such an index argue that its future potential is huge.

Nevertheless, sustainable development, with its demand for integration of environment, development and economy, and its concern with both present and future, global and local, is often considered too complex to capture in a single figure. Hence, experts working in this field have also sought to produce groups of indicators that cover different aspects of the umbrella term 'sustainability'.

○ What is the difference between an index and an indicator, and why is it difficult to find an index of sustainable development?

● An index is an aggregate, or collated, figure that is based on a number of individual indicators; an indicator is a number that relates to one specific aspect of sustainability. The concept of sustainable development is concerned with complex interplays across spatial and temporal scales, and the integration of environment, society and economy. Hence, it is difficult enough to capture movement in a national economy at any one time via GDP, let alone this extremely broad set of issues.

Sustainability indicators have been developed at every layer of decision-making, from local government and sub-national regions, to national, regional (e.g. European) and international levels. In all these cases the indicators are designed to achieve one or both of two objectives: informing strategic decision-making and/or engaging the public imagination. For both these audiences, the authors of sustainability indicators are faced with a balancing act between being true to the complexity of the data they build the indicators on, and reaching out to non-experts with approachable messages. This section aims to introduce you to the purpose and potential of the indicators, and to prepare you to be a critical reader of them.

Box 6.2 What is a 'good' indicator?

It has been said that there's no such thing as a good indicator, just one that does the job it's been given. However, there are some rules of thumb that have been learnt in recent years. The International Institute for Sustainable Development (IISD) has been working with a network of sustainability indicator experts since the mid-1990s with the aim of identifying and promoting best practice, and includes the following in their checklist (remember it as R, R, S, S):

1   *Relevance*   Is the indicator linked to critical decisions and policies, either at individual or global level? If not, it won't catalyse change.

2   *Reliability*   Is the scientific/technical measurement at the root of the indicator sound? Are measurements robust, or do results vary widely according to researcher and technique? Credibility counts; the public are mistrustful of official information.

3   *Simplicity*   Can the target audience pick up the central message quickly and intuitively?

4   *Sensitivity*   Can the indicator detect a small change in the system? Indicators will vary: some will require attention to small changes, and others to large. Can a time-series be constructed for the indicator, reflecting trends over time?

The selection of indicators is a balancing act (Figure 6.10). There are the seeds of contradictions within this checklist, and you should look out for tensions between simplicity and reliability, relevance and sensitivity. You might want to refer back to this list when you look at the current examples on the Web.

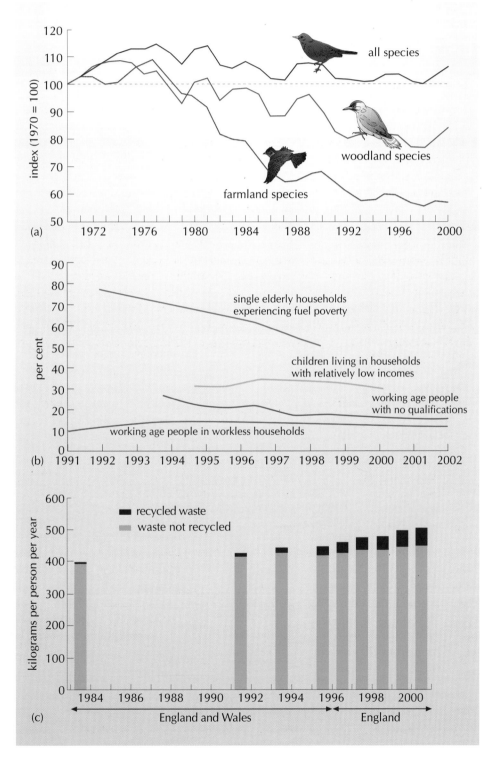

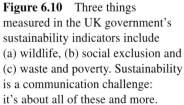

Figure 6.10 Three things measured in the UK government's sustainability indicators include (a) wildlife, (b) social exclusion and (c) waste and poverty. Sustainability is a communication challenge: it's about all of these and more.

199

The list of statistics that you will find recommended in UN and other documents encompasses a huge range. Thus, 'gender inequalities in wage', 'concentration of faecal coliform in freshwater' and 'total overseas development assistance (ODA) given or received as a percent of GNP' all appear in one outline of potential indicators. The list is a sobering reminder of the reach and ambition (or perhaps perplexing messiness) of the concept of sustainable development.

Here are a couple of questions derived from UN guidelines about how to choose sustainability indicators that will help you understand the thinking of the people producing them.

⦿ 'Protected area as a % of total area' tells us something about biodiversity in a country. But what questions would you ask next?

⦿ 'Protected area as a % of total area does give some indication about biodiversity in a country, although its historical land use, and political, social and economic history will result in wide disparities with other countries, even those with very similar climate and vegetation types. However, time-series data will help to tell us whether the rhetorical commitments to biodiversity protection have been backed up by legislative (and practical) change. The existence of a park does not mean that biodiversity is necessarily protected; that will depend on good environmental governance.

⦿ What does the number of Internet subscribers or telephone lines per 1000 inhabitants tell us about sustainable development?

⦿ It is a widely held belief in the policy world that communication and participation are pivotal to progress in sustainable development. Here Internet and telephone access are being used as a proxy for these aspects. Given that personal internet use in the developed world is recognized as being used predominantly for porn, shopping, gaming, sports results, and so on, rather more than the active pursuit of sustainability, this indicator needs to be taken with a pinch of salt. But these measures do give a rough and ready idea of the ease with which people can share information, debate and agree action without having to physically meet. You may want to qualify the aptness of the chosen statistic by noting that some less-developed countries are seeing rapid growth in the use of mobile telephones, which would not register in these figures.

Not for the first time in this course, we want you to think about the ways in which numbers are powerful in environment and sustainability debates. Also, we want to shine a light on the fact that they are rarely 'neutral' and value free. As the old saying goes, history is written by the victors. Indicators are much the same. They are generally written by government. Although the construction of most indicator sets involves extensive consultation with other stakeholders, including NGOs, the funding, research and publication is almost always undertaken by government bodies. The selection, methodology and presentation of sustainability indicators all involve making decisions about what is or isn't important and/or appropriate. As we have aimed to show throughout this chapter, sustainability is not some fixed point that can be mapped and described. Rather it's a concept that is constantly redefined by the many interests that have a stake in it.

Even where physical processes of environmental change are being referred to, the play of politics and values is never far away. The position of the authors of indicators in relation to their funders counts for a great deal: consultants and civil servants working for government will be working to their brief. As you go on to analyse sustainable development, or indeed any other kinds of indicators, keep this simple fact in mind.

Activity 6.4: Pros and cons of sustainability indicators

Summarize the strengths and weaknesses of sustainability indicators as a tool for communication and decision-making. You don't have to restrict yourself to commenting on just one scale of indicator, such as national: you can also make a note of particular strengths and weaknesses of local, regional and international indicator sets if you wish. (Note that you may want to organize your answer with reference to the four features of the indicators checklist on p. 198; the initials 'R, R, S, S' may help you remember them.)

Answer

Everyone's summary of strengths and weaknesses will be slightly different. In our analysis we have made both general comments, such as about the methodological challenges involved, and specific observations, for example about the strengths of local and national indicators.

	Strengths	Weaknesses
Relevance	Helps to catalyse change by making complex interlinked issues vivid for professionals, and progresses the process of 'mainstreaming' sustainable development thinking.	Indicators can be tokenistic for local and national government; ('we are trying to understand the issues fully before we act; the indicators are a measure of our commitment'). Also relatively under resourced.
Reliability	Draws on data from a wide range of established sources.	Methodologies are complex, but can also disguise the mix of quantitative and qualitative assessments.
Simplicity	If you can identify a composite index of sustainability that captures people's imaginations, you have a very powerful political tool in your hands.	Have failed to find space in the media's or the public's imagination.
Sensitivity	Presents opportunities for comparison of progress towards sustainability goals across time and space.	The stories indicators tell can be confusing and/or counterintuitive (how does road building — often an economic good but also often an environmental bad — show in the indicators?)

6.4 Conclusion

Chapter 5 set up some questions: how can the science and policy of climate change be interpreted and acted on within our political and ethical frameworks? Chapter 6 has looked at one of the main responses — that is, the rise to prominence of the concept of sustainable development. It has charted some of the main features of the concept, and gone on to assess the value of sustainability indices and indicators that aim to give some kind of benchmark against which to measure progress. We have moved in this chapter beyond an exclusive concern with climate change, and begun to see how climate change inevitably demands that we look in a holistic way at the inter-relatedness of environment, economy and society (Figure 6.11, overleaf). What we have yet to do is to place the high-minded notion of sustainable development within everyday political and social life. The final chapter in the block places sustainability within the context of globalization, and looks at how new thinking about governance might help us to debate and act on global environmental change problems.

Figure 6.11 An ice sculptor works to draw Londoners' attention to the realities of climate change.

You should now go to the Web and do the activities associated with Chapter 6.

6.5 Summary of Chapter 6

6.1   Climate change marks a distinct change in the way environmental problems are understood. The aggregate of individual actions is now seen to be resulting in physical global environmental changes, as opposed simply to despoliation of the natural world or exhaustion of resources.

6.2   A range of disciplines, including ecology, thermodynamics and environmental economics, have shaped both environmentalism and the concept of sustainable development.

6.3   There are counter arguments to environmentalism that have stood the test of time, having been consistently posed since the early 1970s.

6.4   Climate change and questions about the nature of development are inextricably bound up together. The issue lent force to the concept of sustainable development and brought about a 'second wave' of support for environmentalism. The concept serves as a political compromise between environment and development concerns. Its implementation has proved much harder than defining it.

6.5   Attempts have been made to express progress towards sustainable development in terms of carefully chosen indicators and indices. Though they have not caught the public imagination, they could serve to take environmental concerns into the frame of thinking of mainstream government and business decision-makers.

Learning Outcomes for Chapter 6

When you have completed this chapter, you should be able to:

6.1 Define and use, or recognize definitions and applications of, each of the terms given in **bold** in the text. (Question 6.7)

6.2 Explain the relationship between climate change and the career of the concept of sustainable development. (Questions 6.1, 6.3 and 6.4)

6.3 Briefly outline how the disciplines of ecology, thermodynamics and environmental economics have shaped environmentalism and the concept of sustainable development. (Question 6.2)

6.4 Describe the intended role and basic features of sustainable development indicators. (Questions 6.5 and 6.6)

Questions for Chapter 6

Question 6.1

What influence has the emergence of the issue of climate change had on the career of the concept of sustainable development? Answer in no more than 150 words.

Question 6.2

State three sources of ideas underpinning environmentalism and the concept of sustainable development, and what unites them. Answer in no more than a few sentences.

Question 6.3

Name up to five difficult questions that stand in the background of discussions of sustainable development.

Question 6.4

Give up to five factors that contributed to the 'second wave' of environmentalism in the second half of the 1980s.

Question 6.5

What are the four main features that are proposed as desirable in a 'good' sustainable development indicator (think 'RRSS')? Offer a sentence or so of summary of each one. Are there problems with this list?

Question 6.6

Summarize in around 150 words what you consider to be the main strengths and weaknesses of sustainable development indicators.

Question 6.7

Outline three long-standing critiques of environmentalism.

References

Constanza, R. (ed.) (2001) *Institutions, Ecosystems and Sustainability*. London: Lewis Publishers,

Daly, H. E. (1977) The steady-state economy: What, why and how? In Pirages, D. (ed.) *The Sustainable Society*, New York: Praeger.

Daly, H. E. and Cobb, J. B., Jr. (1990) *For the Common Good. Redirecting the Economy toward Community, the Environment, and a Sustainable Future*. London: Green Print.

International Institute for Sustainable Development (IISD) [online].
Available from: http://iisd.ca/measure [Accessed 28 April 2003]

Pearce, D. W. (1993) *Blueprint 3: Measuring Sustainable Development*. London: Earthscan.

Rees, W. E. and Wackernagel, M. (1994) Ecological footprints and appropriated carrying capacity: Measuring the natural capital requirements of the human economy. In Jansson, A. et al. (eds), *Investing in Natural Capital: The Ecological Economics Approach to Sustainability*, Washington DC: Island Press.

World Commission on Environment and Development (1987) *Our Common Future*. Oxford: Oxford University Press.

Chapter 7 Changing the world

Prepared for the course team by Joe Smith

7.1 Introduction

Human societies have to take urgent action to end their dependence on fossil fuels (Figure 7.1). They also have to prepare to adapt to the uncertainties inherent in global environmental changes, particularly climatic ones (Figure 7.2). These are two of the most striking conclusions from the early chapters of this book. Blocks 1–3 all point to a simple conclusion: we have to alter the whole path of our development and decision-making in order to make our societies both environmentally adaptable and sustainable. This chapter takes on the task of trying to chart some of the ways in which this might come about.

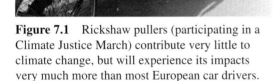

Figure 7.1 Rickshaw pullers (participating in a Climate Justice March) contribute very little to climate change, but will experience its impacts very much more than most European car drivers.

Figure 7.2 The aftermath of torrential rain in Tenerife. A rare act of God — or by-product of fossil-fuelled development that is an indicator of things to come?

Section 7.1 sets the context for these changes by going further into what the term 'globalization' means in the context of environment and sustainability. It introduces three different views on the relationship between globalization and the environment. Each of these views is an argument about how we might get out of the mess we appear to be in. The following section asks how our decision-making can advance sustainability to make our societies more adaptable to environmental change. It looks at the chances of achieving both accountable global governance and grassroots participation. The final brief section has three parts. It takes the three views outlined at the beginning of the chapter and looks at cases and arguments to see how each see sustainability being arrived at. The conclusion will tie some of the threads of the chapter together by reflecting on the importance of the media, and specifically web media, as a key location for moving forward debates about sustainability.

4   *Ecological*   Global movements of species, specifically in tandem with globalizing human activities of development, trade and tourism. Publicity about global *flows* of pollutants in the 1960s and 1970s drove many to support environmentalism. More recently, ozone depletion and climate change represent perhaps the most dramatic evidence of globalized and linked processes of environmental change.

  How have the inventions shown in Figure 7.4 assisted globalization?

(a)

(b)

Figure 7.4   How are technology and globalization linked?
(a) goods container terminal;
(b) laptop with webpage.

  Containers helped to accelerate economic globalization from the mid-1970s onwards, reducing costs and speeding up haulage of goods (in turn, having huge environmental consequences in the form of increased road freight). Communications technologies have reduced or eliminated constraints of time and space on human interactions, feeding cultural and political globalizations.

  What is meant by the words 'flow' and 'network' here?

  Flows are the movements of goods, people, cultural objects and ideas, and information across space and time. 'Networks' in this context refer to patterns of interaction between independent people, places or institutions.

7.2.2 Globalization and the global environment: three views

Not for the first time in this course, you are faced with a term that is important, but difficult to define precisely. Although the fact that plenty of people from different standpoints are making use of the term is some measure of its importance, it can be confusing to find that there are different ways of framing what it means for humans and the environment today and in the future. In this section, we've organized the range of political responses to climate change and environment–economy interactions more generally under three headings: *business learns, radical break* and *sustainability steps*. It's a bit easier to think about what the terms mean if you begin to give them a personality. Three good examples are shown in Figure 7.5.

(a)   (b)   (c)

Figure 7.5 Three different takes on sustainability: how far apart are they? (a) 'green' businessman Ray Anderson; (b) ecologist and campaigner Vandana Shiva; (c) environmentalist and adviser Jonathan Porritt.

Table 7.1 Economics, politics and environment: three perspectives

	Business learns	*Radical break*	*Sustainability steps*
What will the future bring?	A global free market dominates. (Figure 7.6).	US corporations are the core of a global empire.	Societies can shape the course of development
What happens to nation states?	Declining throughout the world.	Expanding powers (developed) and declining (less-developed countries).	Reconfiguration of state power throughout the world.
What future for rich and poor countries?	Erosion of global differences: fast growing markets (and middle classes) in previously poorer countries.	Increasing misery and marginalization of most in less-developed countries: wealth for a few.	Erosion of distinctions between developed and less-developed countries; middle classes grow globally, though pockets of poverty remain in rich countries.
How do they respond to global environmental threats?	Voluntary business agreements; corporate social and environmental responsibility; carbon trading; but risks worth taking.	Reinvent the state to rein in capital; tax environmental harm not work; locally based economies (localization); precautionary approach to technology.	Global governance and local participation; partnerships between stakeholders; measuring sustainability claims; balance risk and progress.

Who should we have in mind when we think of these three categories? For *business learns*, think of the sharp-suited business people working for one of the major oil, computing, car or food companies. These have grown from being national concerns (albeit often with an international reach) to immense bodies globally networked, often with revenues larger than many less-developed countries and a power in politics that, though difficult to measure, can influence the thinking of the world's most powerful democratically elected governments.

Box 7.1 What is a nation state?

There are a few essential features of most nation states:

- They have territorially defined populations who recognize their government.
- The state is served by a specialized civil service (backed on occasions by a military service).
- The state is recognized by other states as independent in its power over its subjects. In other words, it has **sovereignty**. This power is expressed through, among other things, a body of legal regulation, but laws also act as guarantees of the rights of a state's citizens in relation to the state and each other.
- Ideally, and often in practice, the population of the state forms a community of feeling or identity based on its own sense of national identity.
- Members of a nation state are citizens; they are not purely subject to, but also participate in, processes of government. They also take part in sharing the responsibilities and benefits associated with membership of the nation state.
- Important features of social interaction, particularly the economy and family life, are viewed as beyond the direct control of the state and its institutions.

(adapted from Bromley, 2001)

Activity 7.2: Climate politics from the top of the tree to grassroots

In this activity, try to combine three things: what you know about climate change from studying previous chapters in this book; what you've learnt about globalization in the last section, and the summary of what constitutes a nation state in Box 7.1. With a short paragraph for each, go through the six questions below, each of which is based on the points in Box 7.1, and note down your thoughts as you consider the unfolding politics of climate change. The activity will help you to think about the changing roles of different players — notably the nation state — in shaping outcomes in environmental politics.

1   How well can national politicians represent global climate change issues in their day-to-day work as democratic representatives?

2   Which interests are national civil servants working on climate change seeking to serve?

3   How does the concept of 'sovereignty' influence climate-change politics at an international level?

4   In what ways might the 'community of feeling' in the US shape negotiations?

5   How can citizen participation in climate debates influence intergovernmental talks?

6   What influence can the state's climate policies really have on the economy or households?

Comment

1   With difficulty! Climate change demands action globally, but in most democratic states a government's actions will be debated and are subjected to its people's scrutiny through elections. Global interests, such as integrating the true costs of burning fossil fuels into fuel prices, are often undermined by politicians seeking to outbid each other in guessing the short-term interests of their electorates. The United Nations struggles to win commitments to collective action by its constituent nation states.

2   Civil servants who negotiate climate change and plan actions within countries are trained to seek out and represent the best outcomes for their nation state; altruism (benefiting another state, perhaps to the cost of your own) is not just unlikely in this context; it might be seen as unprofessional. American and Australian climate-change negotiators have a responsibility to their state long before any responsibility to United Nations processes, whatever their personal view may be.

3   The concept of sovereignty ensures that nation states cannot generally be coerced into a course of action by other states, particularly for climate-change issues. In climate-change negotiations this means that some states (most prominently the United States) can reject an agreement that has been arrived at by the great majority of other nation states by referring to its own sovereignty. But the concept of sovereignty is not static: the European Union has acted as a unified party in climate-change negotiations. Most interpret this as nation states pooling some of their sovereignty to allow more efficient decision-making and to give the EU as a whole a stronger collective voice in negotiations.

4   The community of feeling or identity of the United States is strongly bound to a notion of individual freedoms. In the late 20th and early 21st centuries, these were expressed (some would say distorted) in a general pattern of energy-intensive lifestyles (large cars, frequent air travel, energy-hungry appliances, etc.). European societies have followed a similar route, though they have not reached the same intensity of resource use. Although they would rarely put it in these words, many NGOs and commentators are absorbed by the question of whether a high-consumption lifestyle can be divorced from a sense of quality of life and self-worth.

5   Citizen pressure, in the form of NGO activity, individual letter writing and other lobbying processes, and individual actions to reduce the environmental impacts of households and communities, add up to significant pressure on the state. The presence of strong citizen voices demanding action on climate-change complemented messages coming from the science community to pressurize governments into international talks on the issue in the 1990s. By contrast, there are also examples of citizens organizing to campaign against environmental policies, for example against energy tax rises.

6   One of the great challenges of climate-change politics is that a global problem that is the result of millions of local actions requires that international agreements can result, through the actions of individual nation states, in changes in the behaviours of local economies and households. Not only are such chains of cause and effect very difficult to predict and influence, but they can stir up strong resentment and opposition, such as the fuel price protests mentioned at the end of point 5.

The failure of the state to deal effectively with old problems, and its inability to respond to new challenges, above all globalization and emergent global environmental change, has seen political scientists tear up their textbooks and start again.

They have had to acknowledge that their linear models of central decision-making by formalized institutions — whereby policies are generated and implemented in a top-down manner — don't represent the reality of contemporary politics. Similarly, political, business and NGO figures find that the word 'government' captures neither reality nor their ambitions for new ways of debating and resolving questions. It is in this context that the loose and open term 'governance' has become so quickly and widely popular.

What's the difference between government and governance?

Governance, from the Greek words *kybenan* and *kybernetes*, meaning 'to steer' and 'pilot' or 'helmsman' is the process whereby 'an organization or society steers itself, and the dynamics of communication and control are central to the process' (Rosenau and Durfee, 1995, p. 14). Of course, you could read these words as a pretty sound definition of government. But that would be to miss the point. *Government* describes a more rigid and narrower set of activities among a narrower set of participants (usually civil servants, elected politicians and some influential or privileged interests). The word 'governance' has been used throughout the course because it is a better fit for the global environmental change issues we've been addressing. It has spread like wildfire through debates on a range of issues, but particularly around environment and development issues, because it acknowledges that there is a range of institutions, rules and participants, both within and beyond the nation state, who are involved in taking decisions. This is happening both at national and international levels, but also in innovative new forms of organization that cut across government boundaries.

The state is seen as having progressively lost its monopoly over the control of citizens and regulation of business and other institutions. It is still a player, but commentators have to take into account a range of other paticipants and scales. Political scientists are having to think in terms of webs or networks of governance. They have to think of these as being both horizontal and vertical, and as representing new ways of distributing the business of managing societies' concerns across local, national, regional and international scales. Involvement of a wider circle of stakeholders is seen as central.

Although this is true of all discussions of new patterns of governance, it has been particularly true of environmental governance. This is probably best demonstrated by the gradual emergence of environmental and social NGOs as major players in international negotiations, such as around climate change. They can claim to represent a global movement, yet can also draw on very local voices as 'witnesses' to environmental problems. They can also keep watch on individual national delegations to underpin their commitment to action. Increasingly, there are instances of NGO representatives being invited to join national delegations, both to represent environmentalist strands within civil society, but also on account of their expert knowledge of the negotiation processes. Another set of stakeholders known as QUANGOs (quasi non-governmental organizations) has taken on roles that might previously have been associated with government, such as the Environment Agency in the UK.

Table 7.2 The distinctions charted thus far between government and governance

Government	Governance
clearly defined participants linked to the state	mixes state and non-state participants (including e.g. NGOs)
linear model	network model
top down	multi-layer
formal institutions and procedures	evolving and ongoing processes
simple and intuitive representation of citizens through election	power is dispersed/opaque
domination through rules or force may be required to ensure universal acceptance of a decision	acceptance of and support for decisions by all players arises out of wide participation in earlier debate

Good green governance in five easy steps...

It would be a serious error to imagine that 'government' has evaporated: it still shapes many aspects of our lives from beginning to end (welfare, taxation, transport — and, of course, the recording of births and deaths). Governments are the central negotiators of environmental-change policies at international level, and of their implementation at national and local level. Nevertheless, there is no denying that, for many areas of life, governance is a better description both of new processes that are already in play and also of ambitions for the shape that decision-making should take in the future. In other words, although the term is both descriptive of new patterns of decision-making it is also prescriptive. This is perhaps truer of environmental decision-making than anything else. Perhaps we shouldn't be surprised at this: new thinking about governance appeared at the same time as global environmental change issues and economic globalization.

Any of the rash of documents that promote good governance tend to make very similar demands, and are likely to include the following (use the acronym OPASI taken from the initial letters to help you remember them).

1   *Openness*   Accessible and understandable language that can reach the general public and improve confidence in complex institutions.

2   *Participation*   'Quality, relevance and effectiveness' depend on wide participation throughout the policy chain. Effective participation demands an inclusive approach from all layers of government when developing and implementing policy.

3   *Accountability*   Legislative (scrutiny and passing of laws and policies) and executive (initiating and executing policies) responsibilities and powers need to be clearly separate.

4   *Subsidiarity*   Taking decisions at the most appropriate level.

5   *Integration*   Policies and actions need to be effective — that is, timely and answering clear objectives, and based on evaluation of future impact (and where possible, relevant precedents). They must have coherence — that is, be easily understood, and hang together in sensible ways.

In Table 7.3 these five features are tabulated against the four main (interacting) levels of governance, concentrating on dimensions relevant to advancing sustainability.

● Why might the precautionary principle or carbon taxes be seen as examples of policies that could be seen as based in a 'non-reciprocal' sense of justice, or compassion?

● These policies could be seen as reflecting a 'bedding down' of non-reciprocal obligations to the future and the non-human natural world. We are bound by these obligations, but this isn't like the deal that was struck when Western European countries set up welfare states, where welfare and economic security were exchanged for strike-free labour relations and social stability. They are, therefore, 'non-reciprocal'.

Home-grown compassion, not public commitments

It has long been held that we conduct all citizenship, and the obligations it implies, in the public sphere (that is, outside the private sphere of the home). However, it has been argued that there are other potential sources of obligation. Andrew Dobson argues that the principal duties of the ecological citizen are to act with care and compassion to strangers, both human and non-human — not just in the present, but also those distant in space and time (Dobson, 2000). These virtues of care and compassion are experienced, nurtured and taught not in public spaces — the established domain of citizenship — but in the private sphere (in other words the family and the home).

Do these features contrast ecological citizenship so sharply with established definitions of citizenship that they shouldn't be considered in the same category? Civic rights enshrined in law are transparent; it is not difficult to see when they are being denied. However, notions such as care and compassion are much more difficult to translate into the language that law makers and civil servants are comfortable with. These notions are clearly part of how many environmentalists would explain their actions, and these are clearly features of the private rather than the public sphere. It remains a big leap for most political philosophers to see these as aspects of citizenship.

● You might think, 'What's the practical use of all these language games? Climate change and biodiversity loss need action not philosophical talk.' or 'Why might political philosophy be as important as measurements of global mean surface temperature in thinking through action on climate change?'

● Although it's true that a global withdrawal of labour by political philosophers wouldn't lead to a food shortage, or result in hazards or misfortune, it is important to recognize that if we want to make good decisions in difficult circumstances we need our thinking to be very sharp. We will need to think hard about what feelings and arguments might be available to underpin action. These are some of the things that philosophical debates can help us to do.

Ecological citizenship is just one way of thinking about peoples' motivations as you go further in exploring the new kinds of politics surrounding sustainability. We've presented it here not as a line of thinking we wish to promote, but as an example of the sort of philosophical territory that conclusions from science and policy knowledge of global environmental change may be pointing us towards. The question that now needs answering is: can all the talk about green governance and ecological citizenship be turned into meaningful action? Can we act fast enough to reduce human impacts on the global environment to a sustainable level? The last section in the block takes up this challenge.

You should now go to the Web and do the activities associated with this part of Chapter 7.

7.4 Making it happen — sustainability in practice

How many ordinary people know that sustainability is the concept that's meant to save the world? How many people who believe in the concept are convinced that it can capture the public imagination? The answer to both questions is 'not many'. It is an easy charge to lay that the idea has been much talked about in some closed circles, but has no purchase on the public imagination and is little practised. This section takes the three different approaches to global environmental change presented in Section 7.1, and offers examples of how their visions have been put into practice. These are intended as no more than sketches that you will combine with web resources linked to this section. By the end of the block, you will be in a good position to weigh up the claims of the different camps to have found routes to sustainability.

7.4.1 Capitalism — naturally

Business can learn to integrate ecological thinking into the core of its thinking and become the hub of a sustainable society. This is the claim of the *business learns* position. As environmentalists have spent over thirty years portraying business as the arch villain of the piece, this is a grand claim! One of the people who have stated it most clearly in recent years is Ray Anderson, head of the US carpet giant Interface (Figure 7.5a). Here is the story of a dramatic conversion to a different way of thinking about business and the natural world.

Ray's story: 'doing well by doing good'

Ray Anderson was in the business of selling vast amounts of carpet around the world. He had no regard for the environment, beyond recognizing the obligation to 'comply, comply, comply' with regulations. The company was a heavy user of petrochemicals, and once the products left the factory gate the company wouldn't see them again; their last home would be landfill. One day in 1994 he was asked to talk to a group of his executives about the company's environmental vision. He realized they didn't have one, and he chanced on a book called *The Ecology of Commerce*, by Paul Hawken (1995). The book transformed the way he thought about the whole business world:

> While business is part of the problem; it can also be a part of the solution.
> Business is the largest, wealthiest, most pervasive institution on Earth, and
> responsible for most of the damage. It must take the lead in directing the
> Earth away from collapse, and toward sustainability and restoration…

> I believe we have come to the threshold of the next industrial revolution. At Interface,
> we seek to become the first sustainable corporation in the world, and, following that,
> the first restorative company. It means creating the technologies of the future — kinder,
> gentler technologies that emulate nature's systems. I believe that's where we will find
> the right model. Ultimately, I believe we must learn to depend solely on available
> income the way a forest does, not on our precious stores of natural capital. Linear
> practices must be replaced by cyclical ones. That's nature's way… We look forward to
> the day when our factories have no smokestacks and no effluents. If successful, we'll
> spend the rest of our days harvesting yesteryear's carpets, recycling old petrochemicals
> into new materials, and converting sunlight into energy. There will be zero scrap going
> into landfills and zero emissions into the biosphere. Literally, our company will grow
> by cleaning up the world, not by polluting or degrading it. We'll be doing well by
> doing good. That's the vision. Is it a dream? Certainly, but it is a dream we share with
> our 7,500 associates, our vendors, and our customers. Everyone will have to dream this
> dream to make it a reality, but until then, we are committed to leading the way.

Ray C. Anderson, Chairman, Interface, Inc.

Figure 7.12 Energy and materials use, waste and processes have all been rethought to meet Interface carpets' sustainability goals.

The company has been applying **life cycle analysis** (LCA) to 'close the loop' of its resource impacts through efficiencies and cutting pollution (Figure 7.12). Perhaps most interesting is the new way it started to think about the business's relationship with customers. It seeks to supply service and value rather than material goods. For example, the company leases floor coverings, replacing only those carpet tiles that wear (and recycling those). The result can be reduced environmental impact, satisfied customers and competitive advantage. But they're still a carpet company, turning a profit, with 7500 employees working in 34 countries.

The company makes some grand claims, but its corporate reporting addresses sustainability. Indeed it claims to have produced the first corporate sustainability report, and followed this up with a dedicated sustainability website. The data in Box 7.2 are drawn from it.

Box 7.2 Interface sustainability preformance

Interface can certainly talk the talk, but it is clear measurable evidence that counts. The evidence in some key aspects of environmental impact show meaningful progress. Here is some evidence drawn from their sustainability reporting web pages:

Waste elimination activities
Interface began its journey to sustainability by focusing on the elimination of waste. It measures its waste in a 'dollar value' — something that helps attract the interest and commitment of employees (especially the all-important financial directors) and investors alike. By looking hard at trims and scraps, overuse of raw materials, inventory losses and/or labour to re-inspect or correct a defective product, they claim cumulative savings since 1995 of over $185 million.

Energy
Another of the company's sustainability indicators is the source and quantity of energy they buy. They aim to: (1) decrease use of non-renewable energy by increasing the efficiency of processes, and (2) increase use of green/renewable energy. The goal is less dependence on fossil fuels, and hence reduced greenhouse gas emissions. Interface has reduced its non-renewable process energy by over 18% since 1996.

Renewable energy in their plants takes the form of biomass (waste woodchip from a local company) and generation and purchasing of green electricity (three Interface sites use photovoltaic arrays and four buy certified green electricity). Their long-term strategy is to increase both efficiency and use of renewable energy.

Water consumption
For a textiles firm, the nature and quantity of water use is an important measure of environmental impact. Since 1996, Interface has decreased its average water consumption per unit of product by 26% through water conservation efforts and rethinking manufacturing processes (such as re-using dyebath water, and redesigning or scrapping certain printing processes).

Reducing petroleum-based raw materials
Through the use of renewable energy, re-materialization (replacing petroleum-based materials with non petroleum-based materials), and de-materialization (creating products with less 'stuff'), they have reduced use of petroleum-based materials by more than 33% since 1994.

Even the brief account of the Interface story in Box 7.2 sketches out some of the central messages of the business learns position:

Eco-efficiency = money in the bank

Business can profit from taking the environment into account (generally known as **eco-efficiency**). Poor environmental performance is seen as a reflection of poor business practice in general. Eco-efficiency promotes the economic benefits of energy and materials savings, at the same time being first to market with new technologies or products. Since business sustainability lobbies promoted eco-efficiency in the early 1990s the creed has gained rapid acceptance, and with good cause. Eco-efficiency success stories are numerous: it has become something of an orthodoxy among global companies. Some commentators have pointed to fourfold increases in efficiency that could easily be achieved by businesses drawing on current and proven technologies (von Weizsäcker *et al.*, 1997). The same authors go further to argue that the true state of environmental problems demands closer to a factor of ten improvement. There are numerous sources of credible eco-modernization case studies and data. You might start by looking at the work of the World Business Council for Sustainable Development (WBCSD) on the Web.

Business needs sustainability

The second argument is more profound: long-term profitability, and the existence of business itself, is threatened if companies can't transform themselves. This assumes that although the costs of environmental and social impacts can be ignored for a period, in the context of globalization of environmental, social and political processes, they will come back to haunt businesses, and ultimately threaten their survival. There are a number of communications and management tools that have been developed to help get business decision-makers into an ecological mindset.

The success of a business is generally measured in reports of financial performance. This information is enormously influential in shaping a company's future, whether it relates to its capacity to expand or the likelihood of merger or takeover. However, financial results are increasingly recognized to be only part of the story: businesses that don't put in place means of measuring and benchmarking (comparing performance against that of other companies) environmental and social performance are at risk. NGOs might destroy a carefully nurtured brand name in the wake of exposure of an environmental or social 'crime'. Alternatively, the fast-growing movement for socially responsible investment may begin asking awkward questions, damaging investment potential. Pressure from NGOs, the persistence of corporate accountability scandals and, more positively, some fresh thinking from leading figures within the business world, have resulted in widespread innovations in reporting.

The Web is an excellent source both of individual company reports (variously called environmental, sustainability or corporate social reports) and comparative indices that aim to tell the story of all three dimensions of sustainability — social, environmental and economic. Companies such as Shell, BP and Monsanto, with a track record in the 1990s of damaging public conflicts with NGOs, have been among the leaders of innovation in sustainability reporting, and the Web is often the best way to access the information, and also to interact with the companies about it (Figure 7.13). Openness, both within and outside companies has become a central claim of business reporting in these areas.

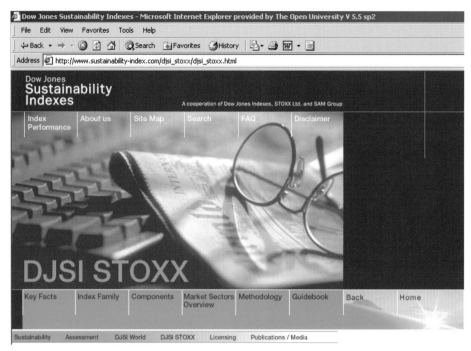

Figure 7.13 Some claim this kind of information published on the Web has the power to make business sustainable.

The Dow Jones Sustainability Indexes (2002) offer comparative evidence about corporate performance, measured according to easily accessible sustainability criteria such as the nature of corporate governance, measurements of environmental performance and the quality of engagement with external stakeholders. However, many environmentalists argue that business performance on social and environmental issues is starting from such a pitifully low baseline that such information exercises are of little value unless they are contributing to a dramatic rethinking of what core business practice amounts to. They insist that relying on business voluntarism may result in one or two heart-warming stories, but will still leave most locked in the old way of doing things. Groups of independent-minded radicals have not waited for business or government action, but instead sought over the last three decades to blaze their own trail.

7.4.2 Green from the grassroots up

Those demanding a radical break with the business-dominated path of economic globalization believe that the claims of the mainstream business community are at best hopelessly inadequate, and at worst deceitful. However, they know they have to come up with some answers of their own. This section outlines ideas that seek to underpin a transition to green economies owned and run at grassroots level. Ambitious? Box 7.3 looks at Findhorn, a groundbreaking community that started out on a windswept caravan park in Scotland.

You can get a fuller picture of how these components contribute to their definition of sustainability by drawing on the plentiful web resources produced by what used to be known as communes, but are now referred to as 'intentional communities'.

Of course, Findhorn is a very special place, although there are others like it, and it's not easy to imagine urban Britain turning to this way of life in a big way. But it is illustrative of a movement of experimentation at local level that is throwing up some ideas that could be scaled up to help make whole societies more sustainable.

Box 7.3   The Findhorn ecovillage — a sustainable future?

More than thirty years ago an unemployed couple tried to start growing vegetables on a very unpromising sandy plot on a caravan site on the coast of Scotland. A powerful founding myth of today's Findhorn community (Figure 7.14) is that their garden grew prodigiously — gathering stunned horticulturalists to the scene. In time, a community grew there too, now numbering 400 people, with a further 4000 people visiting annually for retreats and courses.

Figure 7.14   Grassroots decision-making is central to the way communities such as Findhorn function.

Findhorn has become one of the best known of a global network of ecovillages. An ecovillage is a small community of between 50 and 2000 people, based on shared ecological, social and/or spiritual values. Working on the principle of not taking more from the Earth than one gives back, ecovillages aim to be sustainable — indefinitely. The ecovillage is a response to the complex problem of how to turn human settlements, be they villages, towns or cities, into sustainable communities, and to integrate them into the natural environment. The Ecovillage Project at the Findhorn Foundation aims to be a synthesis of the best current thinking on human habitats. Quality of life, cooperation and co-creation with nature are some of the driving principals. They suggest that ecovillage principles can be applied to both rural and urban settings, to developed and less-developed countries. These principles are put into action through a commitment to some or all of:

- ecological building;
- renewable energy systems;
- local organic food production;
- sustainable economics based around local businesses;
- social and family support within the community.

It may be a mistake to think of the arguments of those promoting a radical break with globalizing capitalism as being a diametrically opposed alternative. Rather, the ideas the radicals have been generating may be a laboratory of raw but inspiring ideas that have worked in a few specific places. Some of these may be adapted and applied by mainstream policy communities in 'the world as it is'. Nevertheless, many have felt the need to work harder to connect radical ideas to real world settings; to engage in some uncomfortable bargains that might deliver at least some progress in the near term.

7.4.3 Getting everyone signed up to sustainability

Those proposing step-by-step progress towards sustainability would include in their plans many of the ideas proposed in the previous two subsections. However, what distinguishes this group is that they stand in the middle of the scale between faith in unfettered business voluntarism and a conviction that radical transformations are required. Their incrementalism is reflected in the kinds of pragmatic solutions they propose; their radicalism shows itself in the way they think about new roles and processes being taken up by all key stakeholders.

Partnerships for sustainable consumption

Moderate NGOs, progressive business and government all have a stake in seeing round-table partnerships come up with practical steps that can bring sustainability closer. One area that has attracted the attention of all these players is consumption. Directing or limiting consumption is politically difficult for even the NGOs to promote. Similarly, 'voluntary simplicity' of the sort lived at Findhorn is not something that mainstream business is going to support. Hence sustainable consumption is an obvious goal around which these partners can gather. Two prominent examples are the Forest Stewardship Council, FSC (Box 7.4) and the Marine Stewardship Council, MSC, both examples of attempts to create sustainable supply chains of raw materials that are subject to intense and unsustainable exploitation.

What might the geographical spread of FSC certification tell us about governance of forestry? Contrast Europe with Africa.

Looking at Figure 7.18, there appear to be wide differences between European and African percentages of certified forestry. A combination of factors may be at play:

- European civil society and government are demanding sustainable forestry practices; management systems in the EU exist in an increasingly tight environmental regulation context;

- governance of African forestry supply chains may make it more difficult to achieve certification;

- some of the initial promoters of the FSC approach may be EU based.

Careful research would be required to know what precisely the reasons are, but the information in Figure 7.18 is a good starting point.

Box 7.4 Forest Stewardship Council—a partnership for the future of forests

The Forest Stewardship Council (Figure 7.17) is an international non-profit organization founded in 1993 to support environmentally appropriate, socially beneficial, and economically viable management of the world's forests. With offices in Mexico and Germany, it is an association of members including environmental and social NGOs, the timber trade and the forestry profession, indigenous people's organizations, community forestry groups, and forest product cert-ification organizations from around the world.

Forest Certification is a way of assessing and badging claims to have put sustainable forestry in place. Operations are assessed against a predetermined set of standards. The FSC's standards aim to establish a global baseline to aid the development of region-specific forest-management standards. Independent certification bodies, accredited by the FSC in the application of these standards, conduct impartial detailed assessments of forest operations at the request of landowners. If the forest operations are found to be in conformance with FSC standards, a certificate is issued, enabling the landowner to bring product to market as 'certified wood', and to use the FSC trademark logo.

Chain of custody is the process by which the source of a timber product is verified. To carry the FSC trademark, a timber has to be independently tracked from the forest, through all the steps of the production process, until it reaches the end user. By mid-2002 there were more than 1500 FSC-endorsed Chain of Custody (COC) certificates in the world. In the space of five years, there was a fivefold increase in the area of FSC forest (Figures 7.18 and 7.19).

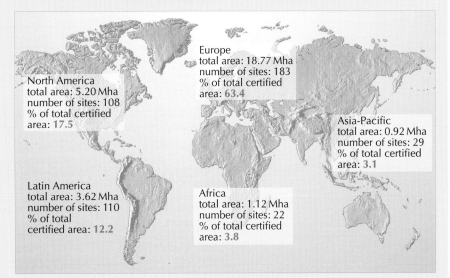

Figure 7.17 The Forest Stewardship Council (FSC) logo asks the sustain-ability question all the way along the supply chain.

Figure 7.18 Certified forest sites endorsed by FSC, August 2002.

Europe
total area: 18.77 Mha
number of sites: 183
% of total certified
area: **63.4**

North America
total area: 5.20 Mha
number of sites: 108
% of total certified
area: **17.5**

Asia-Pacific
total area: 0.92 Mha
number of sites: 29
% of total certified
area: **3.1**

Latin America
total area: 3.62 Mha
number of sites: 110
% of total
certified area: **12.2**

Africa
total area: 1.12 Mha
number of sites: 22
% of total certified
area: **3.8**

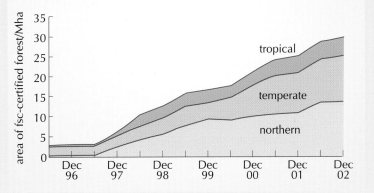

Figure 7.19 Rate of increase of FSC-certified forest (in million hectares) over time (December 1996–December 2002).

The FSC is a compelling and exciting case, but remains a rare one. For sustainability steps to be a convincing way forward, there need to be ways of scaling up the occasional success story and to make them mainstream.

One way of increasing the number of cases like the FSC is to communicate about successes and provide information about how to introduce sustainability. The Web has reduced — almost eliminated — barriers of space and time that used to limit communication. This, allied to more flexible patterns of governance, such as the inclusion of all stakeholders in decision-making, is seen as a key tool in accelerating the shift to a sustainable society. 'Best Practice Databases' are one of the most visible means of promoting success (Figure 7.20).

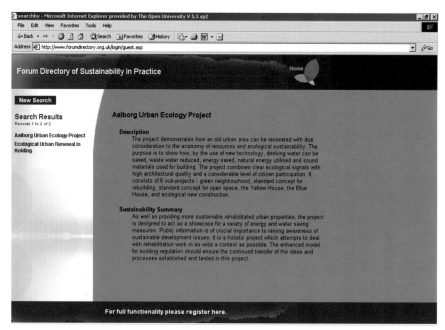

Figure 7.20 'Best Practice databases' disseminate sustainability success (Forum for the Future, 2002).

If you put together enlightened business, concerned and often organized civil society, and a communications system of the like the world has never seen before, you can expect some progress. However, it is widely felt that this progress will remain marginal, and unsustainability will continue as the norm unless government becomes involved, and starts to give some regulatory shape to sustainability principles.

Activity 7.5: Which path to sustainability?

This activity invites you to assess the usefulness and viability of the three different approaches to achieving sustainability outlined in this section. To do this we want you to ask yourself the following questions and make notes on your answers:

1   With which of the three positions do you most identify?

2   Do you find that the examples offered in this section convince you that societies can adapt to environmental change and become sustainable?

3   Are they exclusive alternatives, or can they be combined?

Comment

Here are some of our thoughts.

1 You may conclude 'all of them and none'. Business can deliver creative solutions to problems, and a capitalist economic system can offer the means of replicating them quickly. But such best practice won't be universalized without external pressure from government and civil society. There is no evidence of widespread preparedness for a shift to 'intentional communities', or a locally based alternative to economic globalization, but society at large can benefit from their hard thinking about what quality of life really means. Of course, stepwise progress towards sustainability appears to be the 'reasonable middle ground' but that is precisely its problem. It is just a little too well reasoned and sensible to grab people's attention at a time when people are taken up with trying to meet their immediate needs and wants.

2 Interface, the Findhorn Foundation and the Forest Stewardship Council are impressive and exciting. In different ways and for different audiences they represent pathfinders for society. But they are very much exceptions.

3 Taken as a messy interconnected whole, these begin to offer some sources of hope. However, it would be a mistake to hold your breath waiting for single answers to global environmental change issues to appear fully formed.

7.5 Conclusion — the increasingly World Wide Web

We have here a variety of new approaches or terms that are interlinked, and have been prominent throughout the course. All of them have played a part in this block's journey through the scientific, political, philosophical and social implications of climate change.

Governance of climate change is about: decision-making under *uncertainty*; understanding and representing vulnerability even when vulnerabilities are difficult to assess or unknowable, and making every aspect of human activity *sustainable* within the context of economic, socio-cultural, political and environmental *globalization.*

One of the things this course has sought to do is to equip you to explore these themes and the connections between them using the uniquely rich, but also problematic, medium of the Web (Figure 7.21). Sustainable development and the Web grew up together. However, it is not just this accident of timing that makes them such close relations. Consider some of the things that are often claimed for the Web. It:

- Plays a role in spreading values globally, and aids development of global civil society — for example, via NGO transboundary organization.
- Promotes transparency — data and argument can be published regularly and in full, reducing the possibility of manipulation.
- Reduces hierarchy, which facilitates working in small teams.
- Is inclusive in terms of breaking down obstacles of distance.

Figure 7.21 A secondary school computer lesson, Zimbabwe. The Web is opening up new flows of information and debate — key components of sustainable development.

If the relatively obscure groupings of policy experts, NGOs and intellectuals who were talking about sustainability in the late 1980s had listed some of the features of a communications environment that progress towards a sustainable world would require, it's a fair guess that this is what their list would have looked like. These features of the Web could enable ideas and decisions about making progress towards sustainability to be quickly and widely agreed and disseminated. In your main web activity for this part of the course, you will train as an environmental web journalist, and write your own story based on web sources. It is an opportunity for you to judge the value of the Web as a place where information and progress can be communicated, claims can be scrutinized and civil society can organize.

Activity 7.6: Changing the world with the Web

Study the e-mail in Figure 7.22. It was sent by the World Wide Fund for Nature (WWF) to a supporter who holds their 'Panda Passport'. The Panda is the WWF logo, and the 'passport' is a scheme that supporters can sign up to on the group's website, wherein they are sent news and campaigning opportunities. This one is about fisheries issues and refers to what it claims to be the 'world's first virtual demonstration' (a fisherman's tale maybe…). Note down some of the ways it uses the web to inform, engage and activate support and pursue campaign goals.

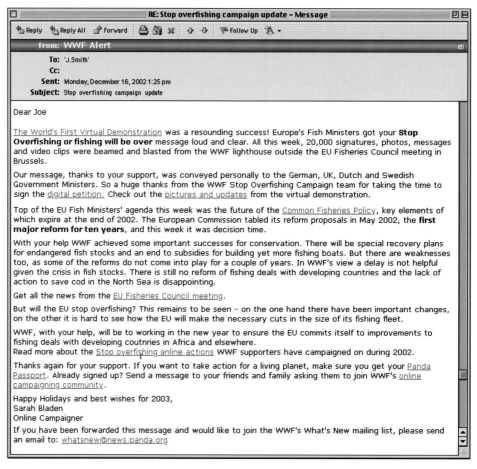

Figure 7.22 A 'Panda Passport' email. An example of creative and integrated use of e-mail and the Web by a major environmental group.

Comment

The e-mail communicates some news to a targeted group concisely, speedily and cheaply. But it does a great deal more than that. The embedded links to websites allow supporters to go and seek more in-depth background, campaign photos and news, or to get involved in further actions (both virtual and real). It holds the potential to develop some kind of virtual campaigning community.

Taking in the whole

The unfolding awareness of human societies' hazardous impacts on environmental systems really turns up the heat on questions about the future. Climate science suggests that those systems on which we all rely are subject to dramatic changes. This simple fact may increasingly serve to motivate a whole range of players to bring about change on the kind of scale that the problems appear to demand. The last section pointed to evidence of:

- a 'new industrial revolution';
- a demanding and proactive civil society;
- intelligent, consensual approaches to bringing these forces together.

There seems enough evidence in the brief case studies in Section 7.4 to suggest that we are capable of innovation in our social and economic systems. Intelligence about these innovations can move fast around our networks — be it business, NGOs or the media (aided these days by the Web).

However, it no longer makes sense to see these systems as separate from the natural world. The unfolding science of climate change is an incredibly potent and pressing illustration of how these systems are inescapably interwoven with environmental systems. This block has taken you from current findings in the science of climate change to the inevitable conclusion that societies must urgently find ways of becoming environmentally sustainable. The next block will take you much further in thinking through how this might be achieved in the context of complex environmental problems. It picks up the path laid here by looking at problems and proposed solutions relating to one vitally important natural resource — freshwater. This issue links to biodiversity, climate change and development issues. It calls for an integrated approach to research, debate and governance if all the talk about sustainability is to be turned into action.

You should now go to the Web and do the activities associated with this part of Chapter 7.

7.6 Summary of Chapter 7

7.1   It is essential that societies seek ways of becoming environmentally sustainable and adaptable to unknowable environmental changes, particularly in climate. This must happen in the context of globalization. The concept of sustainability is coming to prominence at a time when established structures of government are being questioned and new ways of thinking about governance are being explored.

7.2   Globalization has a number of dimensions that are relevant to discussion of environmental change and sustainability. In addition to the widely used economic meaning of the term, political, social/cultural and ecological dimensions of globalization are drawn out.

7.3   Three different views on the relationship between globalization and the environment can be identified, termed in the chapter 'business learns' sustainability (in its own self interest), 'radical break' with globalization (and pursuit of sustainable grassroots alternatives), and 'sustainability steps' (incremental progress based in partnership, but emphasizing a role for government). There are empirical examples of each of these approaches (e.g. Interface carpets, the Findhorn community, the Forest Stewardship Council).

7.4   Comparison of the concepts of government and the more recently prominent term 'governance' demonstrates some of the strengths, but also the threats, implicit in a shift to more flexible and open-ended decision-making structures.

7.5   New forms of governance imply new ways of practising citizenship: writers now argue for cosmopolitan and ecological citizenship.

7.6   Communication and debate will be important if any — or a mix — of these approaches are to thrive, hence the media, and specifically quality web journalism, are a key location for advancing towards sustainability.

Learning Outcomes for Chapter 7

When you have completed this chapter, you should be able to:

7.1   Define and use, or recognize definitions and applications of each of the terms given in **bold** in the text. (Question 7.1)

7.2   Summarize, giving examples, the three approaches to achieving sustainability, here described under the headings 'business learns', 'radical break' and 'sustainability steps'. (Question 7.2)

7.3   Explain the distinction between 'government' and 'governance', and the reasons for associating the latter with the pursuit of sustainability. (Questions 7.3 and 7.4)

7.4   Critically assess the proposal that new ideas about citizenship, including cosmopolitan and ecological citizenship, offer a framework for understanding how individuals link to and act on global processes and politics. (Questions 7.5 and 7.6)

7.5   Critically assess the contribution the Web can play in advancing sustainability. (Question 7.7)

Questions for Chapter 7

Question 7.1
Name four dimensions of globalization outlined in Section 7.1.

Question 7.2
Outline, in no more than 100 words, the distinctions between the three approaches to achieving sustainability outlined in Chapter 7.

Question 7.3
Organize the following under the headings 'government' and 'governance'.

> clearly defined state actors;
>
> linear model;
>
> multi-layer;
>
> power is dispersed/opaque;
>
> top down;
>
> network model;
>
> domination through rules or force may be required to ensure universal acceptance of a decision;
>
> simple and intuitive representation of citizens through election;
>
> mixes state and non-state actors (including e.g. NGOs);
>
> evolving and ongoing processes;
>
> acceptance of and support for decisions by all players arises out of wide participation in earlier debate;
>
> formal institutions and procedures.

Question 7.4
List five features (think 'OPASI') frequently associated with good governance, and give brief summaries (please write no more than 100 words for the whole answer).

Question 7.5
What makes ecological citizenship distinctive? Give two reasons (a short paragraph on each).

Question 7.6
Match the following approaches to sustainability with the ideas they promote: business learns, radical break, or sustainability steps.

> best practice databases;
>
> ecological tax reform;
>
> corporate sustainability reporting;
>
> Local Economic Trading Systems;
>
> Forest Stewardship Council.

Question 7.7
In around 100 words, outline what claims are made for the Web as a medium that might aid transitions to sustainability.

References

Anderson, R. C., Ray's story [online] Available from: http://www.interfaceinc.com/getting_there/Ray.html [Accessed 31 November 2002]

Arnstein, S. R. (1969) Ladder of citizen participation. *Journal of the American Institute of Planners*, **35**, pp. 216–224.

Bromley, S. (2001). *Governing the European Union*. London: Sage.

Commission on Global Governance Report (1995) *Our Global Neighbourhood*. Oxford: Oxford University Press.

Dobson, A. (2000) Ecological citizenship: a disruptive influence? In Pierson, C. and Tormey, S., *Politics at the Edge, PSA Yearbook 1999*. London: Macmillan.

Dow Jones Sustainability Indexes (2002) [online] Available from http:/www.sustainability-index.com/djsi_stoxx/djsi_stoxx.html [Accessed 8 January 2003]

Findhorn Foundation website [online] Available from: http://www.findhorn.org/ [Accessed 31 November 2002]

Forum for the Future (2002) [online] Available from http:/www.forumdirectory.org.uk/index.html [Accessed 19 December 2002]

Hawken, P. (1995) *The Ecology of Commerce: a declaration of sustainability*. London: Phoenix.

Held, D. et al. (1999) *Global Transformations: Politics, Economics and Culture*. Cambridge: Polity Press.

Rosenau, J. N. and Durfee, M. (1995) *Thinking Theory Thoroughly: coherent approaches to an incoherent world*. Boulder, Co.: Westview Press.

Smith, M. J. (ed.) (1999) *Thinking through the Environment: a Reader*. London: Routledge.

Smith, M. J. (1998) *Ecologism: Towards Ecological Citizenship*. Milton Keynes: Open University Press.

Urry, J. (1999) [online]. Globalisation and citizenship. *Journal of World-Systems Research*, **2**, pp. 311–324. Available from: http://csf.colorado.edu/jwsr

von Weizsäcker, E. and Lovins, A. B. (1997) *Factor Four: Doubling Wealth — Halving Resource Use: the New Report to the Club of Rome*. London: Earthscan.

World Resources Institute (2000) *World Resources 2000–2001 People and Ecosystems: The Fraying Web of Life*. Washington DC: World Resources Institute.

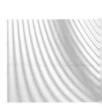

Answers to Questions

Chapter 1

Question 1.1

(c) is the only accurate answer. The IPCC does not conduct its own research; it is a peer review process. Only the Summaries for Policymakers are negotiated in IPCC plenary sessions. A good job too — they would never finish! (Box 1.1, p. 12)

Question 1.2

(a) Hydrology and glaciers; sea-ice; animals; plants.

(b) Shrinkage of glaciers; thawing of permafrost; later freezing and earlier break up of ice on rivers and lakes; lengthening of mid- to high-latitude growing seasons; poleward and altitudinal shifts of plant and animal ranges. (Section 1.6, p. 24)

Question 1.3

(a) crop yields; (b) water resources; (d) energy consumption. (Section 1.7, p. 27)

Question 1.4

The correct matches are as follows (Table 1.1, p. 29).

Risk category	Examples
risks to unique and threatened systems	impacts on mangrove ecosystems
risks from extreme climate events	increases in frequency and intensity of tropical cyclones
risks due to distribution of impacts	severe famine and drought in East Africa
risks due to aggregate impacts	net human welfare loss due to a 2 °C warming equivalent to 5% of GDP
risks due to future large-scale discontinuities	possible large retreat of the Greenland and West Antarctic Ice Sheets

Question 1.5

The main reason the air inside a greenhouse is warmer than the surrounding air is that the glass traps warm rising air that has convected to the top of the greenhouse. There is nothing equivalent to a sheet of glass at the top of the troposphere! The real reason the Earth is 33 °C warmer than it would otherwise be without its atmosphere is the recycling of infrared radiation that takes place throughout the atmosphere as a result of greenhouse gases. Such gases selectively absorb solar radiation and re-emit infrared radiation. (Section 1.9.2, p. 32)

Question 1.6

(b) Nitrogen; (f) oxygen. Molecules of all the rest contain more than two atoms, and therefore are greenhouse gases. (Box 1.8, pp. 36–7)

Question 1.7

3 t of N_2O. Using the values for DGWP in Table 1.3 (p. 41), the relative radiative forcing effect of the different quantities of different gases is as follows:

$$850\,t \text{ of } CO_2 = 850 \text{ tCO}_2e\ (850 \times 1)$$
$$3\,t \text{ of } N_2O = 888 \text{ tCO}_2e\ (3 \times 296)$$
$$30\,t \text{ of } CH_4 = 690 \text{ tCO}_2e\ (30 \times 23)$$
$$50\,g \text{ of } SF_6 = 1110 \text{ tCO}_2e\ (50 \times 10^{-6} \times 22\,200)$$

Question 1.8

Carbon dioxide is by far the main contributor to the enhanced greenhouse effect globally because of the sheer scale of emissions of this gas relative to any of the other five gases that are regulated under the Kyoto Protocol, even though they are all significantly more powerful greenhouse gases. In 2000, Europe emitted 3144 Mt of carbon dioxide, 16 Mt of methane and 1 Mt of nitrous oxide. Methane and nitrous oxide are 23 and 296 times more powerful greenhouse gases, respectively, than carbon dioxide. However, the scale of carbon dioxide emissions relative to emissions of the other gases is such that even taking into account their larger DGWPs, carbon dioxide is responsible for 80% of the contribution to the enhanced greenhouse effect as a result of emissions from Europe. This is typical of other industrialized countries and therefore of the situation globally. (Activity 1.2, p. 41)

Question 1.9

The key steps are (Figure 1.25, p. 43):

- human activity produces greenhouse gas *emissions*;
- greenhouse gas emissions result in higher atmospheric greenhouse gas *concentrations*;
- higher greenhouse gas concentrations lead to *positive radiative forcing* (the enhanced greenhouse effect);
- positive radiative forcing results in a higher *GMST*;
- increasing GMST causes *climatic impacts* such as sea-level rise.

Chapter 2

Question 2.1

(a) This mainly involves the hydrosphere (water) and the atmosphere (water vapour).

(b) This mainly involves the atmosphere (positive radiative forcing) and the land surface (radiating more heat back to space as the Earth warms).

(c) This mainly involves change in the atmosphere (positive radiative forcing) and cryosphere (sea-ice, snow cover, land-ice).

(Section 2.2, pp. 52–3)

Question 2.2

(c) 2 to 4 years, (d) 30 to 100 years, (b) 50–200 years, (e) 100–200 years, (a) up to 10 000 years. (Figure 2.3, p. 54)

Question 2.3

(a) Earth observation satellite measurements (data from 1979).

(b) Stratospheric observations (data from 1940s).

(d) Direct sea-level measurements (since about 1900).

(e) Precipitation and wind measurements (since early 1900s).

(f) Surface ocean observations (since the 1850s).

(c) Tree ring data (data from up to 1000 years ago).

(Box 2.2, p. 63 and Figure 2.3, p. 54)

Question 2.4

(a) is true. (b) and (c) are both false (Box 2.3, p. 68). The IPCC concludes that there is no compelling evidence of change in the frequency and severity of tropical storms, and no long-term changes in severe local weather events.

Question 2.5

(a) 5 000 PgC. 1 GtC is the same as 1 PgC.

(b) Neither. The cost of mitigation from both technologies is the same ($\text{€}17/\text{tC} \equiv \text{€}62.39/\text{tCO}_2$; Box 2.1, p. 56).

Question 2.6

Total cumulative historical emissions from burning fossil fuels were 270 GtC ± 30 (Table 2.1, p. 57). The error is therefore ± 30 GtC. The 1998 rate of fossil-fuel consumption is 6.6 GtC yr^{-1} (Table 2.2, p. 58). The error is therefore equivalent to just under 5 years' current consumption (30/6.6 = 4.5).

Question 2.7

(a) A volcanic eruption produces aerosols. These increase solar scattering, reflect more radiation back to space and therefore have a net negative effect on radiative forcing. Volcanic eruptions cool the climate.

(b) Cleaner emissions mean fewer aerosols enter the atmosphere and there is therefore a net positive radiative forcing. This aspect of clean coal technologies contributes to warming the climate. On the other hand, cleaner technologies could also be more carbon efficient, which means less CO_2 emissions and therefore cooling!)

(c) High clouds have a net warming effect. More high clouds would therefore have a net positive radiative forcing effect.

(d) During the day, clouds reflect solar energy back to space. Less of them would reflect less energy and therefore result in a net positive effect on radiative forcing.

(e) Snow-covered forested areas reflect less light back to space than snow-covered deforested areas. This aspect of deforestation would therefore have a net negative effect on radiative forcing. (However, as is the case with the (b), we also have to take into account the release of the carbon that was stored in the forest. This would contribute positively to radiative forcing.)

(f) There would be a decrease in surface albedo. Loss of sea-ice therefore has a positive effect on radiative forcing.

(Section 2.4, pp. 60–3)

Question 3.7

(a) This is correct. Emissions trading can take place between any members of the Annex I group of countries.

(b) This is incorrect. Saudi Arabia is a developing country and therefore is not part of Annex I. It is part of non-Annex I, and is therefore not eligible to take part in the emissions trading mechanism.

(c) This is incorrect. The Clean Development Mechanism applies to projects in developing countries only. Norway is not a developing country.

(Section 3.4, p. 107)

Question 3.8

The headline target is a 5.2% reduction of emissions by 2012 compared with 1990. When you take into account that under a business-as-usual scenario, emissions would normally have grown substantially in the 22-year period 1990–2012, the real reduction that the Kyoto targets represent is approximately 20%. This is ambitious! (Figure 3.20, p. 112)

Chapter 4

Question 4.1

(a)   Small island states contribute a negligible amount to greenhouse gas emissions. Even if they were to cease all emissions immediately, this would have only a negligible impact on global warming. On the other hand, small island states are particularly vulnerable to climate change. Apart from haranguing the world's gross climate polluters such as the US, China and Europe (something AOSIS does particularly well), the main decision they face is how much to invest in measures to adapt to anticipated climate impacts (e.g. ecological and hard engineering approaches to reduce coastal vulnerability — for example, mangrove swamp restoration and protection by sea walls). Alternatively, they can choose to try to cope with any climate damages as they arise.

(b)   The European Union has a population of 380 million, each of them emitting four times as much pollution as 1 Chinese citizen (giving Europeans an effective climate footprint equivalent to about 1.5 billion Chinese citizens). The EU is a big player in the climate change game. Decisions that it makes can have a significant impact on the future levels of greenhouse gas emissions. But reducing emissions will cost money. So too will investing in adaptation measures to try to offset some of the damages that climate change will inevitably bring (e.g. reducing the costs of serious winter flooding such as that experienced in Eastern Europe in Autumn 2002). Then again, Europeans are relatively rich compared to the 5 billion people living outside the OECD. They can afford to clean up after climate-related damage, and this might also be a sensible strategy. Europe faces a much trickier sum to do — how much to spend on mitigation and adaptation, and how much residual damage to cope with.

(Section 4.2, p. 124)

Question 4.2

(a)   The four main steps involved in integrated assessment models are (Figure 4.3, p. 127):

(i)   the construction of alternative scenarios of future greenhouse gas emissions;

(ii)   the translation of emissions scenarios into alternative scenarios of greenhouse gas concentrations using climate modelling;

(iii)   the computation of projections for global mean temperature changes and associated impacts on climate variables (sea-level rise, precipitation, cloudiness, etc);

(iv)   the computation of the socio-economic impacts of such changes in the climate system;

(b)   Arguments in support of the IPCC's 1998 policy decision not to look at the economics of climate change in the context of the TAR include:

(i)   The climate system is extremely complex. There are uncertainties in each step of the integrated assessment of climate change (Figure 4.4, p. 128). Moreover, uncertainties compound from one step to the next. The assessment of economic impacts is the fourth step in integrated assessment, and therefore relies on the outputs from each of the other three stages of analysis. Of all the stages involved, the economic assessment of climate change (taking into account the costs of residual damage, adaptation and mitigation) is therefore the most uncertain.

(ii)   An economic approach to assessing climate impacts means placing values on the social and environmental impacts of projected climate change. This raises complex ethical questions about the monetary valuation of such impacts (see Chapter 5).

Question 4.3

(a)   Population, economic activity (incomes and lifestyles), and technological change are the key drivers of global emissions trends (Section 4.5, p. 137).

(b)   Several factors affect mitigation/stabilization including:

(i)   Assumptions about the baseline: higher baselines increase costs and vice versa.

(ii)   The target stabilization level: lower stabilization levels increase costs and vice versa.

(iii)   The target date for stabilization: the sooner that a target needs to be reached, the higher the costs and vice versa.

(iv)   The degree of burden sharing involved in meeting the stabilization target: the more participation there is in any climate-change regime, the less each member has to do and (potentially) the lower the costs, and vice versa.

(v)   The nature of the rules governing emissions trading and the Clean Development Mechanism: strict rules and stringent criteria will decrease the number of opportunities for finding cheaper emissions reduction abroad and vice versa.

(Section 4.2, p. 125)

Question 4.4

(a)   The A1 and B1 scenarios both assume that global population peaks around 2050, declining thereafter, and are both technologically optimistic.

(b)   In the A2 scenario, technological change is more fragmented and slower than in the other storylines.

(c)   Of the three key assumptions made by the IPCC in its scenario analysis, 'no new climate policies in the future' undermines the credibility of the storylines. Even in the face of considerable scientific and political uncertainties, the international response to climate change has been significant, and represents active precaution. It could be argued that it seems implausible to assume that either (i) the scientific consensus on the evidence for climate change will collapse, or (ii) that governments will suddenly stop acting in a precautionary manner (Section 4.6, pp. 138–44).

Question 4.5

The most challenging is clearly option (b) (high global emissions baseline, 450 p.p.m. atmospheric stabilization target). This is because from the information given, it contains the highest baseline and lowest target stabilization level. The gap between business as usual and target is therefore the greatest. In the other two options we know that in each case the stabilization targets are both higher (therefore less difficult to achieve) and the baselines are lower (medium rather than high) (Section 4.7, pp. 144–8).

Question 4.6

The correct matches are (Section 4.8, p. 153):

Approach to equity	Key phrases
opportunity-based	standards of living
poverty-based	protection against climate impacts
liability-based	actions of others
rights-based	global commons

Chapter 5

Question 5.1

The opportunity-based approach is the most commonly held by climate-change negotiators. Developed countries hold on to the right to protect their lifestyles, but equally, countries from the less-developed world don't want to be impeded from following the same path, even though this may be fossil-fuel intensive. The contraction and convergence position is held primarily by NGOs, but has been supported by some less-developed countries and some Green and Social Democratic politicians from the developed world (p. 162).

Question 5.2

(a)   Minimal transfers of wealth from developed to less-developed countries.

(b)   Gradual progress on emissions reductions in line with improving technical capacity.

(c)   A wide range of development paths open to less-developed countries.

(d)   No restrictions on development (but assumes this will be 'sustainable').

(p. 163)

Question 5.3

Economists usually view the value of something to us in the present as higher than the value of the same 'good' in the future. Hence a resource or species has to have a very high value today to be considered worth saving for the future. The interest rate is crucial in these calculations. With a lower interest rate, a resource would be discounted less and therefore be worth more to us. With the kinds of interest rates sought by commercial and international banks (around 15% for the World Bank) the short-term exploitation or dismissal of natural resources becomes an integral feature of investment and economic growth (p. 168).

Question 5.4

Externalities are costs that are (or might be) born somewhere or somehow, but are not included in the calculation of the internal costs of a good or service. Environmental economists put prices on, for example, the climate-change consequences of a growth in road traffic catalysed by a new road scheme. Hence the price of such a scheme will need to increase to include not just the costs of the scheme itself in terms of materials, labour and land-use change, but also social and environmental costs, such as increased local and global pollution, communities being severed, and so on. The price of such a scheme would always have been passed on to end users in one way or another (in taxes, or in some parts of the world through tolls), but would go up once such externalities have been included (pp. 171–2).

Question 5.5

Lovelock drew together work in geology, climate science and ecology to argue that the Earth is a single, self-regulating, living system (p. 176).

Question 5.6

Midgley sees Gaian theory as a way of correcting the individualistic frame of Enlightenment thinking dominant in science since the 17th century. She sees this as having spilled over into the way we think and act in terms of economics, politics and ethics. This has resulted most recently in an inappropriate extension of the principle of competition in Darwinism to all readings of the social and natural worlds, to the exclusion of the cooperative dimensions that the Gaia hypothesis emphasizes (pp. 177–8).

Question 5.7

See Table 5.3.

Question 5.8

See Table 5.4.

Chapter 6

Question 6.1

The poor and their environments are the most vulnerable to climate change, but it will cost rich countries too. In addition to the depletion of basic human needs of food, fuel and water, the extinction of the fundamental source of all ecological services that human societies rely on — biodiversity — is likely to be accelerated. Climate change limits the poor's chances of development. The costs of adaptation to and mitigation of climate change in rich countries add to the energy behind climate-change politics. Together, these factors have done more than anything to underline the need to integrate environment and development, and hence promote sustainability to a central role in our local and global responses to the challenges of the 21st century (pp. 185–7).

Question 6.2

Ecology, thermodynamics and environmental economics are all a hidden presence in sustainability debates. Although they don't always use the same language, they have interests in systems, feedbacks and limits/systems collapse in common (pp. 194–6).

Question 6.3

How, practically, can we represent the interests of future generations in the present?

How do we balance the interests of future generations against those of present generations who don't have equal access to economic development?

How do we represent the non-human natural world in our decisions?

Does it matter if we, today, 'spend' one natural resource in the present if we replace it with another that is valued by future generations?

How do we interpret and decide on conflicting proposals that both claim to be pursuing 'sustainable development'?

(p. 197)

Question 6.4

(a)   A strong body of evidence emerged in reports from NGOs, UN and scientific bodies.

(b)   Transboundary impacts, such as acid rain, demonstrated that industrial and domestic processes in one region resulted in environmental degradation in another.

(c)   In the case of the Antarctic ozone layer, local actions were shown by scientists to have the capability of resulting in global impacts that were attributable to pollution.

(d)   Sociologists of environmentalism suggest that developed societies had become 'rich enough to worry': as people are more secure in terms of meeting immediate economic needs, they are freed to consider a wider orbit of concerns, including their local and global environment.

(e)   Evidence suggested that economic development in less-developed countries was not being delivered as promised: the environment was being damaged but to little gain.

(pp. 198–9)

Question 6.5

See Box 6.2 (p. 198).

Question 6.6

Strengths:

- Help to make complex interlinked issues vivid for professionals.

- Begin the process of 'mainstreaming' sustainable development thinking.

- Draw on data from a wide range of established sources.

- Present opportunities for comparison of progress towards sustainability goals across time and space.

Weaknesses

- Have failed to find space in the media's or the public's imagination.

- Methodologies are complex, but can also disguise the mix of quantitative and qualitative assessments.

- The stories indicators tell can be confusing and/or counter-intuitive (how does roadbuilding (often an economic good but usually an environmental bad) show in the indicators?).

- Indicators can be tokenistic for local and national government ('we are trying to understand the issues fully before we act; the indicators are a measure of our commitment').

- Relatively under-resourced and are rarely highlighted to the media or public (too many tales of internal inconsistencies laid bare in the indicators maybe?).

(p. 202)

Question 6.7

Three criticisms of early 1970s environmentalism continue to circulate today:

(a) Over-confidence in computer based projections of interactions between human societies and economies and environmental change. Society–environment interactions are simply too complex to be modelled in this way. Many assumptions are made which could be presented differently by someone with different political intentions.

(b) Many feel that western environmentalists want to 'pull the ladder up' behind them. In other words they believed that those who have already enjoyed the benefits of economic growth in the developed world wish to deny those benefits to others for fear of the environmental consequences.

(c) Environmentalists fail to recognize the adaptability of human systems, and the ingenuity of technology. Capitalism is at its most dynamic and adaptable in the face of economic or environmental challenges, whether in seeking new oilfields or new ways of extracting oil, or in moving towards cleaner industrial production.

(pp. 187–8)

Acknowledgements

Grateful acknowledgement is made to the following sources for permission to reproduce material in this book:

Chapter 1

Figures 1.1, 1.6: Stephen Peake; *Figure 1.2*: Mike Levers; *Figure 1.3*: World Meteorological Organization and United Nations Environment Programme; *Figure 1.4a*: Press Association; *Figure 1.4b*: Debby Besford/Science Photo Library; *Figure 1.5a*: Courtesy of Bob Girdo; *Figure 1.7*: Introduction to Climate Change, United Nations Environment Programme/GRID-Arendal; *Figure 1.8*: Special Report of Emissions Scenarios. Intergovernmental Panel on Climate Change; *Figure 1.9*: Still Pictures; *Figure 1.10*: Meadows, D. H. et al. (1972) *The Limits to Growth*, Earth Island Ltd, by permission of D. L. Meadows; *Figure 1.12*: Weather forecast for Africa, CNN; *Figure 1.13*: Houghton, J. T. et al. (2001) *Climate Change 2001: The Scientific Basis*, Intergovernmental Panel on Climate Change; *Figure 1.14*: McCarthy, J. J. et al. (eds) (2001) *Climate Change 2001: Impacts, Adaptation, and Vulnerability*, Intergovernmental Panel on Climate Change; *Figure 1.16*: NASA; *Figure 1.17*: *Climate Change 2001*, Intergovernmental Panel on Climate Change; *Figure 1.18*: © European Centre for Medium-Range Weather Forecasts ECMWF, http://www.ecmwf.int/; *Figure 1.20*: Science Photo Library; *Figure 1.24*: 500 PPM Website.

Chapter 2

Tables

Table 2.2: Metz, B. et al. (2001) *Climate Change 2001: Mitigation*, Intergovernmental Panel on Climate Change; *Tables 2.3–2.5*: Metz, B. et al. (2001) *Climate Change 2001: The Scientific Basis*, Intergovernmental Panel on Climate Change.

Figures

Figure 2.1a: National Oceanic and Atmospheric Administration Paleoclimatology Program/ Department of Commerce/Maris Kazmers, SharkSong Photography, Okemos, Michigan; *Figure 2.1b*: Melanie Conner/National Science Foundation; *Figure 2.3a*: *Climate Change 2001: Synthesis Report*, Intergovernmental Panel on Climate Change; *Figure 2.3b*: *Climate Change 2002: Summary for Policy Makers,* Intergovernmental Panel on Climate Change; *Figure 2.4*: © Sesame Workshop; *Figures 2.5–2.7, 2.9, 2.11*: Houghton, J. T. et al. (2001) *Climate Change 2001: The Scientific Basis*, Intergovernmental Panel on Climate Change; *Figure 2.8*: Associated Press; *Figure 2.10*: Petit, J. R. et al. (1999) Climate and atmospheric history of the past 420,000 years from the Vostock ice core in Antarctica, *Nature*, **339**, 3 June 1999, pp. 429–436; *Figure 2.13*: Bruce Miller.

Chapter 3

Figure 3.1a, b: Houghton, J. T. et al. (2001) *Climate Change 2001: The Scientific Basis*, Intergovernmental Panel on Climate Change; *Figure 3.2a*: Mary Evans Picture Library; *Figure 3.2b*: Alamy/Motoring Picture Library. National Motor Museum; *Figure 3.2c*: Hulton Archive; *Figure 3.2d*: Photri; *Figure 3.2e, f*: Courtesy of Earth Sciences and Image Analysis Laboratory, NASA, Johnson Space Center; *Figure 3.3a, b*: Science Photo Library; *Figure 3.4*: Scripps Institute of Oceanography (SIO), University of California 1998; *Figure 3.5*: Tegart, W. J. McG. et al. (1990) *Climate Change*, Intergovernmental Panel on Climate Change; *Figure 3.6*: PA Photos Ltd; *Figure 3.8*: GADO: cartoon is based on the 'Fortress World' scenario from GEO3, published by Earthscan for the United Nations Environment Programme, 2002; *Figures 3.10, 3.21*: Methodological Issues, National Communications from parties included in Annex I to the Convention. Report on national greenhouse gas inventory data from Annex I Parties for 1990–2000, UNFCCC; *Figure 3.11*: UN/ DPI Mark Garten; *Figure 3.12*: Angela Barber/Kurdish Human Rights Project; *Figure 3.13*: Seize the Day CD cover, www.seizetheday.org; *Figure 3.14*: Associated Press; *Figure 3.15a*: Courtesy of Geoexplorer; *Figure 3.15b*: Courtesy of Munich Re, Munich; *Figure 3.15c*: Mike Dodd; *Figure 3.15d*: Jim Wark/Still Pictures; *Figure 3.15e, 3.16b, d, 3.18, 3.19, 3.23a*: Stephen Peake; *Figure 3.16a*: Joe Smith; *Figure 3.16c*: Chris Stowers/Panos Pictures; *Figure 3.17*: The Kyoto Protocol to the Convention on Climate Change, UNEP/IUC; *Figure 3.22*: Wrigley (1998) The Kyoto Protocol: CO_2 and CH_4 and climate implications in *Geophysical Research Letters* **25**(13):2, 285–8, American Geophysical Union; *Figure 3.23b*: Courtesy of British Energy; *Figure 3.34*: Darko Bandic/AP.

Chapter 4

Tables

Table 4.1: Fankhauser, S. (1998) *The Costs of Adapting to Climate Change*, Working Paper 16, GEF Secretariat; *Tables 4.2, 4.3*: *Climate Change 2001: Mitigation*, Intergovernmental Panel on Climate Change.

Figures

Figures 4.1, 4.4: *Climate Change 2001: Impacts, Adaptation, and Vulnerability*, Intergovernmental Panel on Climate Change; *Figure 4.5, 4.17*: Stephen Peake; *Figure 4.6a*: Penner, J. E. et al. (1999) *Aviation and the Global Atmosphere*, Intergovernmental Panel on Climate Change; *Figure 4.6b*: Geophysical Fluid Dynamics Laboratory; *Figure 4.6c*: *Climate Change 2001: The Scientific Basis*, Intergovernmental Panel on Climate Change; *Figure 4.7*: © Peter Jackson; *Figure 4.8*: Dr Ben Matthews; *Figure 4.9*: CO_2 Emissions from Fuel Combustion 1971–1999, OECD/IEA, 2001; *Figure 4.10*: U.S. Greenhouse Gas Emission Intensities, 1990–1999. U.S. Environmental Protection Agency, Inventory of U.S. Greenhouse Gas Emissions and Sinks: 1990–1999, April 2001, EPA 236-R-01-001, pp. 1–11; *Figures 4.11–4.16, 4.18a, 4.19*: *Climate Change 2001: Mitigation*, Intergovernmental Panel on Climate Change; *Figure 4.20*: Associated Press; *Figure 4.21, 4.22*: de Elzen, M. et al. (2000) Framework to Assess International Regimes for Burden Sharing, RIVM.

Chapter 5

Figure 5.1: NASA Earth Observatory; *Figure 5.2*: NASA Earth Observatory; *Figure 5.3*: Greenpeace/Davison; *Figure 5.4*: B. Lewis/Network Photographers; *Figure 5.5*: © Sven Torfinn/Panos Pictures; *Figure 5.7*: Tracy Finnegan; *Figure 5.9*: © The Advertising Archives; *Figure 5.11*: Mary Evans Picture Library; *Figure 5.12a*: Eurostat, 2002, 'Transport and environment: statistics for the transport and environment reporting mechanism (TERM) for the European Union, data 1980–2000, unpublished electronic update, January 2002', European Environment Agency; *Figure 5.12b*: EEA, 2002a, 'Annual European Community greenhouse gas inventory 1990–2000 and inventory report 2002, EEA Technical Report No 75, European Environment Agency, Copenhagen; *Figure 5.13*: © The Advertising Agency; *Figure 5.14*: Nash, R. T. (1989) *The Rights of Nature: A history of environmental ethics*, University of Wisconsin Press; *Figure 5.16*: The Wellcome Library; *Figure 5.17*: Cristina Pedrazzini/SPL; *Figure 5.18*: © 1997 Megan Schefcik.

Chapter 6

Figures 6.1, 6.9: Joe Smith; *Figure 6.3*: Lonely Planet Images/David Tipling; *Figure 6.5a*: © Luiz C. Marigo/Still Pictures; *Figure 6.5b*: © Chris Martin/Still Pictures; *Figure 6.5c*: © NASA; *Figure 6.5d*: © 2001 Greenpeace/Thomas Bollinger; *Figure 6.5e*: Jeremy Hartley/Panos Pictures; *Figure 6.7*: AP Photos/Massimo Sambucetti; *Figure 6.8*: © Courtesy of New Economics Foundation; *Figure 6.10*: UK Government Sustainable Development DEFRA, Royal Society for the Protection of Birds, British Trust for Ornithology; *Figure 6.11*: PA Photos/Stefan Rousseau.

Chapter 7

Figure 7.1: © Courtesy of Corp Watch, www.corpwatch.org; *Figure 7.2*: © Associated Press, EFE/ Cristobal Garcia; *Figure 7.3*: © Mark Henley/Panos Pictures; *Figure 7.4a*: PA Photos/Paul Sakuma; *Figure 7.4b, 7.10, 7.15*: Joe Smith; *Figures 7.5a, 7.12:* © Interface Fabrics 2003; *Figure 7.5b*: © Pier Paolo Cito/AP Photos; *Figure 7.5c*: © PA Photos/Sean Dempsey; *Figure 7.6*: Courtesy of Ecover Ltd; *Figure 7.7*: Steve Morgan/Greenpeace; *Figure 7.11*: Mike Dodd; *Figure 7.13*: Dow Jones Sustainability Indexes; *Figure 7.14*: Courtesy of the Findhorn Foundation; *Figure 7.16*: © New Economics Foundation; *Figure 7.17*: © FSC; *Figure 7.18*: UNEP-WCMC, WWF and FSC; *Figure 7.19*: UNEP-WCMC; *Figure 7.20*: Reproduced by permission. Forum for the Future, www.forumdirectory.org.uk; *Figure 7.21*: Chris Sattlberger/Panos Pictures; *Figure 7.22*: WWF Alert (2002) Stop overfishing campaign update. Reproduced with permission from WWF. © 2002. WWF World Wide Fund For Nature (Formerly World Wildlife Fund) All rights reserved.

Every effort has been made to trace all the copyright owners, but if any has been inadvertently overlooked, the publishers will be pleased to make the necessary arrangements at the first opportunity.

Index

Entries in **bold** are key terms. Page numbers referring to information that is given only in a figure or caption are printed in *italics*.

A

Aarhus Convention *220*, 221

accountability in governance 219, *220*, 221

adaptation to climate change 105, 121–4, *127*, *185*
 costs and benefits 160–61

aerosols (atmospheric) **23**
 effect on radiative forcing 61, 62

AGCMs (atmosphere general circulation models) 69

Agenda 21 *13*, 191

agriculture
 adaptation of, to climate change *123*
 impact of climate changes on 75
 intensive *88*

aircraft emissions *132*

albedo 52
 effect of changes on radiative forcing 62

reduction due to climate change 52

Alliance of Small Island States (AOSIS) 16, 98–100

altruism in climate change negotiations 217

Anderson, Ray *211*, 227

Annex I countries **97**–8, 99, 110–11, 113, 150–51
 cumulative emissions 134–5

Annex II countries **97**–8, 101, 113

Antarctica, warming 26

anticipatory adaptation to climate change **122**

AOGCMs (atmosphere–ocean general
 circulation models) 69

AOSIS (Alliance of Small Island States) 16, 98–100

Arnstein's, S. R., ladder of participation 222

Arrhenius, Svante *89*

atmosphere 51–4
 circulation patterns 68
 composition 34, *35*, 39, 40, *65*, *87*, 89, *90*, 176
 properties affecting GMST 61–2
 role in greenhouse effect 32–7
 structure *34*
 see also aerosols, atmospheric; Earth,
  energy exchange with atmosphere;
  greenhouse gases, atmospheric levels

atmosphere general circulation models
 (AGCMs) 69

atmosphere–ocean general circulation
 models (AOGCMs) 69

B

Bangladesh, sea-level rise 27

baselines 145

Beckermann, Wilfred 171

'Best Practice databases' 236

'BINGOs' 193

biodiversity 200
 impact of climate change on 75, *186*
 sustainability indicator *199*

biogeochemical cycles 39

biosphere and climate system 51

borehole measurements, climate change indicators 63

Bové, Joseph 209

Bromley, S. 215, 216

Brundtland report 190, 196

burden sharing 125

Bush, George, senior *92*, 164

Bush, George W. 102–3, 164, 171

'business learns' response 210, 211–12, 214, 227–30, 237

'business as usual' scenario 105, 106, 111–12, 121–2, 144, 146,
 163

business, stakeholders in sustainable development 193

C

Calder, Nigel, on ice age scare 23

capital, man-made and natural 195

car ownership 139–40

carbon aerosols *61*, 62

carbon cycle 39, 53, 53–60, *127*

carbon dioxide
 atmospheric
  changing levels 64, *65*, 70–72, *76*, 80, *87*, 89–90
  greenhouse gas *35*, 39, 40–42, *61*
  monitoring *88*, 89
  and planetary temperatures *17*, 62–3
  stabilization of levels 125
  units 56–7
 emissions 52, 54–5, 57–9, 69–70, 70–71, 124–5
  baseline 125, 144–8
  future 134–8
  limiting 110–14
  reductions 102–3

emissions *contd*
    see also emissions entitlements;
        emissions intensity; emissions scenarios;
        international emissions trading
    vibrational modes 36–7

carbon dioxide equivalent (CO$_2$e) **41**

carbon taxes 226

Carey, George, on climate change 14, 16

cars; *see* internal combustion engines

CDM; *see* Clean Development Mechanism

Centre for Alternative Technology *232*

Charlton, N. 176

citizenship 217, **221**–6
    and shopping behaviour 223–4

civil society 213–14

clathrate compounds 29 (footnote)

Clausen, Eileen, on climate change 15, 16–17

Clean Development Mechanism (CDM) 107, 108, 109–11, 125, *126*

climate, distinct from weather 21

climate change 21–2, 65–8
    associated lifestyle features 164–6
    communicating 17–18, 78–9, *131*
    delay in realizing 87–91
    early signs 23–5
    impacts 24–9, 100–1, *127*
        future 72–8
        on poor people 186–7, *189*
    measuring 63
    political consequences 13–18, 159–61, 180, 190–94
    possible future 67, 69–78
    reasons for concern about 28–30, 53
    responses 104–5, 105–6
        political 210–14, 216–18
    role of road transport 173
    uncertainties concerning 49–50, 57, 68–71, 77–81, 129
    vulnerability assessments 101
    see also United Nations Framework Convention on
        Climate Change

climate cycles 65

climate equity 161–3, 164, 166

climate models 40, 59–60, 69–71, 78–9, 131, *132*
    see also integrated assessment models; JAVA climate model

climate sensitivity 60

climate system 51
    components 51, 52
    external factors 61
    internal factors 61
    processes in 52–4

Clinton, Bill, on climate change 15, 17

clouds
    change in cover 68
    effect of, on radiative forcing 62

coastal zones
    adaptation of, to climate change *123*
    impact of climate change on 75

Cobb, J. B., Jr 197

Commission on Global Governance 215

Commitments under UNFCCC **93**, 96–104, 107

communications technology *146*, 200, 210, 221, 236, 238–9

communities of feeling/identity 216
    in United States 217

competition 178

complementary currencies 232–3

computer models 130–31

Conference of Parties to UNFCCC **94**

consumers
    effects of sustainable development on 104
    shopping behaviour 223–4
    see also sustainable consumption

containerization 210

contraction and convergence model 153, **161**, 162

Convention on Biological Diversity 93

Convention to Combat Desertification 93

cooperation 178, 233

corals
    bleaching 26
    climate change indicators 63
    paleoclimatological studies *49*

corporate social and environmental responsibility 212

cosmopolitan citizens 223–4, 225

Costanza, R. 168, 195

costs and benefits
    of internal combustion engine 172–3, *174*
    of responses to climate change 123–5, 128–9, 144, 160–71
    see also externalities

couplings between climate system components **52**

crop yields, effects of climate change on 27

cryosphere and climate system 51

D

Daly, Hermann 194, 195, 197

damage costs 124

Darwin, Charles 178

Dauncey, Guy 14

decision-making and environmental change 207, 214–15, 218
   integrated *191*
   see also governance

decision support tools 130

deforestation 52, *189*

descriptive scenarios 139, 140

desertification 52

determinants of emission levels 138

developed countries
   environmental concerns in 188–9
   responsibility of, for mitigation costs 160
   and UNFCCC 96–7, 101, 108, 113–14, 151–2
   see also Annex I countries; Annex II countries

developing countries
   cumulative emissions *134*, 135
   debts 189
   increasing emissions from 160
   and UNFCCC 96, 96–7, 98–101, 113, 114–15, 151–2

DGWPs; *see* direct global warming potentials

dipole moment 36
   and infrared activity 36–7

direct climate impacts (climate change) **100**

direct global warming potential (DGWP) of greenhouse gases **39**, 40–41

discounting the future 168–9, *181*

discourse 191

disease; *see* human health

do little or nothing ('business as usual') scenario **105**, 106, 111–12, 121–2, 144, 146, 163

Dobson, Andrew 225, 226

Dow Jones Sustainability Indexes 230

E

Earth, energy exchange with atmosphere 37–9

Earth images 159

eco-efficiency 229–30

ecological citizenship 225–7

ecological economics 195

ecological footprinting 197

ecological globalization 208, **208**–9, 210

ecological tax reform 232, 233

ecology 194

economic globalization 189, 209, 210, 214

economic and social impacts (climate change) *76*, **100**, *127*, 128, 129, 140–42

economics
   for sustainability 195–6
   see also environmental economics

economies in transition, role of, in UNFCCC 98, 112–13

Ecover factory *212*

ecovillages 231

El Niño Southern Oscillation 68, 71, *76*

electromagnetic radiation *33*
   emitted by planetary bodies 36

emissions entitlements 162

emissions intensity 135
   indicators 136–7

emissions scenarios 138–44, 145

emissions trading; *see* international emissions trading

energy consumption *165*
   by businesses 228
   effects of climate change 27, 75

energy modelling 131

enhanced greenhouse effect 33

Enlightenment world view 177–8

entropy 195

environmental economics 168–71, 177, 180, *181*, 195

environmental movement 188–93, 213, 218
   see also non-governmental organizations

equity 148–54, **159**, *191*
   see also climate equity

ethics
   and climate change 166–7, 178–9, 180
   evolution 175–7

European Union
   governance in *220*
   greenhouse gas emissions in 41–2

externalities 171–2, 232

extreme weather events 68, 71–3, *76*, *122*, *207*
   see also flooding

F

FAIR (Framework to Assess International Regimes for Burden-sharing) model 151–2, *153*

fair trade 213, 223, 224

Fankhauser, S. 123

feedback within climate system **52**–3

Findhorn community 230–31, 237

first commitment period (of Kyoto Protocol) **107**

First World Climate Conference 92

fisheries 238
   ecology 195
   impact of climate change on 75

'flexibility' mechanisms; *see under* Kyoto Protocol

flooding, effects of climate change 27

flowering season changes 27

flows, global 209–10

food
impact of climate change on production *186*
transport and processing *165*, 223–4

Forest Stewardship Council (FSC) 234–5, 237

forestry
adaptation to climate change *123*
impact of climate change 75, *185*, *186*, *189*

fossil fuel companies, stakeholders in sustainable development 193

fossil fuels 20, 103, 104
effects of combustion 53–60, *61*, 62
see also oil industry

Fourier, Jean Baptiste Joseph *89*

Framework Convention on Climate Change 13

Friedan, Betty, on ice age scare 23

fuel tax protests 217

future generations, and climate change decisions 166–71, *181*, *191*

futurity 191

G

Gaia hypothesis 174–5, **176**–9, 180, *181*

Galapagos Islands, coral bleaching in 26

GCOS (global climate observing system) 31

GDP (gross domestic product) 197

GHGs; *see* greenhouse gases

Global Climate Coalition 79

global climate observing system (GCOS) 31

global commons 161

global mean surface temperature (GMST) **21**, 30–32, 60–61
effects of greenhouse gases on 37–9, 67, 69–70, *70*
increases in 30, 65–7, 76–7, 80, 87–8
measuring 31

global warming 9–10, **30**–31
see also climate change; greenhouse effect

globalization 194
economic 189, 209, 210, 214
and environmental change 207, 208–14

GMST; *see* global mean surface temperature

governance 194, 215, 219–22, 238
citizen participation in 222–3
of climate change; *see* UNFCCC
as distinct from government 218–19

governments 218, *219*
stakeholders in sustainable development 193, 200

greenhouse effect 30, 32–9

greenhouse gases (GHGs) **30**, 35–9, 69, 70
anthropogenic 43, 51, 57–8, 61
atmospheric levels 38–9, 40, 64, *65*, 69–72, 77, 80, *87*, 89, 92, *127*, 128
stabilization of, under UNFCCC 94, 121, 145
DGWPs 39, 40–41
lifestyle features associated with *164*, 165–6
and sea-level rise 30, 42–4
transport emissions *174*
see also carbon dioxide; emissions intensity; water, atmospheric

'greenwash' 193

gross domestic product (GDP) 197

Gummer, John 196

Gulf Stream 76–7

Gwynne, Peter, on ice age scare 23

H

habitat destruction 188, *189*

Hawken, Paul 227

Hawking, Stephen, on climate change 15, 17

heat index *72*

Held, D. 223

Hill, J. N. 129

holistic approach to sustainability **194**, 201

horse dung crisis scare 133–4

human activities
and climate change 43, 51, 57–8, 63, 67, 77–8, 133
and Earth systems 176–7, *181*
see also greenhouse gases, anthropogenic

human health
adaptation to climate change *123*
impact of climate change on 27, 74, 75

human population 136–8, *139*, 141–2
rising 18–20, 150

hydrofluorocarbons (HFCs)
changing atmospheric levels of *65*
as greenhouse gases 35, *61*

hydrological cycle 33
impact of climate change on 75

hydrosphere and climate system 51

I

IAMs; *see* integrated assessment models

'ice age scare' 22–3

ice core studies *49*
climate change indicators 63

ice cover changes 26, 52, 68, 71, *76*

IIASA; *see* International Institute of Applied Systems Analysis

Ilisu dam *101*

Index of Sustainable Economic Welfare 197

Industrial Revolution *88*

inequality
    costs and benefits of adaptation/mitigation 160–61
    income distribution 149–50
    increasing with globalization 209
    vulnerability to climate change 185, 186–7

inertial systems **53**

infrared radiation
    absorption by molecules 36–7
    and greenhouse effect 37–9

instrumental records 63

insurance 105, 122

integrated assessment models (**IAMs**) 27, 125–6, **127**–9, 144, 151, 154

integrated assessments of climate change **121**–5

integrated decision-making *191*

integration in governance 219, *220*, 221

'intentional communities' 230–31, 237

interest rates 168

Interface Inc. 227–8, 237

Intergovernmental Panel on Climate Change (IPCC) 9–13, 20, 66, 69–70, 78–80, 129
    establishment 92
    First Assessment Report 92
    Second Assessment Report 107
    Working Groups 12–13
    see also Third Assessment Report (TAR)

internal combustion engines; *see* road transport

international emissions trading 107, 108–11, 125, 160, 161–2

International Institute of Applied Systems Analysis (IIASA) 131

International Institute for Sustainable Development 198

Internet access 200

IPCC; *see* Intergovernmental Panel on Climate Change

'IPRT' formula 137–8

J

JAVA climate model *131*, 162

Johannesburg Summit (2002) 192, 196, *220*

K

Keepin, B. 131

Kilimanjaro, Mount, ice melt on 26

Kyoto Protocol 15, **100**, 106–16, 144, 150
    compliance regime 114
    degree of success 110–14
    effect on global temperatures 114
    'flexibility' mechanisms 108–11, 114
    gases regulated under 41
        European Union emissions 41–2
        see also greenhouse gases
    rules and red tape 125
    US rejection of 102–4, 171

L

ladder of participation 222

land surface and climate system 51

land-use changes 19–20, 52, 59, *61*
    see also agriculture

Landfill Tax 233

large-scale discontinuities *76*, 80

Lauti, Teleke, on climate change 14, 16

Lempriére–Ross mark 79

LETS; *see* local exchange trading systems

life cycle analysis 228

Limits to Growth (Club of Rome) *20*, 187

limits to human development *191*, 192

Local Agenda 21 *13*, **191**

local exchange trading systems (LETS) **232**–3

localization 212–13, 214

locally produced food 223, 224

Lovelock, James 174–5, 176–8, 179

M

Mauna Loa CO_2 data 90

McDonald's 209

Margulis, Lynn 176

Markham, Adam, on climate change 14, 16

Matthews, Ben *131*

Mazza, Patrick 14

Meacher, Michael, on climate change 15, 16

Meadows, D. H. *et al.* 20

methane
    atmospheric, changing levels 64, *65*, 80, *87*
    as greenhouse gas *35*, 41–2, 53, *61*

methane clathrates (hydrates) 29 (footnote), *76*

Meyer, Aubrey 162

Midgley, Mary 177–9, 180

mitigation of climate change **106**, 121, 122–5, *127*, 145, 147–8, *185*
    costs and benefits of policies 161

models 130–34, 138–9

moral community 175

N

Nash, R.T. 175

nation states 215–16, 217, 223

natural capital 195

negative feedbacks within climate system **52**–3

net radiative forcing 40

networks, global 208, 209, 210, 214

New Economics Foundation *193*

new social movements 212–13

New York City, summer temperatures in 27

NGOs; *see* non-governmental organizations

nitrous oxide
    atmospheric, changing levels of 64, *65*, 80, *87*
    as greenhouse gas *35*, *41*, *61*

no regrets responses to climate change **122**

Non-Annex I parties 97

non-governmental organizations (NGOs)
    'ark' *16*
    images used by *16*, 189–90, 212
    political activity 217
    stakeholders in sustainable development 193, 218
    view of emissions trading 109

normative scenarios 139, 140

O

Objective of UNFCCC **93**–5

obligations 179–80
    in private sphere 226
    to biotic community 225
    to future generations 166–71

ocean general circulation models (OGCMs) 69

oceans
    carbon dioxide absorption 52
    circulation patterns 68, *76*
    evaporation from 52

OECD countries 101, 113

oil crisis (1973) 20

oil industry *88*, 101
    see also petroleum-based materials

'OPASI' 219, *220*, 221

OPEC countries 101

openness in governance 219, *220*, 221, 229

opportunity-based approach to climate equity 153, **162**–4

opportunity costs 168

organic food 223, 224

ozone layer 188, *189*

P

Pachauri, Rajendra 79

paleoclimatological studies *49*

'Panda Passport' 238

participation in governance 219, *220*, 221
    see also ladder of participation

Parties to UNFCCC 93, **94**

Pasek, Joanna 171

Pearce, David 195

perfluorocarbons (PFCs)
    changing levels of 65
    as greenhouse gases *35*, *61*

petroleum-based materials, reduced use of 228

phenology 27

Plass, Gilbert 89

policy community 176, 215, 234

political globalization 209

polluter pays principle **233**

pollution
    as externality 171–2
    transboundary 188, 210

Ponte, Lowell, on ice age scare 23

population; *see* human population

Porritt, Jonathan *211*

positive feedback within climate system **52**

poverty
    and impact of climate change 186–7
    sustainability indicator *199*

precautionary principle 191, 226

precipitation patterns 69

Principles of UNFCCC **93**, 95–6, 151

protected areas 200

Q

QUANGOs 218

R

radiation; *see* electromagnetic radiation

radiative damping 53

radiative forcing 40
    uncertainties in understanding 60–63

'radical break' response 210, *211*, 212–13, 214, 230–34

range land/livestock, impact of climate change 75

Rasool, S. I., on ice age scare 23

reactive adaptation to climate change **122**

Reddish, A. 137

redundancy 192

Rees, W. E. 197

re-materialization 228

renewable energy 104, 106, 125, *126*, *196*, 228

Revelle, Roger 89

rights-based approach to climate equity 153, 162

Rio Earth Summit 93, 191, 196

road transport *163*, *165*
    costs and benefits of 172–3, *174*

Roy, Arundhati 209

S

Samoa, shore recession 27

scenario 138

scenario analysis; *see* emissions scenarios

Schneider, S. H., on ice age scare 23

Schumacher, Fritz 194

sea-ice thickness 68, 71

sea-level change 14, 27, *54*, 68, 70, *70*, *76*, 79
    and greenhouse gases 30, 42–4

sequestering of carbon dioxide **40**

Shiva, Vandana *211*

SI system of units 56–7

sinks 52, *126*

Slade, Tuilome Neroni 99–100

'small-world effect' 18

Smith, Mark 225

snow cover 68, 71

social capital 233

social exclusion, as sustainability indicator *199*

social impacts of climate change; *see under* economic and social
    impacts (climate change)

social/cultural globalization 209

solar variation, effect on radiative forcing of 62–3

sovereignty 216, 217

Spencer, Tom, on climate change 14, 16

stakeholders in sustainability *191*, 193, 230

state power 212–13, 214
    see also nation states

storms; *see* extreme weather events

subsidiarity in governance 219, *220*, 221

sulfate aerosols 62

sulfur dioxide emissions 70–71

sulfur hexafluoride as greenhouse gas *35*, *61*, 65, *65*

supranational bodies 223

sustainability reporting 229

'sustainability steps' approach *211*, 213, 214

Sustainable Biosphere Initiative 194

sustainable consumption 213, 234–8

sustainable development 94, 95, 101, 104, 142, *146*, 163, 180,
    186–201, 227–30, 236–8
    intellectual foundations 194–6
    see also 'sustainability steps' approach

sustainable development indicators 191, **197**–201

systems mapping 134–5

T

TAR; *see* Third Assessment Report

taxation; *see* ecological tax reform; carbon taxes; fuel tax protests

telephone access 200

thermodynamics approach to sustainability 194–5

thermohaline circulation *76*

Third Assessment Report (**TAR**) **10**–11, 12–13, 14, 23–4,
    28–30, 63, 66–7, 78, 128, *132*
    scenario analysis 139, 140–44

timber supply, effects of climate change 27

'Time Dollars'/'Time Banks' 232, *233*

time-scales associated with climate change **53**, 90–91, 94

Töpfer, Klaus, on climate change 14, 16

tourism *165*

tree ring data as climate change indicators 63

Tuvalu, vulnerability of, to climate change 14, 16, *185*

Tyndall, John 33, 34

U

uncertainty
    in climate science 49–50, 57, 68–71, 77–81, 129
    in construction of road transport models 139–40
    in costs of climate change 124–5, 144
    in estimation of future emissions 134–8
    in integrated assessment modelling 128, 129
    in integrated assessments 172
    in Objective of UNFCCC 93, 94, 95
    in Principles of UNFCCC 95
    in risk assessment 24
    in temperature records *66*
    in understanding of radiative forcing 60–63

United Nations Environment Programme (UNEP) *13*

UNFCCC (United Nations Framework Convention on Climate Change) **92**–106, 150

    classification of countries 98

    Commitments 93, 96–104, 107

    Objective 93–5

    Principles 95–6, 151

    see also Kyoto Protocol

United States

    and climate science 89–90

    emissions intensity indicators 136

    Kyoto Protocol rejection by 102–4, 171

    use of resources 217

units

    of atmospheric carbon/carbon dioxide 56–7

    concentration of greenhouse gases 40

    of greenhouse gas emissions 111

urbanization *88*

Urry, J. 209, 223

V

Villach Conference 92

volcanic dust 62–3

voluntarism 212, 214, 230

von Weizsäcker, E. 229

vulnerability to impacts of climate change 160

    inequalities in 185

    of poorest people 186–7, *189*

W

Wackernagel, M. 197

waste 195

    elimination of 228

    production of *165*

    as sustainability indicator *199*

water

    atmospheric 33–4, *35*, 52, 68, 71

    consumption by businesses 228

water resources

    adaptation to climate change *123*

    effects of climate change on 27, *186*

    impact of climate change on 75

Weyant, J. P. 129

'wine glass representation' of distribution of global incomes and equity *149*

World Business Council for Sustainable Development 229

World Commission on Environment and Development (WCED) 190, 196

World Resources book 209

World Summit on Sustainable Development (Johannesburg, 2002) 192, 196, *220*

World Trade Organization 114, *115*

World Wide Fund for Nature 238, *239*

World Wide Web 229, *230*, 236, 237–8, *239*

WSSD; *see* World Summit on Sustainable Development

World Meteorological Organization (WMO) *13*

Wynne, B. 131